GRANDFATHER STORIES

Other Books by Samuel Hopkins Adams

CANAL TOWN

BANNER BY THE WAYSIDE

PLUNDER

SUNRISE TO SUNSET

GRANDFATHER
STORIES

Samuel Hopkins Adams

RANDOM HOUSE

New York

"Canal Bride," "Marcia and the Celebrity," "Piety and
Pie," published by permission of *Woman's Day*, The A & P
Magazine. All of the remaining stories in this book ap-
peared originally in *The New Yorker* except for "Two
Grandfathers," "A Third Ward New Year's," "The In-
imitable Mr. Carlyle," "A Deal in Gems" and "A Finger
Lakes Boyhood."

To

the alma mater of five generations

of Adamses, this book is reverently dedicated.

Samuel Hopkins Adams, '91

CONTENTS

GRANDFATHER STORIES

TWO GRANDFATHERS

Back in the last century grandparents were less durable than they are now. Few children got far into their teens with a full quota. That, through the years of my growing-up, I was blessed with three, plus a step-grandmother thrown in for good measure, made me an object of envy to my contemporaries. Looking back to my boyhood years of the 1870's and early 1880's, I incline to believe that the young got more out of the old than they now do.

The relationship was patriarchal and preceptorial on the one side, respectful and receptive on the other. How far it was mutually beneficial, I would not presume to estimate. There were times when grandparental authority, superimposed upon parental, seemed a little too much of a good thing. On the whole, however, the association was profitable to the young, though perhaps less pleasant than it seems in memory. Retrospect tends to be sentimental.

My two grandfathers, both typical of upstate New York character, were of different eras. Grandfather Adams, born at the tag-end of the eighteenth century, quite plainly bore its impress. He even consciously affected its archaisms. Grand-

father Hopkins, of the next generation, was, by the other
grandfather's standards, too much of a modernist. I have
heard Grandfather Adams call himself "a plain, everyday
American," though I doubt that he fully meant it. It would
never have occurred to Samuel Miles Hopkins, D.D., an erudite Professor of Church History in a Presbyterian Seminary,
thus to characterize himself. He was too conscious of his min-
isterial prerogative. Though there was a distance of only seventy miles between the two homes, my grandparents saw
little of one another. It was probably just as well.

Vacations brought change and expansion into my life.
Early in the summers I went to visit my maternal grandparents in Auburn. The Hopkins house, of mid-Currier & Ives
architecture, stood at the top of the Grant Avenue rise over-
looking the city. Twenty or more members of the family
might be guests there at one time; children and grandchildren, nephews, nieces, cousins and collaterals, all, by some
legerdemain of hospitality on the part of my grandmother,
tucked away somehow between cellar and cupola, the latter
being the size of a modern bungalow.

No tales of canal life were to be heard in this household.
Grandfather Hopkins sometimes read to us in the evening,
or, to our delight, recited without consultation of the text—
for he had a phenomenal memory—long passages from *The
Lays of Ancient Rome* or the entire *Ancient Mariner*. He
was the old type of scholarly gentleman, impressively handsome, of great dignity, and with courtly manners. Some of my
female relations openly mourned that he was a Presbyterian
since, in their belief, "Uncle Sam would surely have been a
bishop before he was forty, with those manners." He was particular to the point of being finicky about his clothes, which
were always of the finest material and most stately cut.
Grandfather Adams alluded to him, not too kindly, as "that
ecclesiastical elegant." The Rochester "plain American" did
not approve of a clergyman who wore a swallowtail coat.

The contrast between my Rochester and Auburn environments was sharp. For the restriction of city streets, was substituted, when I reached Auburn, the freedom of open country. Just beyond Grandfather's place was a thick woodland opposite a wild gully. The place itself comprised some three acres of garden, vinery and sunken croquet lawn. Next door stretched the pasture lot of the institution lugubriously called the Home for the Friendless. There, we children, having pried loose a board in the high fence, staged a series of bullfights and buffalo hunts, much to the detriment of the Home's milk supply until, one grim day, a uniformed policeman came and took us, weeping, into custody.

How many servants my grandparents kept nobody quite knew. They were all over the place: cook, waiting maid, chambermaid, washerwoman, an ancient cockney dame, Mammy Thompson, who acted as communal nurse, and several casuals who came to clean house. There was also a brooding old party named John Donovan, who mowed the lawn, trimmed the grapevines and currant bushes, and picked the vegetables. He was an alumnus of Auburn State Prison and touchy on the point. I remember one horrific day when Bailey Serviss, a boy from across the street, greeted him as, "Hey, Stripes!" The old man took after Bailey with a scythe and would probably have mowed him down at the knees, had not Grandpa opportunely appeared and wrested the weapon away.

All this plethora of servants did not, as might be thought, indicate a luxurious scale of living. Domestic service was modestly paid in those days. Anything more than ten dollars a month was considered almost profligate. I suppose that the total wages of the household, inside and out, never rose above twenty dollars a week.

When Grandfather Hopkins acquired a point on Owasco Lake, a few miles away, and moved us all up there for a month of wild life, living standards were simplified to the verge of hardship. No servants were taken along. All the work of a decidedly primitive camp devolved upon the family, with us children, as it seemed to me, bearing the brunt of the most distasteful chores. Grandfather said that it built character.

Perhaps it did. But, by the end of a month of peeling potatoes, drying tin dishes, dressing fish, bailing boats, burying garbage, and cleansing and filling grimy kerosene torches, I for one, was glad to get back to Rochester and civilization.

If these ancestral reminiscences deal chiefly with my Adams forebear, it is not because of any personal preference for him. As a matter of fact, Grandfather Hopkins was far more companionable. I had an affection for him warmer than any feeling for the more austere and less approachable relation. But he had led, from boyhood, a sheltered life of predestined scholarship in library and classroom, whereas Grandfather Adams, though by no means devoid of cultivation, had as a young man, operated a stump-puller with eight-foot wheels in the construction of that mighty engineering feat, the Grand Erie Canal, and later worked on the canal, itself. The difference in appeal to youthful imagination needs no emphasizing.

Grandfather Adams lived in a simple cottage on unfashionable South Union Street in Rochester, New York. Before any of us grandchildren were born, he had sold a once prosperous farm and retired on an insufficient income. Retirement did not mean idleness for him. The name, Myron Adams, frequently appeared in signature to communications to the newspapers, severe in style and often richly archaic in expression. Upon invitation he would address public meetings, his favorite topics being the evil of strong drink, the degeneracy of the times, and the conspiratorial activities of the Democratic party. He also wrote papers on subjects as diverse as the influence of sunspots on the weather and the domestic tomato as a causative factor in cancer.

The South Union Street household was made up of Grandfather, his second wife, and a man-of-all-work who was earning his way through the Baptist Theological Seminary. To this day I do not know our step-grandmother's given name. Grandfather addressed her as "Mrs. Adams" and would have been shocked at any such unwarranted familiarity as "Myron" on her part. Placidity and good humor were her memorable characteristics. Conversation between her and her husband was restricted to household economics and the old gentleman's health, which was more rugged than he believed it to be. She fussed indulgently over his ills, real or imaginary, and encouraged his self-dosing with the popular crypto-alcoholic nostrum, Hop Bitters, which was always at hand.

He pretended annoyance at her solicitude. Actually he enjoyed and depended upon it. Most of her time was spent in the kitchen with the door open a crack to listen for symptomatic coughs or sneezes. Though formal, their relations were not unfriendly. He respected her particularity as a housekeeper and her frugality at the market, and had been known to extol her cooking to outsiders.

The third member of the household was the meek, bespectacled, fledgling theologian to whom Grandfather always referred as "my man, Geordis." Why, we never knew, his name being Howard Holder. "Geordis" he remained, notwithstanding, in family usage. He was small, quiet, earnest and much concerned with his studies, which he repeated as he went about his chores, in a rapid mumble. Geordis was a conscientious worker. He did all the heavy work of house and garden and took good care of Horace G. (for Greeley), the family horse. In recompense he received lodging in the barn, two meals a day in the house, and two dollars a week wage. Apparently the arrangement suited; Geordis was never heard to complain.

Horace G. was the apple of Grandfather's eye. The horse was of indeterminate ancestry, uncertain age, and lethargic habit. Family tradition held that before any of us was born, Grandfather had outswapped the chief of a band of gyppos, somewhere out beyond Spencerport, for him. His conformation was lumpy, his disposition aloof, and his appearance unbelievably shaggy, shabby and moth-eaten. But he could maintain a steady jog of five miles an hour indefinitely, which is all that his owner exacted of him. Daily he was exercised, hitched to a rattletrap buggy in summer, an ancient sidebar cutter in winter, and driven through Rochester's busiest thoroughfares, in calm disregard of the sensation which the venerable rig occasioned on fashionable East Avenue or crowded Main Street. When we young Adamses reached the age of social self-consciousness we used to shrink from the conspicuousness of riding behind Horace G. Grandfather was immune to any such embarrassment.

"Horace G. may not be as pompous as Dan Patch," he admitted, "but no horse has a more respectable character." In Grandfather's mouth the word, respectable, reverted to its primal meaning, worthy of all respect, estimable in a high degree. Pompous, of course, meant of fine and impressive appearance.

Family piety ran strong in the Adams line. At least once a week we grandchildren were required to pay our formal respects at South Union Street. There were five of us in regular attendance. The age-span from Jenny, the eldest, to Charlie, the youngest, was ten years. In between were John, Sireno and myself, all born at the beginning of the 1870's.

It took years for us to become at all well acquainted with Grandfather. In the early days of our duty visits there was a romantic halo about his person, due to a misconception. Up to the time when I was ten years old, I cherished, in common with my cousins, the proud illusion that he was a retired horse-thief. The ground for our faith was a framed certificate, hanging in the sitting room. It was the one worldly touch on walls otherwise given over to the pious aridity of crewel-work texts and the mortuary reminders of Currier & Ives. In clear and elegant script it set forth that Mr. Myron Adams of East Bloomfield, New York, was a member in good and regular standing of the Wayne County Horse-thief Society, witness the sign and seal of the secretary, Anno Domini, 1821. There was, of course, no way of our knowing that the Society was formed for the purpose of discouraging raids on farm stock, and was also a social and festal organization comprising the young bloods or "Corinthians" of the county.

John, Reno and I bragged unconsciously to our envious playmates of the strain of criminality in our blood. Only Jenny was of another mind. For some reason incomprehensible to the rest of us, she pretended to regard the record as faintly discreditable. Jenny was precociously ladylike.

It was difficult to reconcile the old gentleman's personality with the glamorous past which we attributed to him. Certainly there was nothing rakish about him as an octogenarian. My early recollection is of a patriarchally bearded and imposing figure in a Boston rocker beside a Franklin stove. From the ample expanse of beard issued a calm and preceptorial voice, dispensing admonition, instruction, exhortation to good and warning against evil conduct, sage advice and stern reproof; seldom praise and never levity. I was in my tenth year before I ever heard him laugh.

It was that occasion which broke the ice between the generations. The five of us had been bidden to breakfast at the cottage, a harsh ordeal, involving, as it did, a seven o'clock arrival, and family prayers in the heatless parlor. It was on a raw March morning that John innocently precipitated the event.

Fifteen minutes was the scanty time allotted for breakfast on our step-grandmother's toothsome battercakes, after which we were herded into the devastating chill of the parlor. Grandfather read from the Scriptures. We sat, shivering and stiffening. Grandfather led in prayer. We knelt on the stone-cold floor with quaking knees. Grandfather lifted up his voice in sacred song. We joined in, doing our conscientious best to control our tremulous jaws.

> Broad is the p-p-p-path
> That leads to d-death,
> And thousands w-w-walk
> Together ther-r-r-r-re.

Then a protracted benediction, after which we were free to make for the warmth and comfort of Benjamin Franklin's patent stove. All but one. This time John cringed in his chair, immobilized by a cramping chill. He was hustled out to the sitting room where Grandma swathed him in a blanket, Geordis fetched a hot brick for his feet, and Grandfather reached for the ever-handy Hop Bitters bottle.

A tablespoonful of a forty percent alcohol solution is calculated to produce effects upon the ten-year-old human organism. John, normally the most decorous of our generation, reacted atypically to the stimulus. Fixing the framed certificate with a glittering eye, he said loudly, "Grandpa!"

"Yes, John."

"I gotta question to ask you."

A galvanic shock went through the rest of us. Interrogate our grandfather? Except for a polite inquiry as to his health, none of us would have dared such a thing. What alcoholic temerity was John about to perpetrate?

"Ask it." The tone was not encouraging.

"Where did you get Horace G.?"

"Hah!" Grandfather ejaculated, the memory of that equine transaction still warm within him.

"I know," John asserted with profound conviction.

"Do you, indeed!" said Grandfather ominously.

"You stole him."

Grandma uttered a faint shriek.

"Didn't you? Didn't you steal Horace G.?"

Grandfather turned to his wife. "The boy is exalted in the head. Send for Dr. Ely."

"Horse-thieves steal horses, don't they?" his grandson insisted. "And you used to be a horse-thief, didn't you? That paper"—he pointed a wavering finger at the wall—"says so. I read it, myself, and I got Jenny to read it after me so's to be sure I was right. How can you be a member of a horse-thief society unless you're a horse-thief? Wasn't he a horse-thief, Jenny?" he appealed to his cousin.

"No, you ninkum!" she snapped.

John looked searchingly at her and then at his grandfather. He read blank denial in their faces. Confidence oozed out of him. "I told all the fellas you were," he said brokenly. "And n-n-now . . ." He choked up.

We listeners sat, sunk in despondency. Our dreams of ancestral derring-do were dissolved. Gone was the vision of a young and dashing Grandpa, riding at the head of his Wayne County cohorts upon some predatory and perilous mission. What a disillusionment! The old gentleman turned his slow regard upon the stricken faces around him.

"So you all consider your grandfather a malefactor," he said.

"I never!" cried Jenny.

"No, sir," Reno and I said. It was a hollow disclaimer. Young Charlie simply raised a wail of disappointment.

A strange alteration took place in the aged visage before us. Something was happening to Grandpa. His face worked. His beard quivered. From it issued a rumble which presently became a roar. We were appalled. It did not at first occur to us that this convulsion in one so mirthless could be laughter. Grandma was the first to recognize it. She began to giggle. Jenny joined in. One after another, we boys, our alarms dissipated, timorously ventured participation; then, as nobody rebuked us, gave ourselves up to whole-hearted glee. The little room rang to Grandpa's deep boom, Jenny's soprano peals, and a pandemonium of gurgles, shrieks and whoops from us boys.

Only Geordis refrained. With an expression of pain upon his meek countenance, he went out to look after Horace G.

Things were never the same again in the South Union Street home. The solvent of shared laughter melted the glacial barriers which Grandfather had unwittingly set up between age and youth. We never became actually chummy with him, it is true, but a cautiously progressive companionship did develop, respectful on our part, condescending on his. To our gratified surprise we discovered that we and he had interests in common. His enlightenment was even more revolutionary; we were revealed to his astonished recognition as human beings.

The visits to the little cottage ceased to be uniformly penitential. Instead of long, unrelieved, impersonal discourses, the old gentleman now developed for our edification and discomfiture, a playful device. He would interlard his conversation with obsolete terms and feign surprise and mortification when his hearers manifested a lack of understanding. We never knew when to expect these pitfalls. In the midst of some reminiscence of his youth he might let fall a casual mention of "the October improvement party at the minister's house," and then pause expectantly.

One or another of his hearers would repeat, "Improvement party?"

"Certes. Surely you know what an improvement party is."

Dubiously shaken heads.

"What ignorami! Why, the veriest abecedarian of my schooldays would exhibit more docity."

Groping for a clue, Jenny would venture, "I'm going to join the Self-Improvement Class next term."

"Self-improvement, indeed! Hunca-munca."

It was now John's turn. He was our scholar. "Was it to improve the minister, sir?"

"No parson who needed improvement from his congregation would have lasted long in East Bloomfield."

After several other feeble essays, which he properly rebuked, Grandfather would vouchsafe to enlighten our ignorance: every October, in the olden time, the church folk gathered at the parsonage with axe, saw and wedge, and moved on to the nearest woodlot to improve—i.e., augment —the parson's woodpile for the impending winter.

As time went on our range of communication broadened. One could never tell what the day's visit might bring forth. It might be a scientific dissertation on snails, a horde of which invaded the cellars of South Union Street one August. It might be a reading from the almanac, with historical commentary. It might be a narrative brought out by reference to the old gentleman's "ort-book," a massive, leather-bound volume of heterogeneous memorabilia, kept under lock and key in his secretary-desk. This was a never-failing source.

After the label-prescribed dosage of his favorite Hop Bitters, he was likely to lapse into light and brief slumber, emerging with some old-time aphorism on his lips, usually of didactic or economic purport.

"Let young Loosetongue hire a turnip cart and preach the end of the world from its tailpiece."

"A pig on credit makes a good winter and a long spring."

"Blow high, blow low, hired money passes with the wind."

"Why pay a malkin to skin a cooked eel?"

And once he scandalized our childish sensibilities by coming out of a doze and announcing briskly, "Only a waste-thrift would plane the under side of a privy seat."

It was the only indelicacy that we ever heard him utter, and the only occasion on which he ever showed embarrassment.

A drunken man who staggered by in the street one Saturday, served as text for a temperance sermon, with a distant, obscure and deceased cousin as horrible example. This relative, it appeared, after having "bowed his manly head to the killing cup," had wandered away into the forest and been eaten by bears. As epitaph, Grandfather recited with solemn fervor a favorite poem, of which the opening stanza is indelibly if perhaps not quite accurately imprinted on my memory.

> Ah, see where the red-glowing grogshop appears,
> As the waves of adversity swell.
> How it burns on the verge of tempestuous years,
> The horrible lighthouse of Hell!

Next to drunkenness he reprehended gambling, with one exception. He stoutly deplored the abolition of lotteries. Consider the good accomplished by them in the past, he argued. Libraries built, cultural institutions established, colleges and seminaries endowed, churches supported, charities enriched, all through the beneficent operations of these temples of chance.

"How," he inquired rhetorically, "would my own alma mater, Hamilton College, have won through its early vicissitudes without the funds allotted to it by that praiseworthy enterprise, the Literary Lottery? If I win a wager from a friend, I profit by the mulct of his money. But who is the worse for the luck of the draw in a properly conducted House of Fortune? Nobody!"

He was exceedingly proud of having attended Hamilton, though he did not finish his course. His name appears in the 1816 Catalogue as a member of the Sophomore class. Owing to some breach in the then rigid tenets of academic discipline ("I did a barney in Spring term" he once revealed to us), he was rusticated under the surveillance of that same East Bloomfield clergyman whose woodpile he helped to improve. Annoyed at the dereliction, his canal-contractor-father, Deacon Abner Adams, withdrew him from "those classic shades" and set him to work as a surveyor.

That he harbored no grudge is proven by his having sent

two of his sons to Hamilton. When I entered, he signalized
the event by giving me a dollar. On my return to Rochester
for my first college vacation, he greeted me as "Fellow Alumnus." Secretly tickled at having caught him in a slip, I pointed
out that a freshman could hardly lay claim to that title. He
turned a chilling eye upon me.

"Do not play the callow dawplucker with me, Samuel," he
said sternly.

I hastened to apologize.

"Consult the dictionary," he directed, pointing to the book-
shelf.

I did so and learned what I should have known from past
experiences, the inadvisability of challenging the old gentleman on a point of verbal usage. Any member of a collegiate
body, I found, graduate, undergraduate, or non-graduate, is
an alumnus.

Why Grandfather left unmentioned for so long the most
glorious (to our appreciation) phase of his career is a puzzle.
He must have known that the Erie Canal which threaded the
center of the city, was an integral part of daily life to Rochester youth. In summer we swam and fished in it. In winter
we played shinny-on-your-own-side at the Wide Waters. Between seasons we extended respectful landsmen's greetings
to the lordly mariners on its surface, and, on rare and beatific
occasions, dropped by invitation from an arched bridge to
the deckhouse roof of some hospitable, time-grizzled captain.

Our juvenile ambitions centered upon the canal. Let others
aspire to become locomotive engineers, Indian scouts, or baseball captains with whiskers; for us the grassy berm, the toiling mules and the smooth-gliding craft were the ultimate in
ambition. Reno, the practical, business-minded member of
the group, was for steam. He would be master of a profitable
stern-propeller, make a pile of money towing, and sign on
Charlie as cabin boy if that young hopeful would learn to
salute and call him "sir." John and I were willing to start at

the bottom as mule-drivers and work up from the dust of the towpath. Jenny had decided to become mistress of the mahogany-fitted tugboat, *Annie Laurie*, even though it involved marrying the captain, a design which would have considerably surprised him, his wife, and their five children. We had nothing but pity in our hearts for those unfortunate children who lived in canal-less regions.

Yet we might never have learned from Grandfather of our vested interest in the great waterway, had it not been for a chance encounter. On a June day of 1881 the old gentleman gave evidence of expanding fellowship by inviting us to go driving with him. Only three of us were available that day: John, Reno and I. Jenny had to do some church sewing, and Charlie had the earache. While Geordis was harnessing Horace G., Grandfather unlocked his private repository and got out from his ort-book a document which he carefully inserted in the breast pocket of his rusty Prince Albert coat. Having buttoned it in, he led the way to the rig and we were off at a reliable five-miles-per-hour.

Out through Brighton we jogged to Pittsford, where our driver turned left. A moment later, John gave apprehensive warning.

"You can't drive there, Grandpa."

"Why not?"

"That's the towpath."

"I am aware of the fact."

"But, Grandpa! Nobody's allowed on the towpath but the canallers."

Reno and I added our protests. Too many times had we been chased from that forbidden territory with horrid imprecations and whizzing rocks not to have a fearful respect for it. Grandpa, it appeared, did not share our alarms.

"Giddap, Horace," he said placidly as he turned right upon the mule's highway.

A span of mules appeared, with a hulking lout at the lines.

Fifty yards back of him loomed the freighter, light and riding high. Grandfather pulled to the offside to give the team passage room. The muleteer stared hard at our rig, scowled formidably, and, as we boys shrank into the smallest possible compass, threw up his hand, grinned, and passed on. From his lofty stance at the tiller the captain, as the boat drew level, saluted. Grandfather civilly lifted his whip. We marveled.

"Grandpa," Reno said in a small voice, "do you *know* those canallers?"

"Hah!" said Grandfather noncommittally.

Several other craft passed. The phenomenon was repeated; nobody interfered with our progress. Presently we came in sight of a man fishing from the towpath. He carried a staff and wore a badge. Our companion scrutinized him.

"That must be a new bankwatcher," he said. "I do not recognize his face."

"What's a bankwatcher, sir?" I asked.

"The degenerate successor to the old-time pathmaster."

"What's a pathmaster?" John inquired.

Before there was time for a reply, the fisherman spied us. He jumped to his feet, lumbered out into the middle of the right-of-way, and brandished the staff.

"Whoa!" he shouted loudly in Horace G.'s face.

Surprised and shocked, Horace G. who was unaccustomed to such discourtesy, stopped. The bankwatcher addressed Grandfather.

"Where do you think *you're* goin'?"

"Down to the lock," Grandfather said mildly.

"Not on this towpath. You're trespassin'. Mizzle!"

With a confident smile Grandfather unbuttoned his Prince Albert, took out the document from the inner pocket, unfolded it tenderly, and presented it. The official glared at it suspiciously.

"What's that?"

"A permit from the Honorables, the Erie Canal Comissioners, certifying my right to use the towpath, ad libitum, and signed by Gov. Clinton." (Obit 1828)

"Who?"

"Governor Clinton. The Honorable De Witt Clinton."

"Never heard of him."

Hot color flushed into the old gentleman's cheeks. "You are a disgrace to the Grand Erie Canal which you serve, sir," he declared.

The bankwatcher grabbed Horace G.'s bridle and attempted to swing him around.

"Drop that bridle," said Grandfather sharply.

"Who says so?"

Grandfather half stood up and glanced east and west. Boats were coming from each direction. He put two fingers between his lips and whistled in astonishing volume. It was an accomplishment which we would never have expected in him. The bankwatcher jerked at Horace G.'s head. The wagon wheels cramped. The body tipped. There was a fair chance of our all being shunted into the water when the diversion came. Five runners on the towpath were converging upon us from the boats, which had veered in. The official hailed them.

"This old fool . . ."

He got no further. The first canaller to reach the spot, a burly, old steam captain, swept the official's feet out from under him. Two others rolled him over the bank, while the remaining pair straightened out Horace G. The assaulted man beat the water bellowing for help, but there was no help. Menacing faces loomed over him. He swam across to the berm opposite, where he crawled out, spluttering and snarling threats of arrest. The steamer captain addressed him.

"Why, you crawfish-catching, turtle-chasing mudchunker, you! Do you know who this old gentleman is?"

The man gaped and gurgled.

"This is Squire Adams, this is. Ever hear of Adams Basin, you gillychick? Why, the Adamses *built* the Erie. You'd run *him* off the towpath, would you? Skedaddle before I come over there and drown you."

The dejected bankwatcher dribbled a trail into the underbrush and vanished. Grandfather warmly thanked the rescue squad for their "officiousness," by which he meant—and correctly, by the old usage—helpfulness. They returned to their boats, and the old gentleman turned Horace G. around for the trip back.

Sheer awe held us passengers silent for several miles. Our grandfather was suddenly revealed as a tradition, a fellow-canaller held in honor by these tough inland mariners. And we had never suspected any such glory. Reno made the break.

"Grandpa?"

"Yes, Sireno."

"Did you really build the canal?"

"I had a hand in it."

"Did you help run it after it was built?"

"As a young man, I held a quasi-official position."

"Is that why they all came running when you whistled?"

Grandfather smiled. "There's an old saying canalside: Once an Erie man, always an Erie man."

John now took his turn. "Is Adams Basin us Adamses?"

"You may so put it."

"Named after you?"

"After my father, the Deacon, and his brother."

"Is it in the geography?"

"Certes."

John drew a long breath. "Wait till I get back to school!" he said.

It was a gala day thereafter when we could get the old gentleman on the subject of the canal. Through his sly trickeries of speech we became steeped in canal lore. We maintained a conscious verbal superiority over our less erudite contemporaries. In casual conversation we would toss off references to hoodledashers, hoggees, occupation bridges, water-hire, and

mudlarking. We could have told a ballhead from a needleboat a mile away. We were precise as to the authority of a
pathmaster, the rates exacted at a toll lock, and the broad
piscatorial scope of a mackerel inspector, though these offices
had been obsolete for generations.

The designation of the vagrant bands that had formerly
ranged canalside was familiar to us: gyppos, pikies, tenkers,
swingkettles, blanketeers, anatomists, redemptioners, and
ashbucket apprentices, and, in the towns, the tough soap-
locks and roadrunners. Where a juvenile inlander on occasion of peril would have hissed, "Cheese it, the cops!" we
warned, "Low bridge! Everybody down!" And we would
never have been so conventional as to suggest a let-up in
operations by such a term as, "Let's lay off," or, "Enough's
enough." Our word was, "Look for a post," the hoggee's signal for a night's rest.

Grandfather's attitude toward the canal was almost rever-
ential. He would brook no frivolity on the subject. Wither-
ing, indeed, was the wrath which Reno brought down upon
himself by jocosely referring to the far bank of the waterway
as the "heelpath."

"A paltry jest," Grandfather exploded. "A cheap and wit-
less play upon words. Berm! Berm! Berm! Fix that sound
American word in your pudding head and never again let
me hear that other vulgarism from your lips."

He would pronounce with lingering affection the titles of
boats long rotted into canal-bed slime: *The Stormy Lass*, *The
Young Lion of the West*, *The Golden Flash*, *The Try-and-
Catch-Me*, *The Two Faithful Brothers*, and *The Merry Fiddler*, successor to *The Mary Fiddler* which was struck by an
electron and burned while mudlarked in the thunderstorm
that caused the Gerundigut breach of 1831. Equally memorable if less poetic was the nomenclature of waterside taverns,
The Hungry Pike, Hoggee's Rest, Death to Chinches (bedbugs), Welcome All, and The Well-Stuffed Gut of brief exist-

ence before the name was suppressed by those upholders of the proprieties, the Canal Commissioners.

In the ort-book could be found places which had vanished from the official maps years before: Pilgrimsport, Gasport, Joppa Basin, Poverty's Pinch, Ratcatcher's Wharf, and Cholera Hitch.

"The canal authorities of today," Grandfather would observe, "are devoid of geographical imagination."

Once again Grandfather became a proud boast on our lips. His new distinction compensated for the loss of face we had suffered when compelled to abandon our claim of having a horse-thief in our immediate ancestry. After all, that was in the past. This was in the present. There was Grandfather's name—our name—on the map for all to see. It gave us precedence—at least, in our own consideration—over Craig Powers who had a mere building named after his father, Powers Block at the Four Corners; over George Pond whose local fame depended upon the larger-than-life statue of Mercury, visible from all parts of the city, on the tower of his uncle's tobacco factory; over Norman Mumford who could prove that his grandfather's pasture lot was the playing field of Rochester's pioneer baseball team, perhaps the first in the state, possibly in the whole United States since it dated from 1827.

All these were shining honors. But they lacked the indelible testimony of the printed word. They were not of general record. We were. Adams Basin might be an inconsiderable canalside hamlet. But there it stood, indelible, in every geography book of our school system. That was an unforgettable day for us when John was called upon in Number Three Geography class to answer the proposition, "Name four important communities in New York State west of Albany."

"Utica, Syracuse, Rochester and Adams Basin," said John in crescendo.

Frequently Grandfather had to admonish us against snobbishness. He was not wholly free from it, himself, however. A visiting New England lady to whom he was presented at a church festival, said, "Adams? Adams? Do you claim kinship with the Boston Adamses?"

"There is a Boston branch, I believe," he answered cautiously.

"I refer to the Presidential Adamses," the lady said haughtily.

"Ah! I was personally acquainted with the Honorable John Quincy Adams. A very respectable gentleman. He may well have been a connection of our line, though, being no brag-hard, he would naturally not press the claim. . . . May I fetch you a glass of water, madam?"

Privately he considered the Boston Adamses rather an effete and unenterprising lot. They clung to an easeful existence in Massachusetts while the hardier pioneers of the breed were risking the perils and hardships of the wilderness that made up Western New York in 1791.

A THIRD WARD
NEW YEAR'S

As early as the 1880's Rochester's most stiff-and-starchy ward was beginning to be affectionately referred to as "the Old Third." It was the self-appointed custodian of the city's ancient ways. In pioneer days, when the town was growing into its pride and prosperity under the impetus of the Grand Erie Canal, it had been called, in recognition of its aristocracy, the Ruffleshirt Ward. Long after it dropped the ruffles from its shirts, it kept them on its traditions.

The fine flower of local custom was New Year's hospitality. On that day the Old Families kept open house with pomp, circumstance and a lavish prodigality of refreshment equalled today only by a gangster's wake. Young and old, rich and (within decorous limits) poor, native and outlander were welcome. Dressed in their best bib-and-tucker, they made the rounds from high noon to 6 P.M., eating their voracious way like a swarm of social locusts. A few adventurous homes kept going until eight and, one year, there was an unverified scandal to the effect that the Kimball mansion revels were prolonged to the licentious hour of ten under the stimulus of a punch in the back parlor, rumored to have liquor in it.

New Year's was pre-eminently a masculine day. Ladies made no calls. They were cast in the passive role of providers, with the young girls, starched and sashed and beribboned, as assistants. For the small boys it was a kind of debut. A year or so at Miss Quimby's Dancing Class was supposed to form one's manners, and the round of January 1st calls was often the first public try-out. For the ten-year-old boy it was something of an ordeal, the rigors of which were mitigated by the prospect of the richest and most variegated cuisine of the year.

Careful tabs were kept on the entertainments. It is doubtful that the accumulated lore was ever reduced to writing; it was handed down by word of mouth from age to age with all the authority of tribal tradition. Before the boy debutant was launched upon the social waves, he was equipped with the gastronomic wisdom of generations.

It was accepted as an article of faith that the Brewsters should serve five kinds of pie, including Marlborough; that the Rogers' chicken salad was beyond all competition; that the Stedmans could be relied upon for that meatiest of rare luxuries, scalloped oysters; that what was known as Charlotte "Roosh" attained its apex of delicacy at Miss Ada Kent's; and that the Pecks offered not only two kinds of turkey, but also duck and goose. The house that was traditionally a "must" for the young was the Chapin mansion on Fitzhugh Street, in that it set forth a superb assortment of exotic fruits and nuts which could be taken from the premises for future use with impunity, a practice elsewhere frowned upon as unmannerly. The Chapins overtly encouraged it. In consequence, long lines of juvenile Third Warders, their coats and trousers distorted to shapelessness, could be seen filing down the front steps and pausing outside the iron fence to appraise and compare their loot.

There was careful preparation for the day. The neophyte was coached in a formula which could not go wrong so long as he stuck to it.

All this valuable information became mine on the day of my debut, in 1881. My cousins, John and Sireno Adams, who lived on the east side of the river where the strange custom of morning calls was observed, had been invited to join me for the afternoon. Grandfather and his wife drove the two across Court Street bridge behind the venerable Adams nag, Horace G., who as his owner frequently said, was no equine dandiprat but had a sterling character. The sidebar cutter drew up in front of my parents' half of the double house on Troup Street, and the four occupants descended.

"Happy New Year's," said John and Reno in unhappy voices. They were apprehensive of the unknown rites before them.

The greetings having been concluded, we three boys were lined up against the sitting-room wall for scrutiny by our elders. Besides the grandparents, there were my mother and Aunt Sophie Hopkins. Father had withdrawn to work on his sermon.

There was little to criticize in our outer appearance. All of us had undergone baths, no extra hardship as it was Saturday, anyway. We were in our best clothes, John in dark blue with brass buttons, Reno in fuzzy brown and new tight shoes with a lustrous polish, and I in my hitherto unworn pepper-and-salt Norfolk suit from Sibley, Lindsay & Curr's Fashions-for-the-Young department. Grandfather was pleased to express his approval. "You look very macaroni. As we said in my day, 'A collar-and-risband sprig of fashion,' each of you."

Aunt Sophie was not so easily satisfied. Taking me by the arm and spinning me like a tailor's dummy, she yanked correctively at the back of my jacket.

"What makes it hump up like a camel, Hetty?" she demanded of my mother.

"Stand up straight, Sam," Mother ordered. She gave the garment a compensatory tug. "There! That's better."

"Ought to be," my aunt sniffed. She had noted the price-tag inside the collar. "Ten dollars for a boy's suit, indeed!"

"Pinchpenny ne'er served any," Grandma quoted placidly. "I daresay it's worth the money."

The preliminary inspection having ended, a communal inquisition followed, led by Grandfather.

"Have you all clean handkerchiefs?"

"Yes, sir." (Producing them.)

"Where are your arctics?"

"In the hall."

"You haven't forgotten your calling cards?" This from Grandmother.

"No, ma'am."

These were handwritten in the mode of Spencerian flourish. A decorative seraph's wing, then the name with accented capitals, then a balancing wing. A list of the houses to be visited was handed to John, as the senior, which he carefully stowed in his pocket. We looked hopefully toward the door but were checked by a command in Grandfather's disciplinary voice.

"Hold out your hands."

Chapped but clean, all six passed muster.

"Flatten your gloves in your top pockets."

We obeyed, fidgeting.

"Stop biting your nails, Samuel." I stopped.

"Why do you shoot your cuffs, John?" John abstained.

"Is that gum you are chewing, Sireno?" Reno shamefacedly discarded his cherished tree-spruce.

Footsteps sounded, descending the stairs, and the face of my Uncle Jack, wearing a sardonic grin, appeared.

"Don't they look sweet!" he said offensively, and recited:

> Be kind to all, my little dears,
> And always wash behind your ears.

"Aw, chestnuts!" I protested.

"Rats!" John added.

"What manners!" said Aunt Sophie.

"I don't suppose any one of 'em has a notion of proper behavior," Grandma said, shaking her head.

John chose to accept this as a challenge. He stepped forward with a gracious smile for an imaginary hostess. "How do you *do*, Miss Julia Whitney?" he inquired in sugared accents. "I trust this happy New Year's Day finds you in good health."

"Very commendable," Grandfather approved.

A jingle of bells sounded outside. A nobby sleigh and pair from Toogood's Livery drew in at the curb. Three bachelor Third Warders in glad array were seated in it. They whistled shrilly.

"Jack! Jack! Here's your rig," Mother called.

Uncle Jack reappeared in the hallway, drawing a muffler about his neck. He was superb in a Prince Albert coat with satin lapels, white pique shirt, a made-up bow of pearly hue, black trousers, and patent leather button shoes. The family were exclamatory in their admiration, as he eased himself into his long, frieze ulster and waved a courtly good-bye with his sealskin cap. Through the door, as he opened it, came derisive shouts.

"Dude! Dude! Get onto the dude!"

Three urchins of the Clarissa Street gang were capering on the sidewalk. Uncle Jack ignored them.

Reno made a jump for the nearest window and threw it up. "You wait!" he yelled at the jeering group. "You just wait! C'mon, fellas."

It was not to be. Aunt Sophie, who was slender but sinewy, got a grip on the challenger's collar which was not to be

shaken off. Mother had me by the ear. Grandma spryly
blocked off John.

"Fighting! On New Year's Day!" she said reproachfully.

"In your new suit!" Mother added.

"Stand still," Aunt Sophie admonished Reno. "You—you
eel."

The Clarissa Streeters vanished up the street, hooting.
The festal rig set out upon its social career in a whirl of
snow. We would-be belligerents were herded into chairs and
our instructions were resumed. Don't track snow into the
houses. Be sure to greet the hostess before eating and to say
good-bye before leaving. Take off gloves before shaking
hands. Keep hands out of pockets. Bow as Miss Quimby
taught. Don't start tag-you're-it or any other game indoors.
Don't ask for a second helping. Leave cards. Act like little
gentlemen everywhere.

It was a large and depressing order.

Grandfather unexpectedly lightened the gloom for us. He
turned to my mother.

"Hester, is it the mode for callers to make their rounds
by equipage?" He had been impressed by the splendor of
Uncle Jack's exit.

"If they can afford it, sir." She explained that several bachelors would chip in a dollar apiece and thus defray the costs
of transportation.

"In that case, we shall bow to the fashion," the old gentleman said. "Make ready, boys. I will, myself, act as your coachee
for the occasion."

This put another aspect on the matter. The sidebar cutter, drawn by Horace G. might not be as elegant as Uncle
Jack's turnout, but, at least, it was in the manner. No other
boys in the ward would be transported with such distinction; not Charley Robinson, whose father was a broker, nor
the Roby brothers of near-millionaire heritage, nor the visit-

ing nephew of the Mumfords whose family were so rich that they lived in a Saratoga Springs hotel all summer.

We piled into the cutter with whoops of joy. There still loomed before us the acid test of unfamiliar social observance. John ventured the suggestion that Grandfather give us his moral support at the start by accompanying us.

"No, no," he said. "Society's pribbles and prabbles are fifty years and more in my past. You must stand upon your own feet."

"Mine hurt," Reno said. "I wanta go home."

He was squelched, and the three of us discharged on the corner of Plymouth Avenue. We had to make a beginning somewhere. But where? John found a solution by closing his eyes, whirling around several times, and pointing, stiff-armed. The house indicated was the Chamberlains'. Each struggling to be last, we went in.

It was not nearly as bad as we had foreboded. Through this and the next few calls we bumbled without open disgrace, by dint of huddling close together and sticking to the formula. Presently our shyness evaporated in the simple warmth of the day's greetings. By an imperceptible transition, we became polished men of the world. John's comments on the weather were models of ease and felicity. I forgot my jacket's deplorable tendency to bunch up in the rear and achieved a dexterity with gloves and handkerchief that would have done credit to Rochester's contemporary Beau Brummel, Mr. Mahlon Day. By the time we had reached the Stoddards', Reno's aplomb had attained to a point where he treated his hostess to the latest thing in variety-show argot.

"Ah, there!" said Reno to the astonished Mrs. Dr. Stoddard. "Stay there."

John and I, horrified, hustled him out before he could commit any further faux pas. On the sidewalk we met with

the first setback of the day from Beekman Little who inquired where we were headed.

"Stedman's," I said. "Oysters." I smacked my lips.

"Over the left," Beek said, and broke the bad news. Chippy
Chapin's mother, marketing at Moggridge's grocery the day
before, had overheard the grocer address Mrs. Stedman in
words which afterward became a Third Ward classic.

"Yes, Mrs. Stedman, I *got* saddlerocks. I got plenty saddlerocks. But, makin' so free and you bein' a steady
customer"—Here he daintily clamped his nose between
thumb and forefinger—"if I was you, Mrs. Stedman, I
shouldn't prefer to put none in."

Mrs. Stedman took his advice and substituted a ham.
Something had gone wrong with the railroad shipments. The
Third Ward went oysterless that New Year's.

It was a disappointment. But there were compensations,
in particular the Whittlesey wine jelly and after that a long
stretch of house-to-house hospitality. We ate our happy way
along and around the corner into Washington Street where
stood the John Rochester mansion, famous for the richness
and extent of its refections. It looked bleak. No festoons ornamented its front windows. The steps had not been cleared
of snow. Reno was sent forward to investigate. Halfway up
the long steps he was met by Boardman Smith, descending.
Boardman addressed him with the superciliousness proper
to his sixteen years.

"N.G., kid. N.G."

"Why is it no good?" Reno demanded.

"N.G. No grub," the other grinned.

"Why not?"

"Basket."

"What's basket?" Reno asked, gaping.

"You're no Third Warder," said the scornful Mr. Smith,
"or you'd know that a basket hung to the door means the

family's away or something and you can put your card into it, if you got any, and come back next year."

That block was distressingly prolific of baskets. There and in Plymouth Avenue we dispensed most of our Spencerian pasteboards.

Better things were in store. Livingston Park, we had learned, was wide open. Every house on the upper slope was "receiving." We did well there, but toward the end, had a narrow escape. The scene of near-disaster was the stately George Buell place. Mr. Buell was the leading wholesale grocer of the city, and set a table in conformity with his high status. Here, at least, there would hang no repellent basket. The windows were garnished with holly and a wreath decorated the entry. We toiled up the sloping walk between the snow-festooned rhododendron bushes and had pushed open the outer door when a warning hiss arrested our progress.

"Cheese it!"

Lawrence Fitch and Vernam Fitzsimons were crouched in the shadowy lobby.

"Listen!" Lawrence whispered.

A reedy, little-girlish voice came to our ears.

> "We are lotht," the Captain thouted,
> Ath he thtaggered down the thtairth."

"Oh, Lordy!" John exclaimed in dismay. "What's up?"

"She's speaking a piece," Vern explained below his breath. "The Buell's niece or something. She's only six."

"We've been waiting for her to get through," Lawrence added.

"Can't they stop her?" Reno asked.

"They *like* it. Every time anybody new comes in, they make her do it all over again. Then they clap like everything."

"And we have to listen before we get any grub?" I asked.

"That's what," Lawrence said.

We held a council of war. It simply was not worth it, we decided, and crept forth from the unhallowed place, followed by the two lurkers. Even without the Buell fare, we had by this time put in a solid foundation of edibles. It was time to crown it with the glorious superstructure of Miss Ada Kent's charlotte russe. We three Adamses climbed back into the cutter. The other two boys attached themselves to the runners, and we were stylishly driven out to Troup Street and around into Washington.

Miss Ada Kent's reputation as a benefactor of youth was ward-wide. She was a small, brisk little cricket of a spinster, already, at twenty-five, a predestined old maid. Her table at Sunday School picnics was always the most lavish. She gave a private strawberry festival in June to which the well-behaved young of the locality were bidden. With the first sufficient snowfall she hired a country bobsleigh and took a chosen few on a hayride. Her popularity in the ward was second only to that of Santa Claus.

A group of our crowd were skylarking in front of the Kent gate when we drove up. The equine pomp of our arrival roused them first to envious hoots and then to good-natured violence. In the free-for-all that ensued, John lost three highly essential buttons from the front of his short pants. It could not have happened more unjustly, or to a more modest and mannerly boy. He was for withdrawing from society in the sheltering depths of the cutter while the rest of us enjoyed the ambrosia of the Kent set-out.

Grandfather vetoed this. A conference was held. Jumbo Emerson contributed a scarfpin to the cause of respectability, a sportive design of a pug-dog's head, set in a bodkin-like shaft. Repairs were made, John was cautioned to move gingerly, and we all trooped up the steps.

Miss Ada's pleasure at our advent was heartwarming.

"Dear boys!" she beamed. "How nice of you to come! I do hope that you have brought your appetites with you."

The main parlor and sitting room were full of grown-ups, eating, drinking and chattering. In the side parlor a special trestle had been reserved for youth, with a snowy, damask tablecloth in the center of which towered a massive charlotte russe. Several little girls of our own age were deputed to wait upon us. We seated ourselves on opposite sides of the makeshift table. Miss Ada hovered solicitously. My chair was next to Vern Fitzsimons' and across from John's.

All might have gone well had not John over-extended himself in reaching for a plate of ladyfingers. Something slipped. An expression of acute anguish froze his face into rigid lines. He sank back. His hands fumbled in his lap. Plainly he was making private and desperate adjustments. I noticed the tablecloth twitch slightly, but did not interpret the movement until too late. Vern Fitzsimons also had observed his opposite's maneuvers. Vern was precociously quick-witted and tactful.

He craned his neck to give himself a view through the window back of John. "Say, John!" he exclaimed with well-simulated excitement. "Your horse is getting fidgety. Better get out there."

John caught on at once. "Okay, Vern," he said gratefully. "Thanks."

He rose and started for the door. The tablecloth started after him. A serried array of knives, forks and spoons broke ranks and cascaded to the floor with a silvery crash. Two candy bowls rolled merrily after and, in final catastrophe, the lofty charlotte russe toppled and became a creamy smear on Miss Ada's best carpet. All the little girls shrieked in chorus. Miss Ada did a maidenly faint.

Grandfather, dozing in the cutter, was wakened by Horace G. giving a mighty start against the dashboard. The old horse had reason to be shocked. John, the mild-mannered, John the model for the rest of us, John, the paragon of correct behavior, was stumbling and staggering down the steps, clutching himself amidships, trailing interminable lengths of white damask, and screaming horrid imprecations. After him swarmed a turbulent crowd of his fellows, hysterical with mirth, and shouting the refrain of a popular song made and provided for such occasions.

> Whoa, Emma! Whoa, Emma!
> Emma, you put me in such a dilemma.

Grandfather scrambled nimbly from beneath his lap robe and intercepted the flight. "Get in, John," he said in a tone of quiet command.

John stared at him glassily, then raised his voice in despairing anathema. "Darn! Darn! *Damn!*" he yelped. "Whaddo I care if I go to hell!"

The old gentleman detached Miss Ada's best napery with a yank, lifted the squirming boy into the cutter, and, with a sharp "Gid-*app*, Horace," drove away, leaving Reno and me to walk home.

A year later, on January 1st, 1882, a basket dangled inhospitably from Miss Ada Kent's doorknob. It may have been the resentful aftermath of John's mischance. Or it may have been a non sequitur. As Grandfather might have said, in his favorite phrase, I don't know. Nobody knows.

THE BIG BREACH

By dint of subjecting ourselves to grinding penury over a period of months, my cousin, Sireno, and I became joint owners
of a Flaubert .22 rifle. The weapon and a cartridge box of
"shorts" cost, as I remember, four dollars at Hamilton & Mat-
thews, Rochester's leading hardware store in the 1880's.
Though the rifle was of limited range and uncertain accuracy,
it was the pride of our lives.

On a brisk September Saturday we two rose early and
tramped out to the Wide Waters, a place where the Erie Canal
broadened out across half a mile of flats. After several hours
of stalking, Reno killed a muskrat. This feat made our day. It
was accomplished just before we and the other Adams grandchildren were due at the South Union Street cottage for our
weekly duty call.

We debated, on the way, as to what we should do with our
muskrat. Only too vividly we remembered a previous hunt
when we had triumphantly brought in the day's bag, consist-
ing of a brown thrasher. On that painful occasion, Grandfather had denounced us as midsummer murderers and hedge-

row hoodlums. He might, we feared, feel the same about our present prey.

"I'll hide it in my shirt-front," Reno said. "It'll be O.K. there."

The other cousins, Jenny, John and Charlie, were already in the house when we arrived. Grandfather sat beside the stove, sipping his favorite temperance tonic, Hop Bitters (alcoholic content forty per cent) while his callers politely nibbled our step-grandmother's caraway cookies. On the marble-top stand at the old gentleman's elbow lay an open copy of *Sartor Resartus*. We faced the imminent prospect of having our minds improved by the reading of Mr. Thomas Carlyle, the leading oracle of the day.

Setting down his glass, Grandfather accidentally knocked the book to the floor. Reno, being nearest, stooped to pick it up. A shirt-button gave. He grabbed for his waistline too late; the furry corpse rolled out.

Grandfather adjusted his hexagonal spectacles and regarded it.

"*What*," he demanded, "is this?"

"It's a muskrat, sir," the hunter replied.

"And how comes it here?"

"We shot it at the Wide Waters," Reno said. (I considered that "we" a cowardly shirking of responsibility.)

"Canalside, eh?" the old gentleman asked in a tone of surprising amiability.

"Yes, sir. He was just crawling into his hole."

"In my heyday on the Grand Western Canal," said Grandfather, giving the Erie its early popular name, "a musquash taken within five furlongs of the waterway fetched a bonus of one dollar and keep the pelt, which might bring in fifteen cents additional."

"Oh, my!" Jenny sighed. "Only fifteen cents. I could have had a muskrat-skin coat."

"Not in my house," Grandfather snapped. "I still harbor a

just ambition against the slithery, slinking, burrowing, under-mining creatures, dead or alive. Pathmaster's penance, we ca-nallers used to call them."

"What's pathmaster, Grandpa?" Charlie inquired.

A pathmaster, Grandfather explained, was the guardian an-gel and unchallenged autocrat of path, berm and water for the fifteen miles of the canal he patrolled and was responsible for the safety of man, beast and boat thereon.

"But no more," he added with that touch of sentiment which he reserved for his beloved Erie Canal alone. "The last pathmaster has sounded his last alarum on his silver whistle."

"What was the silver whistle for?" Charlie asked.

"To summon help at need, to be sure. . . . And so, when I heard the shrill call sounding through the darkness and the rain one night, I knew there was danger afoot."

There was a musing tone in Grandfather's voice that held promise of a reprieve from Mr. Carlyle if we could only hold the old gentleman to the path of reminiscence.

John said quickly, "Who was it that whistled, sir?"

"Tom Culver," was the reply. "No better canaller could be found between Hudson's River and the Long Level."

"What year was it?" John asked persuasively.

It was 1829 or 1830, Grandfather thought. Anyway, it was the year of the five-day August rains when every tributary stream roared over its banks and Erie Water rose a foot an hour.

Grandfather had been to Clyde on a trade in marsh-eels for pickling and barrelling and, that night of rain, was riding his sorrel mare westward along the pike toward Lyons where he would find lodging. From out the blackness on his left came a feeble whistle. He reined in.

"What's that?" he shouted.

A gasping voice answered, "Pathmaster's summons. Lend a hand, whoever you be."

Under the rules, regulations and penalties of the Honorables, the Canal Commissioners of the State of New York, a pathmaster could commandeer help, and the order must be obeyed.

Detaching his saddle lantern, Grandfather dismounted and approached the canal on the berm side. The embankment was spouting like a leaky colander, for it was riddled with musquash holes which had been forced clear through by the pressure of the water. To his expert eye, it was a hopeless case. He climbed the slope and swept his light downward.

Flat on his belly below, Tom Culver was floundering from place to place, feebly striving to plug an irregular circle of widening holes. His progress was that of a broken-backed animal. His arms would flail upward, grasp and wrench away a branch of an alder or a willow, stuff it into a hole, and tamp it down with such rubble as he could scrape up. Grandfather called to him to give over.

"You'll do no good there," he shouted. "She's going to breach."

"You're a liar!" the pathmaster yelled. "What do you know about canal berm? Get down here and do some work."

"I was plugging breach when you were mumbling pipsissiway suckets in your cradle, Tom Culver," Grandfather retorted, and held up his light.

"It's Squire Adams," Culver exclaimed. "You think she'll breach?"

"I know she'll breach. Get up and get out of there."

"I can't. My leg's broke and my ribs is stove in."

Grandfather went down and took him under the armpits and dragged him to refuge under Farmer Stitt's occupation bridge which the Commission had kindly built for the farmer to join the two sections of his land, separated by the canal. A dram of Hooper's Jamaica Ginger from the traveler's hip flask fortified the injured man. He thanked Grandfather.

"You used to be an Erie man yourself, Squire," he said between groans. "You know the saying, 'Once a canaller, always a canaller.' You're an older man than me, but I'm pathmaster here. Will you take my orders?"

"Yes, sir," Grandfather said.

"Get to your horse and raise the countryside."

"And leave you here with your broken bones?" Grandfather objected.

Tom Culver cursed him in full canal terms. "If she breaches now and we don't check her, she'll be the Falls of the Genesee, come morning," he said. "Here! Take my badge and whistle. You're Deputy Pathmaster of this section with full authority. Now get 'em out."

Grandfather paused, then said to us, "You might think it would be difficult to harry decent folk from their beds for a thankless task in the wind and rain of a black night, it being then close on to ten o'clock."

"Yes, sir," John assented.

"As it doubtless would be," the old gentleman continued, "in this thin-blooded age, when loyalty is a dull spark and patriotism the echo of Independence Day rhetoric. But to the York Stater of a hardier time the Grand Western Canal was the pride and glory of the nation, vaunted as the eighth wonder of the world. We had wrought it with our hands and filled it with our sweat. We stood ready to fight and die for it. Our fervor was stimulated by the orators who rhapsodized it and the poets who sang of it in deathless numbers through the pages of the New York *Evening Post*."

"I wrote a commencement song about the Erie Canal," Jenny put in. "Fatty Cook, our principal, wouldn't pass it. He said I couldn't rhyme 'Erie' with 'We love you dearly.' Can't I, Grandpa?"

"Not with my approval," the old gentleman said, "however commendable the sentiment," and he resumed his account.

Remounting his mare, he said, he headed for Lyons. On the

outskirts of the town he saw a light in Ephraim Rowbottom's tavern, Pride of the West, and pulled up. The innkeeper was sitting belatedly over his accounts.

"What fetches you out this foul night, Squire?" he cried.

"Erie's breached," said Grandfather. "Who's on your books?"

Ephraim consulted his day ledger. "Gents, sixteen; ladies, five," he said.

The new deputy stepped to the stair foot. "All good men and true, up and out!" he shouted. "Erie's breaching at Stitt's Crossing."

The stairwell was immediately lined with nightcaps. There was a sharp exchange of questions and answers. A quick poll was taken. Thirteen men agreed to go. The other three were too old.

"Report to Tom Culver at the occupation bridge," the official bade the volunteers. He turned to Host Rowbottom. "Who's in the taproom?"

"Usual harvest of inglers and bunghole sippers," said the innkeeper. "Little good of them you'll get."

Grandfather threw open the door. "Anyone here for a night's work to save the canal?" he called. "Speak up!"

A small group of drowsy drinkers stared at the newcomer and then at one another. One spoke in a whiny voice. "It's rainin'."

"I don't have no argyment for goin' out into weather like this," another said.

"I'll give you one," Grandfather said. "Shilling an hour with pick, shovel or ax, at Stitt's Crossing."

"Got no tools," the first fellow grunted, though Grandfather could see that he was impressed by the liberality of the terms.

"Tools furnished gratis to any man that wants to work," Rowbottom offered.

Grandfather got four out of the taproom, though he mistrusted their worth. With the thirteen from abovestairs he had made a good start. He went out into the night, and in a few rods riding was in the flourishing town of Lyons. Here he was confident of aid.

Being an active member of the Wayne County Horse-thief Society, a fraternal group ostensibly dedicated to stamping out horse-stealing, he knew where to find co-operation. He had but to locate the Honorary Chief Constable, whom he found playing draw poker at the Eagle House.

Within ten minutes, peaceful Lyons was a pandemonium. Churchbells pealed. Rifles and pistols cracked. A coachee paraded Main Street, blaring on his horn, and the 1812 carronade on the green wakened everybody for miles around with one tremendous BOOM! The air rang with rallying cries.

"Breached!" "She's breached!" "Erie's dreening out at Stitt's Crossing!" "All out to staunch the break!"

At the Eagle, Grandfather picked up the news for which he had been hoping. The hurry-up boat was moored in Harris's Basin, two miles west.

"Was it called 'hurry-up' because it went fast?" Charlie asked.

"Ten furious miles an hour with a bone in its teeth," Grandfather answered.

Every section of Erie, he explained, had its own patrol-and-repair boat. It was commanded by a section superintendent, manned by a picked crew of former canal builders—toughened experts, every one—and equipped with planks, girders, joists, ropes, chains, picks, spades, mauls, mattocks and other gear. Horses chosen for speed drew it.

Grandfather got back into the saddle and rode to Harris's Basin. No light showed aboard the hurry-up boat, but in a shack on the wharf a small betty-lamp burned low. Grandfather pounded on the door and shouted, "Breached!"

Everyone seemed to wake at once. Voices called in the dimness. Feet pattered. A man who had been sleeping in his clothes opened the door.

"I'm Superintendent Glenn," he said. "We've been expecting trouble. Where?"

"Stitt's Crossing."

"That's Tom Culver's section."

"Tom's hurt. I'm acting deputy."

The superintendent cupped his hands to his mouth. "Horses! Ready aboard in three minutes. Check your kits. Go with us?" This last to Grandfather.

"No. I've got to get more workers. You'll need 'em."

As he swung back into the saddle, he saw the crew swarming aboard the thirty-foot needleboat, and three impatient horses bent on to the towrope.

"Cast off!" snapped the Super and the boat was whisked away.

Easing his mount, for the pace had been hard, the deputy trotted back through Lyons and took to the towpath. From that vantage point he could spy out some of the side-road homesteads from which he might stir up aid.

Most of the roused inmates responded with alacrity. The Erie had brought a new and wonderful prosperity to their farms, for which they were grateful. If Clinton's Ditch was in danger, they would put in their best licks to save it. House after house gave up its volunteers.

As Grandfather was about to head back to Stitt's, cattle, huddled in the corner of a field, brought to his mind the realization that draft animals might be needed. A narrow trail led him to a darkened log house. Leaning from his saddle, he rapped smartly on the door.

A window opened, disclosing a gaunt figure of a man in a butternut nightshift and peaked headgear. A musket was leveled at the caller's midriff.

"It's loaded," the figure said.

"Put it down," said Grandfather. "I'm Deputy Pathmaster Adams. The canal's breaching."

"Let 'er breach," the man said. "It ain't my canawl." And he quoted a ribald jingle derisive of Governor Clinton.

Grandfather recognized the type. The man was a hater of the great Governor and his life-work, the Erie; a makebate, a dawplucker, a malcontent politicaster. Nevertheless he had two strong, workmanlike arms.

"We need your help," Grandfather told him.

"You don't git it."

"Not for pay?"

"That's different, Mister. How much?"

"Shilling an hour."

"You've hired you a hand."

"Got any critters?"

"Yoke of oxen."

"Six shillings for the night's work."

"Keno! You can have 'em."

"Got any boys?"

"Nope. Got a wife. She's old but she's hale. Four bits for her."

"Fetch her along," Grandfather said.

He wheeled the mare, feeling well satisfied with his evening's rounds. Counting Lyons, he figured, there should be a good hundred workers on hand to aid the hurry-up crew, who should be at the place by this time. He would report back there and surrender his brief authority to the Super.

At Stitt's Crossing, fires threw a red glare upon the low, dribbling clouds. As Grandfather broke through the brush into the open, a scene of wild confusion met his eyes. There were at least one hundred and fifty people scurrying about. More were arriving every moment, on foot, on horseback or muleback, or in home-made flats, poled on the lessening wa-

ter. Nobody seemed to be in charge. Grandfather caught at
the shoulder of a man who was dragging a spile toward the
berm.

"Where's Tom Culver?" he demanded.

"In the barn yonder," the man answered. "Dead by this
time, for all I know."

"Why isn't the hurry-up boat here?"

"Mudlarked two miles west, I hear."

"Who's running things?"

"Not knowin', can't say. Tail onto the end of this spile if
you want to help."

One spile was not going to do any good against the current that was pouring through the five-yard breach. Nor were
the haphazard efforts of the unorganized crowd, so far as
Grandfather could see. Lines of men were pushing wheelbar-
rows and dumping soil which was immediately washed into
the cornfield below.

Others were busy with mauls and sledges, trying to put up
a retaining wall. As fast as the piles were driven, the flood
plucked them out and whirled them away. An unpleasant
sound, as if a soft-mouthed giant were smacking his lips,
reached Grandfather's ears. A shoulder of berm as big as a
springhouse let go and slithered down, carrying with it several
struggling volunteers, who floundered to safety as best they
might. Of repair work on such a large scale, he had had no
experience. But he remembered a saying of his father, the
canal contractor: "For a big breach, big timber."

The wood in sight of where Grandfather stood was no better than toothpicks. He ran up on the occupation bridge and
blew his whistle.

"Woodsmen and sawyers report here," he shouted.

A number of men came on the run. Here was someone who
could tell them what to do. He sent them to Farmer Stitt's
timber lot, an eighth of a mile east, with orders to fell and

trim two-to-three-foot softwoods and float them in the water. The current would carry them to the breach.

One of the woodcutters protested that rolling logs of that size up the slope of the berm would be impossible. Grandfather blew his whistle again and called for ox teams. The canal-hater's oxen and another yoke plodded up, dragging their chains. They got their orders to snake the timber out and float it as fast as it was cut. Grandfather figured that the logs should begin to come down within half an hour.

"What were you going to do with the logs when you got them, sir?" John asked.

The old gentleman smiled. "That is what I kept asking myself every time another chunk of soil flaked loose from the berm. My only plan was to do the best I could and pray that it was right."

He was forming up a gang of polemen to handle the timber on its arrival, he went on, when the wind carried a bugle-note to his ears. ("Sweetest sound ever I heard in my life," he interpolated.) The hurry-up boat came foaming through the water, the hoggee whaling his tandem with an ox-quirt borrowed for the occasion. The boat had been pried loose of the mudbank and was making its best ten miles an hour.

Grandfather ran down to meet the Super who made a flying leap from the prow and stood, staring in dismay at the cataract that roared through the widening breach.

"Good Lord of mercies!" he groaned in Grandfather's ear. "Every keel between here and Montezuma Marsh will be mudlarked by sunup. If only we had timber."

"Timber coming down!" Grandfather assured him, and pointed.

As if in answer to prayer, the current whirled down toward them two fine tree boles, a hemlock and a sycamore. Recovering quickly from his amazement, the Super yelled, "Poles!"

His crew swarmed over the gunnels of the boat and took

each his proper place. Grandfather's worries were lifted from his overburdened shoulders as the experts with their peaveys checked the speeding timber and prodded it into place. Exultantly he watched two more great logs come dashing down, then a group of half a dozen. Those woodsmen were doing a job. Grandfather got a pole for himself and fell to work.

At this point the old gentleman commanded pad and pencil and drew intricate designs to show us the wonders of engineering improvised by the hurry-up men to improvise a dam and save the berm. John may have understood. He assumed a knowing expression and put several appropriate questions; but the whole matter was beyond my comprehension. I was content with the conclusion, which was that when the sun broke through the clouds at dawn, the flood was under control.

The fires went out. The people went home. Farmer Stitt threatened to sue the Canal Commission for damage to ten acres of corn. Superintendent Glenn shook hands with Grandfather and offered him a permanent job. Grandfather curled up on the occupation bridge and went to sleep, still a Deputy Pathmaster on guard over his section.

"Did Tom Culver die?" Jenny asked.

"Not he," the old gentleman replied. "He lost his leg and his job. A one-legged pathmaster would not measure up to the standards of the Honorables, the Canal Commissioners of the State of New York."

Jenny, flushing with indignation, declared her conviction that the Honorable Canal Commissioners were old meanies.

"Do not misprize that body of just and patriotic men," the old gentleman rebuked her mildly. "They not only paid for Tom's peg leg, but also voted him a pension of five dollars a month *in perpetuum*. Upon this, eked out with what he could earn trapping musquashes at a dollar bonus, he lived handsomely to the ripe age of forty-five. The Grand Western Canal," Grandfather added with pride, "looked after its own."

THE PARLOUS TRIP

To the end of his long life, my Grandfather Adams preferred canal to rail travel. All he asked was a good, reliable four-mile-an-hour Erie packet behind a tandem of stout horses. His predilection was rooted in sentimental memory, of the good old days when Clinton's Ditch was the eighth wonder of the world, and the traffic of nations was borne upon its waters.

As for trains, he always said tartly, every last one of them was dirty, sooty, bumpy, uncomfortable, dangerous, and faithless to its schedule. Particularly did he dislike the Auburn, or Old Road, which in its day provided what was perhaps the longest trip for its distance in the United States. The seventy-six miles between Rochester and Auburn took the train three hours and forty minutes if on time, which was improbable. It was a wearisome succession of twenty-one conscientious stops at such places as Fishers, Victor, Paddlefords, Oaks Corners, Shortsville and Aurelius. Grandfather's last journey on it was in 1888, when he was close to ninety years of age.

Two days before he was to go by train from Auburn to his home in Rochester, he was discovered in private negotiation

for a one-horse rig to take him to Weedsport, where he proposed to flag a canal boat and make the trip in dignity and
comfort. He was with difficulty dissuaded by the argument
that passenger accommodations were no longer provided on
the boats, and that he would catch cold if he slept on deck.
Didn't anybody ever catch cold in the drafty cars, he asked.
Nevertheless, he took the Old Road. He did not catch cold, as
it turned out, but he did get a cinder in his eye, and arrived
home demanding to be shown the time when anybody ever
got a cinder in his eye on the Erie Canal.

Pinkeye developed. Grandfather sat with one segment of
his face bandaged, a fretful Cyclops in a darkened room, and
threatened proceedings against the New York Central. Three
of my cousins and I paid a call, both dutiful and anticipatory,
upon him at his little house on South Union Street. His normal attitude toward youth was one of austere taciturnity, but
he could, on occasion, be pleasingly reminiscent, and we went
hoping that his enforced segregation might have loosened his
tongue. To ask him to tell us stories would have been to invite a slurring remark about juvenile curiosity, and possible
dismissal. Patience and strategy were called for.

Jenny opened proceedings by solicitously asking Grandfather about his health. He said he was poorly. Reno, who
could exhibit tact on occasion, expressed the hope that
Grandfather would be at home the rest of the summer. It was
a fortunate lead. The old gentleman said that this was the last
railroad trip he was ever going to take, by Joshua! He could
recall only one worse one, and that was his first.

He communed with himself about the date of it. 1834? No,
it must have been the fall of '35. Late fall, too—probably
November. There was a whirl of snow. The Rensselaer &
Saratoga hadn't been running more than a couple of weeks.
We sat quiet, exchanging covert glances of triumph.

"Ballston to Troy—twenty-four miles," he murmured. "Six
hours. My, my!" A long pause. "Might better have roaded it

in a coach. Got there sooner and saved five shillings," Grandfather reflected. "But I always was a venturesome man." Another hiatus. "I wrote an article about it for the printer," he said.

It was now safe to ask judicious questions. In fact, it was advisable. Jenny took the initiative.

"What printer, Grandfather? Mr. Greeley?" she inquired. Grandfather's tenuous professional association with the *New York Weekly Tribune* (to which he always gave the long "i" proper to stalwart Republicanism) was a matter of continuing pride to him.

"Mr. Horace Greeley," he said. "That was some years after my trip, when he had started his great journal."

We all turned hopeful eyes upon the bookcase where stood the scrapbook of Grandfather's occasional journalistic ventures, mainly agricultural in theme and paid for at the satisfactory rate of fifty cents a column.

"Will you read the article to us, Grandfather?" Reno asked.

The old gentleman shook his head regretfully. "It remained unpublished. I entitled it 'Perils and Vicissitudes of Commerce by Rail.' Mr. Greeley wrote me a personal letter about it. He said that its publication would be injurious to the spirit of progress."

Jenny expressed her belief that Mr. Greeley was mean, and was promptly rebuked. Mr. Greeley, my grandfather said, had been the greatest man in the United States and ought to have been President. If he had ever ridden on the Rensselaer & Saratoga, he would surely have published the article.

"Was the Rensselaer & Saratoga worse than the Auburn Road?" Jenny asked.

It was, my grandfather said, though he conceded that the train itself was a fine and pompous spectacle. The Model Locomotive Engine, Erie, shone like a polished boot as it exhaled whiffs of fragrant hardwood smoke from its stack. There were two cars, richly upholstered in crimson morocco with coach-lace trimmings. One had a panel picture, "The Wounded Tiger," painted on its side. The other was similarly ornamented with "Napoleon Crossing the Alps."

"I took 'Napoleon,'" my grandfather said. "The rear car was advised to be safer."

"Were you scared, Grandpa?" asked young Charlie.

No, he was not alarmed, he said, though others were. Before the start, Mr. Wood, the engineer, had walked up and down the station platform taking snuff, tipping his beaver castor to acquaintances, and assuring the people there was no danger. "He inspired confidence," Grandfather said.

The conductor, Mr. Hoag, wore a fashionable, puce-colored surtout, bright with brass buttons. He was, according to Grandfather, an affable and officious gentleman who circulated democratically in the crowd, making friends for the railroad. The third member of the crew was an eighteen-year-old hobbledehoy in a leather jacket who stacked fagots for the firebox. A betting man in a bottlegreen greatcoat also circulated in the crowd, waving a packet of bank notes. He offered three to one that the train would not make Troy in two hours, and even money against its making it in three.

"The railroaders didn't like it," my grandfather said. "But he had paid legal tender for his ticket. What could they do?"

Five minutes before the train was to start, an oxcart drew up beside the track. The driver stood and cursed the engine, the engineer, the conductor and the fireboy, and hoped the locomotive would drag them all to the bottomless pit of perdition, and serve them right. He enumerated the risks of travel by rail: boilers blew up, wheels came off, bridges broke down, snake rails curled up through the floors of cars and spitted people like fowls, engineers got drunk and ran their trains into rivers, drowning all hands, and so on.

"It was mostly boggledebotch," Grandfather said, "but it

scared some timid folk. Several wanted their money back."

"Did they get it?" I asked.

"Mr. Hoag paid on the nail. Said that nobody had to travel on *his* train unless they'd a mind to."

"What ailed the oxcart man?" Sireno asked.

"The locomotive had run over his pig. He saw all the trains off and warned the passengers. The railroad had him arrested for slander, but the judge loosed him with a warning."

Now well launched, Grandfather proceeded to give us a word picture of his experience. Mr. Hoag, he said, set a small tin horn to his lips and blew five rapid toots. Late passengers clambered aboard. Engineer Wood mounted to his place and tested the reflexes of his machinery. Conductor Hoag swung himself to the sideboard that ran along the outside of "The Wounded Tiger," took a graceful pose, and waved his tall castor. The locomotive hiccuped and belched a gobbet of smoke into the air, the wheels spun, the cars jolted into motion, the people raised a huzza, and the oxcart man delivered a final imprecation. They were off.

Starting on a level stretch, the train gathered headway with impressive power and rhythm. Urchins running beside it were soon outdistanced. Beyond the town limits, a horseman on a parallel shunpike entered into competition with the train. For a time it was nip and tuck, but soon the thundering machine drew away, to the cheers of the passengers.

"That was speed," my grandfather said. "But when we came to the forest, we stopped before every curve."

"What for?" Reno asked.

"So the boy could walk ahead to look for fallen timber or wild animals on the right of way."

"Wild animals!" said Charlie excitedly. "Were there?"

"No; but, as I was about to state when I was interrupted," the old gentleman said severely, "the week before, a she-bear with two cubs trespassed on the right of way. She chased the fireboy and tried to bite the engine. It caused great alarm among the passengers and delayed the traffic half an hour."

"But it didn't happen to your train," Charlie said. "Didn't anything happen to your train?"

"Yes," my grandfather replied. "We slowed down to a stop in a clearing without any reason. A dandified passenger with a deep bass voice walked along the cars and kept asking, 'Has any person present got a piece of string? Our locomotivator has broke down.' Everybody laughed consumedly."

"Why?" Reno asked.

"It was considered a very risible jest. It must have been, too. Many comedians later took it up."

Grandfather mentioned several: Yankee Hill, the dialect comic, incorporated it into one of his famous soliloquies; Buffalo Dixon, who could project his stentorian voice across the Hudson, hollered it at his admiring audiences; Thatcher, Primrose & West's minstrel show took it over, the end man asking for a safety pin instead of the piece of string. Grandfather had even heard that the low comedian of *The Black Crook* had invented a variant, but as to that, he said, he would not know. He directed his bloodshot gaze first upon Reno and then upon me. We tried to look unself-conscious. *The Black Crook* was a leg show and not for youths of respectable upbringing.

"Mr. Orlando Montague was doubtless the original inventor of the jest," my grandfather said. "He was deservedly notorious as the wit of Troy."

"What a lovely name!" said Jenny, who was fifteen and romantic. "Was he a poet?"

"No. He was a blacksmith. Called himself an ironmonger. Claimed to have invented the first free collar."

"Train," young Charlie said. "I want to know more about the train."

"The engineer and the fireboy tinkered and puttered and got the locomotivator going again," said Grandfather. "It wheezed and sputtered, but it operated. At the next crossing, there was a gang of charcoal burners. They cheered."

"I cheered when the Fast Mail went through Dunkirk," I said. "It was all white and went fifty miles an hour."

"We were going twenty-five," my grandfather said, "but that was downgrade. The lady next me said her prayers."

"Then did the betting gentleman lose his bet?" Jenny asked.

"He won. When we reached the next upgrade, Mr. Wood stopped the engine and came back and said to Mr. Hoag, 'She ain't steaming right.' Mr. Hoag said, 'That's your business, not mine,' and Mr. Wood said, 'She'll never make it. It's this danged slithery snow.' We all got out and the engine tried to haul the empty cars, but it stopped halfway up the grade and slid back."

"Did it slide off the track?" Charlie asked hopefully.

"No. It stayed on," Grandfather said. "Mr. Hoag tooted his horn and waved his arms and called out, 'All able-bodied men to tail on and shovel!' I heard him, but I didn't heed him. I sat down on a stump."

"Weren't you able-bodied, Grandfather?" Jenny inquired.

"I was able-bodied enough. But I didn't see why I should use *my* steam to get the Rensselaer & Saratoga train where it was going. The betting man felt the same way. He made a speech and said he was a free American citizen and he had paid his tariff to the railroad and he wasn't helping anybody's spavined teakettle to do its job. That riled the engineer, and he offered to fight the betting man, freehold, fair, or rough-and-tumble. The engineer got out a dollar and put it on a stump, and the betting man got out his dollar and put it beside the other, and both took off their coats." Grandfather paused for effect.

"Did they fight?" asked Charlie breathlessly.

"They would have, I expect, but a pockmarked gentleman with a glass eye came between them. He said he was a magistrate of the City of Troy and he would arrest both of them if they breached the peace, so that ended that. The magistrate addressed me and said I could be seen to be a man of substance and wouldn't I set an example by helping out the railroad men? I told him I would not. It was a matter of principle. The engineer spoke up saucily and said what kind of poxy principle was that, to keep a lot of folks there in the cold? I said to him, 'I've traveled hundreds of miles on the good old Erie Canal, and nobody with brass buttons ever yet asked me to get out and push.' Then he offered to fight *me*."

"I don't suppose the magistrate would let him," Reno said regretfully.

"I have always been a peaceful man," Grandfather said.

The magistrate, Grandfather went on, remembered that his wife's relatives had a farm not more than two miles away, which they worked with a team of oxen, powerful animals that could snake the cars up the hill slick as a mink. "But the Van Woggleums are Dutch and mortal smart bargainers," the magistrate said. "I doubt they'd hold out for ten shilling, at best."

He passed the hat. Grandfather would not give a cent. He said he had paid to travel by steam and he wouldn't give a fip for any other way of travel. He stood by his principles.

The sum was made up without him and a committee dispatched to the farm. There followed a three-hour delay—an hour for the committee to reach the farm, a half for chaffering over the price, another hour to get back, and the remainder for hauling the cars up the grade. Meanwhile, the temperature fell several degrees below freezing, and a gnawing north wind set in. Two woodsmen, with their axes, were among the waiting passengers. They felled a dead tree, cut it up, built a comforting fire, and took up a contribution. "Pretty near got their fare back, I wouldn't wonder," said my grandfather.

Flasks were produced and passed. Without further charge the woodsmen cut hemlock boughs for seats, and Mr. Montague, who belonged to the Troy Harmonia, led in song to pass the time. Grandfather said the passengers sang hymns, and "Hail Columbia," and an inferior tune called "The Defense of Fort McHenry." "Too up and down and twiddle-deedeedly," he said, and hummed it.

"Why, that's 'The Star-Spangled Banner'!" Jenny cried.

"Such was the name later attached to it by the ignorant," Grandfather retorted. "In any case, it would require a steam calliope for proper rendition."

When the oxen came, a final complication developed. Conductor Hoag sat down in front of the locomotive and refused to budge. "He said," Grandfather told us, "that if it ever got to the Skeneckers that his train had to be snaked out by a pair of oxen, he might as well advertise himself for twopence and a bucket of ashes, for he'd never dare show his phiz again in a respectable taproom."

"What's a Skenecker?" Reno asked, and I added, "What did he mean by a bucket of ashes?"

I got the first reply. Twopence and a bucket of ashes, the old gentleman said, was the standard advertisement for an evaded apprentice who was not worth having back. A Skenecker was an operating hand on the rival Schenectady & Saratoga line.

"He was right, too," Grandfather said. "The other railroaders called him Two-Ox Willie to the day of his quittance."

"Then they did get him off the track?" Jenny said.

Grandfather replied that a slight whoobub had taken place, in which Mr. Hoag got his collar torn and an unnamed passenger received a black eye. Afterward, the locomotivator and then, singly, "The Wounded Tiger" and "Napoleon Crossing the Alps," were hauled to the summit by the oxen, and the engine, with a fresh head of steam, resumed its proper function.

"We made four more stops and pulled up at the town line of Troy," Grandfather went on. "The engineer unhitched his locomotive, and the fireboy fetched four horses and laid them

on to draw us through the streets. There was a law. The alder-
men wouldn't allow a locomotive inside the city. They said it
would scare the livestock with its noise and foul the windows
with its smoke. The horses landed us in front of the Troy
House at exactly eight o'clock, Baptist time."

"What's Baptist time?" asked Jenny.

Grandfather explained that some years earlier the Peculiar
Baptists had set up a clock in their steeple. Thereafter, Troy
had taken its time from that.

"Is that all that happened to you, Grandfather?" Charlie
asked.

"No," Grandfather said. "I caught a quinsy from waiting in
the cold and had to put up at the Mansion House. It was
very costly—a dollar a day. Besides, I had to call the doctor.
He purged me and puked me and charged me two shillings
every call. All the fault of the railroad."

This appeared to be the end of the story. Reno asked,
"Could you have licked the engineer, Grandfather?"

"I did," Grandfather said.

We hunched our chairs forward eagerly.

"It was the day I left," he said, speaking in a tone of solemn
satisfaction. "I was paying my scot when Mr. Wood came out
of the Mansion House taproom with his beaver cocked over
one ear. He said, 'Ho, you cheap canawler!' but, being a
peaceful man, I let it pass. Then he said something that I'd
take from no railroader. He said he could spit a better canawl
than ever old Clinton built with all the poxy Adamses from
Adams Basin to Lock Seventeen helping him. Then," Grandfather said, "I punched his eye."

THE MONSTER OF
EPIDEMY

The Cholera cometh; take care!—take care!
Look well to thy dwelling; beware!—beware!
He breatheth corruption and loveth the spot
Where offal is suffered to lie and to rot.
Then look to thy cellar, thy closet and yard.
For all kinds of filth he hath special regard.

In his less austere moments, Grandfather Adams used to chant this verse to a lilting measure and then regale his grandchildren, half a century after the event, with his memories of the pestilence that swept upstate New York during the summer of 1832 when from his home near Rochester, he had occasion to make several business trips up and down the Erie Canal. After another half century or so, I came upon the jingle in a bound volume of the *Cholera Bulletin*, a weekly put out by a group of physicians in New York City, where the plague was just as virulent, but of course, Grandfather, in those days of sketchy communications, didn't hear much about that. The

Bulletin contained, also, a mass of information which corroborated the old gentleman's observations.

The occasion of Grandfather's first reminiscent excursion into the medical past was a slight indisposition on the part of his youngest grandson. Charlie, on this June afternoon visit to the Adams cottage, sat, huddled on his chair in the sitting room, punctuating Grandfather's reading of the Rev. T. De Witt Talmadge's sermon with ill-suppressed grunts. Grandfather lowered the newspaper and stared over the top of his spectacles at the offender.

"What ails the boy?" he demanded.

"I'm sick," was the doleful reply.

"What have you been eating?"

"Cherries," Jenny answered for him. "A whole pint."

"Mrs. Adams! Mrs. Adams!" Our step-grandmother appeared at the kitchen door. "Fetch a tablespoon. . . . No, a teaspoon will serve. . . . Samuel, hand me that bottle. . . . Open your mouth, Charles."

Protest against a grandfatherly command would have been futile, as all of us well knew. Sniveling, Charlie obeyed. The dose of Hop Bitters went down with a splutter and a gulp. The victim gasped as the potently alcoholic liquid burned its way into his interior.

"That should ease you," the old gentleman said.

Charlie had his doubts. "I got a stomach ache," he complained.

"Hah!" Grandfather commented. "A stomach ache! What should a spratling like you know of stomach aches!"

"Well, it hurts just the same," the spratling said, rubbing the seat of the trouble.

The old gentleman let the Rev. T. DeWitt Talmadge slip to the floor. "What would you say to a stomach ache that extended canalside from Albany to Buffalo?"

Not knowing what to say to it, Charlie held his tongue. Reno spoke up.

"Did you have it, Grandpa?"

"A dummock's question. How could any individual have it? Everybody had it. York State had it." He quelled Charlie's mumblings with a slowly waggled forefinger and launched into his narrative.

It was late in the spring of 1832 that the Cholera (often dignified in contemporary records with a capital "C") first threatened. It had crossed the Atlantic and attacked first Montreal, then New York City. Medical commissions from upstate communities visited both ports and brought back reassuring word. The malady was both controllable and curable, they declared. It was also non-contagious. Of the three hundred and sixty-two members of the Exchange Coffee House, a highly select club in Montreal, only one member had succumbed. Those elements with which society could most profitably dispense—the low, the dissolute, the unthrifty —were the disease's customary victims. For, as one of the commissions pointed out, it was mainly "found among the most miserable and degraded of the population—white, black and colored," and "arises entirely from their habits of life." Reputable folk had only to guard against such predisposing causes as "intemperance, fatigue, night air, and sleeping with open windows," and all would be well with them. Secure in its sense of respectability, upstate New York appointed committees and calmly awaited the issue.

Late in June Albany experienced an epidemic of severe stomach aches. These were soothingly designated as mock or common cholera without the warning capital letter. Several victims died. "Cholera morbus," amended the authorities. According to local legend and my grandfather's memory, the first acknowledged case of Asiatic Cholera, July 3rd, was "Pig" Baker, the municipal swineherd whose free-roving charges acting as combined Street Cleaning Department and Garbage Disposal Plant of the 25,000-population capital. Another citizen was stricken on the same day. Within the week several undeniable cases appeared and four deaths were reported in a riverside hovel occupied by a family said to be of alcoholic habit.

Alert, but still undismayed, settlements westward made preparations. Durham boats freighted hogsheads of tar to the canal communities. Utica bought fifty bushels of lime for the use of its poor. Camphor, soda and stomachics were heavily stocked by the grocery trade. A touring Britisher wrote my grandfather:

> All along your Grand Erie Canal my
> attention has been engaged by tar fumes,
> rising to befoul the sky. Do your
> countrymen, then, think to scare off
> the Cholera daemons by such Chinese
> sorceries? What ignorami! The deadly
> epidemy is not so conveniently
> to be repulsed.

"Not such ignorami as he supposed," Grandfather chuckled. "They were not practicing magic but cleansing the polluted air of its choleraic miasms."

In Syracuse he witnessed a test designed to determine the true origin of the disease. There were two principal schools of medical thought, the telluric and the meteorastic. The tellurists held that the soil, itself, was Cholera-polluted and transmitted the malady to humans through fruits and vegetables. The meteorasts ascribed it to the atmosphere while differing among themselves as to whether it was an electric generation in the upper strata or miasmic, exhaling from the earth.

The matter was put to the proof at the Presbyterian church. A ten-pound round of beef was fixed upon the spire. At the end of an hour it was brought down for examination. It was rotted through. Although a few diehard tellurists may have suspected that the butcher who supplied the beef was in the pay of the meteorasts or eager to rid himself profitably of a not very fresh cut, the test settled the issue for most Syracusans. The Cholera was not of earth but of air.

The experiment flabbergasted those loyal citizens of the town who had religiously believed that the atmosphere of Syracuse was amply protected from taint by the prophylactic vapors exhaling from its salt beds. The Freeholders had already held a meeting at the Mansion House for the purpose of "taking into consideration and adopting the best means to be pursued with regard to the anticipated Plague that is expected soon to be among us." The meeting voted an emergency appropriation to fight the disease, called for volunteers to visit the sick, divided the city into sanitary districts, each with a public-spirited citizen in charge, and distributed lime vats to help dissipate the poisonous vapors.

One of the early volunteers was a Dr. Kirkpatrick, a Princeton alumnus who had quit his practice to become superintendent of the Onondaga Salt Springs. He was an avowed "contagionist," believing against the weight of professional authority that the disease was transmissible from man to man. His first assignment was to administer a syringe treatment to a stricken neighbor. He completed the operation, collapsed, and died of fright. Similar cases were reported from other towns.

Albany had taken official cognizance of its peril by the time Grandfather arrived around mid-July. Two highly respectable burghers, Erastus Corning and Stephen Van Rensselaer, appointed as a Board of Health, generously voted themselves three hundred dollars apiece, plugged their noses with cotton, made a tour of inspection, ordered foul premises cleared up, and exhorted the public to abjure strong drink and be of good cheer. Unable to reconcile mandates so self-contradictory, the more prosperous started a quiet exodus which probably scattered the contagion and certainly spread the news of it which the local papers had been suppressing.

At this time the teetotal movement was strong in the state capital. The various Sober Societies, as the temperance organizations were then generically called, claimed a local complement of more than four thousand. They went into action. Evangelists marched through the streets with bottled water from the city's famed State Street Spring and documentary pledges in two languages, prepared for signature or the equally binding "X his Mark," the latter being seldom necessary in that literate community where three-fourths of the population could read and write either English or Dutch—many of them, both. One formula was a revival from earlier days, the Minister's Oath, devised by a group of crusading Massachusetts clerics.

Recognizing the evils of drunkenness and resolved to check its alarming increase, we do solemnly pledge ourselves not to get drunk except on Christmas, at Sheepshearing, Independence Day, and Muster Day.

"Nobody could get from waterfront to the Capitol without a score of accosts from these well-meaning zealots," Grandfather told us.

A stock argument for sobriety was that only two out of the total four thousand temperance members had died of the cholera."

"Probably a lie," said Grandfather who, though an ardent abstentionist himself, was a stickler for facts.

Gradually the comforting faith that the respectable elements of society were immune—the credo so industriously promulgated by the authorities—weakened. Early in August that influential national periodical, *Niles Weekly Register*, a powerful prop of the thesis, acknowledged with obvious dismay:

Several worthy and prudent persons have lately died at Albany of the Cholera.

In the teeth of the best medical authorities, the plague had clearly surmounted the barriers of class and character and was striking right and left. Three emergency pest-houses, hastily put into commission, filled and overflowed. People fell, writhing, on the streets. Houses were found with forgotten dead in them. Coaches arrived empty and departed full. Theatres and museums closed. Stores boarded their windows. Food became scarce; potatoes went to a dollar a bushel. Camphor, which was highly regarded though wholly inert as a medicament, rose from thirty cents to five dollars a pound, with calomel and brandy following suit. Physicians who were normally satisfied to get four shillings for a night call or a dollar for reducing a fracture, demanded and received six dollars a day for serving the city. Burials rose from fifty cents to two dollars per cadaver. Half the homes in town were in mourning.

Though disturbed by the news from their capital, the York Staters were too sturdy a breed to be stampeded into panic. But they did take a more serious view of the threat than at first. Pious folk attributed the visitation to the vengeance of Heaven upon the sins of the people. The remnant of the old Federalist aristocracy ascribed it to President Andy Jackson and his "blasphemous Democracy." The Sober Societies blamed it upon the national habit of tippling. "Flagitious youth," said the purists. "Freemasonry," cried the militant anti-Masons. Some cleric with a knack of the dramatic catch-word preached a sermon on The Monster of Epidemy, and the phrase was taken over as a text in a score of pulpits. These "Cholera sermons" were complained of by the Rochester *Liberal Advocate* as being a potent auxiliary of the disease. Because of them "consternation seized the inhabitants and thousands fled," recorded the editor over his *nom de plume* of Obadiah Dogbery.

Cities, towns and hamlets set aside days for penitence and supplication. There were public prayers and preachments, fright-inspired conversions in the open streets and much hasty signing of pledges. Henry Clay moved in the Senate for a day of national fasting and prayer, but nothing came of it. People remembered that, as Speaker of the House, he had welcomed the Cyprian sisterhood to the halls of Congress and even set aside rooms for their solace and entertainment.

"Some of us," commented Grandfather, "doubted whether Harry of the West would appear to advantage before the Throne of Grace as the inspirer of any petition."

"Sanatory proposals," official and unofficial, now flooded the authorities. The tar smudge observed by the sardonic British letter writer was perhaps the most widely used device, though the lime vat must have run it close. A Dr. Clericault advanced a scheme for perpetual bonfires to consume the evil aerial influences. An unidentified hygienist suggested salvos of heavy artillery to dissipate the hovering poisons, and, from a derisive comment in the *Cholera Bulletin,* it would appear that this was actually tried. The Syracuse test having established beef as an absorbent of the miasms, other towns set out raw chunks on poles to keep the air pure. "A high authority," cited in the Utica *Sentinel & Gazette,* prescribed as a useful prophylactic porridge poultices on the belly and wooden shoes against the penetration of telluric toxins through the soles. Two propositions were relentlessly hammered into the public consciousness; that strong drink was an invitation to infection and that to sleep with open windows was a wanton solicitation of death.

Rochester, while officially accepting the theory of non-contagiousness, took early protective measures by instituting an inspection of marine traffic from Canada, at first regarded as the danger point. When the epidemic struck from the canal, a waterfront cooperage was set aside under the management of an intrepid volunteer constable.

"He was a true hero," Grandfather said. "Monuments have been raised to men of lesser achievement. Yet Simmy's very name is forgotten and no man knows where he is buried."

"Did he die of the cholera, sir?" John asked.

"Well, no," the old gentleman answered after a momentary hesitation. "No, he did not. We may touch upon that at some future time."

He dropped the subject of Simmy and went on to say that no patient, native or alien, was turned away from that primitive refuge.

The leading civic spirit of Rochester at the time was Colonel (and Elder) Ashbel P. Riley, a rigorous sabbatarian who at one time threatened to stop the Sunday mailcoaches, even if he had to wrestle down the horses with his own mighty hands. Garbed in sober blacks, he circulated throughout the city, seeking and gathering in the sick for delivery to the cooperage, collecting drugs and supplies for their use, acting as sick-ward aide, and, at the height of the onset, not only carrying out and burying the dead, but conducting their funeral services.

"A Scriptural figure, terrible in his righteousness," said my grandfather with a measure of awe undissipated after a half century.

Such makeshifts as the Rochester cooperage, the abandoned Utica warehouse, and the Albany almshouse were known as Cholera Refuges. This long antedated the day of hospitals, except in the largest cities, and the emergency establishments lacked much of being satisfactory substitutes. A typical ward was a room of perhaps forty by seventy feet containing four rows of cots, its windows carefully blanketed against the deadly peril of night air. That institution was rare, indeed, which could boast of allocating a bed to every patient.

The beds of the better sort were cast-iron frames attached to plank bottoms covered with hay or straw. When these were full and no more doubling-up was possible, patients were assigned to wooden packing boxes placed in the hallways. Attending physicians reported an inexplicable rise in "spontaneous gangrene, product of hospital air" (once more the envenomed air!) which modern diagnosis might identify as bedsores, product of hospital filth. Flies and mosquitoes swarmed, and an inventive genius from Utica tried unsuccessfully to sell the authorities his patent steam bedbug-killing machine.

"The quack salvers had a heyday," Grandfather said. "The most successful was Dr. Hashalew, who claimed to be sole possessor of a secret and certain cure compounded by a deceased Seneca Indian medicine man. Years before, I had met the fellow. He then called himself Professor Popple and performed feats of magic in a booth attached to an itinerant fair. Now he traveled in his own coach with a painted banner guaranteeing a twenty-four-hour cure for cholera or your money back. As most of his patients died, few claims were presented."

There was, of course—Grandfather went on—a desperate shortage of doctors and nurses. The high pay offered to the latter attracted a disreputable crew. Midwives, magnetic healers, operatives of the medic-shows (itinerant nostrum vendors), herb and root diggers, electric shock-machine fakers, and even gypsies gathered to the lure of twelve, sixteen, twenty shillings per day. With few exceptions they were a noisome and unruly lot. They robbed the sick, stole the bedding, feasted on the victuals contributed by the charitable, got drunk on the medical comforts, and held high revel. It was charged to their inefficiency and neglect that hospital deaths often exceeded house mortality.

"I'd rather have taken my chance at home," was Grandfather's considered opinion.

It was with good reason that the Erie Canal, the pride of the nation, came to be looked upon as the villain. Penny-a-mile-

and-found passenger craft were carrying a heavy traffic of cheap contract labor from the cholera-ridden countries of Europe up the Hudson and through the canal to mine silver, build railroads, and toil in the potasheries to the west. The pestilence was breaking out aboard these boats so frequently that toward midsummer the health officials of towns along the canal took to sending them on their way (often with a capital "C" painted or branded on their prows) with the most unseemly haste.

Things finally got so bad that Rochester wrathfully accused its fellow-cities to the east of refusing to let the boats discharge infected passengers and even, in the case of some who were ill and had reached their destination, of paying their fares to another point in order to get rid of them. One boat, the *Western Barque*, with fifty-six English, Irish and Swiss immigrants aboard, drew into Syracuse "so foul," according to a letter later found among Grandfather's papers, "that dainty persons passing to leeward were fain to puke." The vessel's crew had already disposed of several corpses by dumping them into the canal. Others still lay between decks. The captain was dying. Syracuse clapped a fifteen-day embargo on westbound traffic.

It was a matter of permanent regret to Grandfather Adams, who, as an active member of the Wayne County Horse-thief Society, had acquired a taste for guerrilla warfare, that he missed the Running of the Locks. Teall's Lock, just east of Syracuse, was that town's quarantine station and guards were posted there to halt cholera-ridden vessels. Boats loaded with contract laborers piled up until the waterway was all but choked. Their barge captains, at best a turbulent lot, lost patience and held a meeting, at which they decided on strong measures. The boats must go through. On the appointed night, the captains, girt for the fray in their brass-buttoned coats and tall, brightly painted beaver hats, formed up their cookees, hoggees and steersmen, and rushed the lock. By common report, they were led by three veteran "canawlers" making martial music on fife, harmonica and jew's-harp. There was no difficulty in dispersing the guard and capturing the lock, but it took all night to lock the boats through the city. The maneuver produced a running battle between the Eriemen and mobs of the local citizenry, with much action, many casualties, and no fatalities. The Syracuse authorities seem to have shown little interest in the proceedings. Presumably, they felt that the contract laborers were too prickly a problem for them to handle and the sooner the locality was rid of them the better. Let Rochester have them. Among the many undesirable craft foisted on that hospitable city was the *Columbia*, carrying fifty-six passengers, of whom five were dead on arrival and fourteen others so ill that they died soon after being transferred to the cooperage.

In August, a blast of wind—laden, so people thought, with a poisonous virus from the canal—swept the hamlet of Lennox, twenty-five miles west of Auburn, and whole households were wiped out in less than twenty-four hours.

Even the most determined optimists now admitted the gravity of the situation. The Utica papers, which had played down the virulence of the malady, declaring it to be less dangerous than smallpox, recanted. Hamilton College, at Clinton, gave the change of attitude academic sanction by calling off its commencement, which in those days was held in midsummer.

The public reaction, as far as Grandfather could make out, was not so much terror as gloom and distrust. City streets were strangely silent; people tended to shun one another. After all, the disease *might* be catching, in spite of medical assurances to the contrary. Dr. Henry Bronson of Albany mustered up courage to declare for what he cautiously termed "contingent contagion," active among (of course) the poor, the uncleanly and the intemperate.

The prestige of the medical profession was at lowest ebb,

although the doctors were doing their utmost, trying everything from bleeding and tobacco juice enemas to laughing gas and the burning of moxas, a primitive and drastic method of cautery, on the patient's arms or legs. They produced figures to prove that only a quarter—well, perhaps a third—of those infected died. Few believed them. A contemporary poetaster sourly sang:

> Cholera kills and doctors slay
> And every foe will have its way.

What doctors and committees could not accomplish, an early September frost did. A few days after its coming, *Niles Weekly Register* sounded the first cheerful note since spring; the epidemy was on the wane. By the middle of the month, no new cases were being reported. The tar smudges were quenched. The lungs of the upstaters were no longer affronted by fumes from the lime vats. Refuges closed. Timorous fugitives returned home. Canal and coach travel slowly increased to normal. Business revived. A quack, calling himself the Fire King, who had given up eating live coals to peddle a sure-cure Elixir Cholerae, was hounded off the canal berm near Chittenango by a hooting mob.

"Folks took heart," Grandfather said, "and boys whistled again in the streets."

THE CAMERA AND THE
CHIMERA

Each Friday, Grandfather Adams used to drive across the Genesee River from his home on South Union Street to visit my father in his Plymouth Church study and give him doctrinal advice for his forthcoming sermon. On these occasions, the old gentleman was likely to encounter several of his grandchildren, for my cousins and I found the rear room, behind Father's study, a great attraction. Here Father kept his butterfly collection; also a jig saw for the scrollwork so popular in the early 1880's, and a Caligraph, on which we could practice typing.

Going to the study one rainy Friday, accompanied by three cousins, I found Father deep in talk with a serious-faced man of about thirty. Grandfather had not yet appeared. The two were conferring over a smallish wooden box, which the stranger handled with care. Father looked up with a smile when the four of us appeared, and motioned us to the back room. The visitor, too absorbed to notice us, did something to his box which thereupon clicked interestingly.

"I'd give a dime to know what's in it," John said as he closed the door of the rear room behind us.

"Snakes!" said young Charlie excitedly. This was not impossible, for Father was addicted to natural history.

"Snakes don't click," said Jenny.

"Here comes Grandpa," John said, looking out the window.

We heard the study door open and Grandfather's deep tones dominating the brief conversation that followed, after which the stranger departed. Assuming that the proceedings would now become exegitical, we four lost interest in them, until we heard Grandfather, his voice raised, address his son as "Myron Adams, Junior."

"Something's up," John said.

"Let's listen," said Charlie. John cautiously opened the door a crack.

"No, no, my son!" Grandfather was saying earnestly. "I warn you. I have seen the elephant, and I warn you."

"What elephant?" Charlie asked eagerly, forgetting to whisper. "Where did he see an elephant?"

The fat was in the fire. The conversation in the study stopped; I swung the door wide. Without turning his head, the old gentleman said in measured accents, "In *my* grandfather's boyhood, little eavesdroppers were set in the stocks and had their ears cropped."

"You're the oldest; say something," John whispered to Jenny, and he and I got behind her and propelled her into the study. She did the best she could.

"We came in because we thought maybe you were telling Uncle Myron about building the canal, or something, and we wanted to hear," she said sweetly and shamelessly.

"You said you saw an elephant, Grandpa," Charlie added.

To betray embarrassment before us would have been beneath the old gentleman's dignity, but for a moment he looked a bit discountenanced. He had been guilty of using slang, something he considered reprehensible in us.

"A figure of speech," he said mildly. "More commonly and crudely expressed in the form of the familiar saw, 'Once bit, twice shy.'"

"What bit you?" Charlie persisted, still hopeful.

"Sit down and hold your tongue," Grandfather commanded, pointing to a discarded pew against the wall. "All of you," he added.

We obeyed, relieved at not having been banished, as he turned to my father and resumed the interrupted colloquy.

"A sober and industrious bank clerk, eh?" he asked, evidently referring to the departed visitor. "And the box? What are its contents?"

"It's a mechanism," Father began. "An invention of his own."

"Inventions are wiles of Satan, and investment in them sheer wastethrift," Grandfather said. "How much did he invite you to put into it?"

"One hundred dollars was mentioned," Father said hesitantly.

"A mere nothing to a rich young minister," Grandfather replied sardonically. "No more than a dozen wedding fees and a few funerals."

"Surely some inventions have both forwarded human progress and proved profitable," said my father. "I even thought, sir, that you might wish to look into it yourself, with a view to a small investment."

The old gentleman glowered at the inoffensive box as if it were an infernal machine. "What is the precise nature of this device?" he asked.

"It is a camera, operated on a new principle."

"Camera!" It was almost a roar. "Is that young man a *cameraman?*"

"Why, yes, sir," my father said. "An amateur. His apparatus

is designed for amateurs, to enable them to take their own pictures by simple pressure on a lever. This camera . . .' "

"Camera! Chimera!" Grandfather broke in. So pleased was he with this neat apposition that he repeated it and added a challenge. "Camera! Chimera! Press your lever. Take my photograph."

"This is only a model," Father explained. "A great deal of adjustment will be needed before it is perfected."

"Just so! And you would risk your savings and tempt mine in such bobcrackery. No, no, my son. Never trust a cameraman. The two slipperiest rapscallions ever I met in my life operated cameras. That was fifty years ago and better, and I have not seen their like since, in jail or out."

"Why, Grandpa, photographs weren't invented then," Jenny said. She had written a class essay on "The Art of Daguerre," and knew all about it.

"Photographs? I said nothing about photographs," the old gentleman retorted sharply. "Cameras. Quimby manipulated a camera obscura and his partner, Carr, a camera lucida, and which was the greater ingler I should be at a loss to tell you."

"Did they take your picture, Grandfather?" Charlie asked.

"They took more than that," Grandfather replied grimly. "As will happen to you, my son," he added, turning back to my father, "if you are not wary of this higgler."

The archaic term encouraged our expectations. When Grandfather reverted to the past in his manner of speech, it was usually the prelude to reminiscence, and this time was no exception.

Grandfather, a spruce young blade, though nearly thirty, drove over to Palmyra in his high-wheeled cart, of the kind called "suicide gig," to make a little deal in flaxseed. Outside the town, he saw a pair of men sitting on the berm of the Erie Canal in the shade of a basswood. Jaunty fellows they were, with hats painted like packet captains' and a flirt of ribbon on their walking staves. Overhead a pear-shaped, straw-bound bottle, plugged with a makeshift brown-paper pledget, swung from a limb in the cooling breeze. They hailed Grandfather and offered him a draught of callebogus, which he declined, having no taste for rum-and-molasses and being cautious of strangers, as was the part of wisdom along Erie Water. What evil impulse induced him even to enter into discourse with such flash gentry was beyond his power to explain, he said sourly; the fellowship of the road, he supposed. At any rate, he stopped to talk, and Quimby, the taller and more voluble of the two, gave a brief account of himself and his partner.

They were businessmen turned artists. Quimby had traveled the back roads and shunpikes, selling Russell's Itch Ointment, a product endorsed by Governor Clinton and Henry Clay. His partner, Carr, had been a Lake Ontario slooper out of Sodus. A common passion for art had brought them together, and with their cameras they had been working the canal with some success. At the moment, they were broke. Quimby turned out his pockets with a dramatic gesture.

"Haven't a bowel," he said. "We fell in with a camp of gyppos last night. I think their dice were dickey. Just when we needed capital to develop the project. Thousands in it. Thousands and thousands, if knowingly handled."

Grandfather, the self-styled artist went on cunningly, looked like a young spark who knew his way about. Would he be interested in a profitable investment, with no risk and quick returns? Grandfather replied that art was art, and he was a man of commerce. Thereupon Carr trundled out from behind a bush a strange contrivance.

Art, it seemed, was not the project that needed development. The device the men showed Grandfather was a patent chinch-killer. It was a five-foot wooden box on wheels, underslung with a metal firebox. The low box was loaded with bags filled with some mysterious substance, and on top of the whole thing was a conical peak, formed by a coiled vent that made it look something like a beehive. On the front of the machine was lettered the word "Eliminator." The pair had bought it, they said, with all rights from the inventor, a Utica man presently in jail for debt.

"What is a chinch?" Jenny asked.

"Inquire of your Uncle Myron," Grandfather answered. "He is the scientist."

Father smiled. "Cimex lectularius, I assume," he said.

"Precisely," said the old gentleman. "The pestilence that walketh in darkness. In other words, bedbugs."

"Oh!" Jenny said faintly. "I've never even seen one."

She would have seen plenty, Grandfather assured her, had she traveled the early traffic routes. Inns, taverns, roadhouses, coaches and canalboats teemed with them, especially the boats. Quimby had suggested that he might like to see an example of how art could be made to subserve commerce. Grandfather had said that he had no objection.

"Wait till a female heaves in sight," Quimby said.

A few minutes later, horses appeared on the towpath, drawing a smallish craft. Grandfather, who knew every boat on Erie Water, recognized her for the *Stormy Lass*, Captain Briggs Le Moyne, a short-haul plying from Syracuse westward. She carried a deckload of pickled eels in kegs, on their way to be sold at wharfside in Rochester. Mrs. Le Moyne, a well-rounded, comely woman of thirty, was at the tiller. Quimby unslung his camera obscura, descended to the water's edge, and sighted through it.

"Lady," he called. "I should admire to take your picture."

"How much?" she asked.

"Beauty is its own reward," Quimby said, with an elegant bow. "Gratis, to you."

Mrs. Le Moyne cupped her hands and shouted, "Whoa!" Fifty yards along the towpath, the hoggee, driving the tandem that was the standard motor power of canal traffic, pulled up.

The rope slackened and the *Stormy Lass* nosed in against the berm. It was easy to see, Grandfather observed, who was boss of that freighter.

"Come aboard," the lady said, and the partners and Grandfather climbed the rail.

Leading Mrs. Le Moyne into the foredeck cabin, Quimby set up his camera while Carr darkened the windows, lighted the small cabin lamp, and arranged the subject's pose. Quimby adjusted his lens, and slanted the camera's interior mirror to the proper angle, so that it cast a diminished image of Mrs. Le Moyne on a frosted-glass screen at the back of the camera. Putting a blank piece of paper against the glass, he set to work to transfer the lines of the image onto the paper with delicate strokes. It took him only a few minutes. The two craftsmen conferred gravely over the finished outline, approved it, and indicated to Mrs. Le Moyne that the sitting was over.

Quimby escorted her outside, and Carr got out his crayons and colored the portrait with some skill. At this point, Captain Le Moyne, emerging from below, inquired suspiciously what was up, only to be squelched by a look from his wife. The whole process was over in twenty minutes and the finished portrait presented to the lady, whereupon Quimby proceeded to the real business of the day.

"Lady and Captain," he said, "do you have chinches aboard?"

Captain Le Moyne could not repress his surprise that such a question should be put. "What of it?" he said.

"I can rid you of them."

"What for?" asked the Captain. "We get along all right with 'em."

The lady addressed her husband. "Clam up," she said. Canal manners and speech, Grandfather explained, lacked refinement. "How much?" Mrs. Le Moyne asked Quimby.

"Five dollars to you, ma'am," he said. "Warranty in writing."

"Done," the lady said. "Le Moyne, fetch these gentlemen a dram."

Having drunk her good health, the partners went ashore and brought back the Eliminator. From one of the bags Carr poured out powder into the metal-lined firebox. He then borrowed Grandfather's pocket flint box and helped Quimby take the mechanism into the hold. Presently they came out. Dark spirals of smoke oozed up.

"It will be advisable to go ashore for a time," Quimby said.

Grandfather thought so, too. "Never have the human nostrils been affronted by such a reek," he told us.

"What was in it, sir?" John asked.

"Asafetida seemed to be the foundation of the stench," Grandfather replied. "There were also suggestions of sulphur, lime, pukeweed, skunk cabbage and camphor."

"Did it clear the boat of the—the objects?" Jenny asked delicately.

At first, the old gentleman answered, there were a few straggling lines of insects making for the rail and toppling into the canal, but the main body remained below, dead, he surmised.

"It would have overcome the two-horned rhinoceros of the Grand National Menagerie," Grandfather said.

After three hours, all doors and portholes were thrown open and the owners were invited to inspect. No insect life was found. Captain Le Moyne reluctantly handed over five dollars, and Quimby made out a paper in ornamental writing.

"Here's your warranty, lady," he said. "If you find chinch, roach, ant, spider or weevil stirring tomorrow morning, I'll pay you a shilling a head."

Grandfather was impressed. After discussing terms with the partners, he cashed a check in Palmyra and paid over seventy-five dollars for a third interest in the enterprise. Dreams of financial glory filled his head. The three of them decided that they would put a score of Eliminators on the turnpikes. They would launch others on flatboats and send fleets up and down the waterways. With the ninety-percent profit that Grandfather reckoned on every operation, they would be millionaire-men in a few years.

There was another motive behind Grandfather's decision. He was suffering, he admitted to us with a reminiscent smile, from a recurrence of the canal fever that afflicted so many of the young blades who had worked on Clinton's Ditch. "Once a canaller, always a canaller," Grandfather murmured. Not all the output of Russell's popular alleviant could have cured the itch in his feet when they were set upon towpath or berm. So he joined Quimby & Carr, and the three of them set out for Buffalo.

They did a thriving business all the way. Charges ran from five to ten dollars per treatment, according to the size of the boat and the financial capacity of the owner. Where the captain's wife was aboard, Quimby worked his camera wiles in advance. Grandfather's wide acquaintance among the boatmen was invaluable. True, there was a general indifference to chinches aboard the boats, but the most hardened canallers would pay gladly for riddance from other pests.

"Sound commercial practice," Grandfather said. "Chinches were a petty annoyance, but roaches ate cargo."

Few craft escaped the solicitations of the three partners. They fumed the *Starry Flag*, the *Mary Fidler*, the *Genesee River*, the *Chief Engineer*, the *Gerundigut Racer*, the *Breath of Cashmere*, Sam'l Larned's wax-figure show-boat, and Prof. Everinghim's *Floating Library*, as well as such waterside taverns as the Sailor's Rest, the Mosquito Bend Inn, the Hungry Pike, and the Hare's Refuge.

"What a memory you've got, Grandpa!" John said.

"Those names are burned into it," the old gentleman returned, "with a dollar mark and a minus sign opposite every one."

At the Buffalo terminus, Grandfather, Quimby and Carr reckoned up their takings and found that they had nearly six hundred dollars. Upon the new partner's insistence, the original two agreed to invest all but living and maintenance expenses, which were small, in new apparatus. The plan now was that Quimby and Carr should retrace their course, branching out for new business, while Grandfather took to Lake Erie to work up trade among the merchantmen. The three were to meet at the terminal basin in ten days.

"I never set eye on hair nor hide of them again," Grandfather said.

"Did they run away with the money?" I asked.

"In the cant lingo of their ilk, they took hoof in hand, hit the dust, and left me holding the nose-bag," the old gentleman answered.

At the appointed time, Grandfather said, he arrived at Buffalo Basin with a wallet full of commissions from Lake Erie shipping. His partners were not there, but the *Stormy Lass* was. Captain and Mrs. Le Moyne rushed upon him and denounced him as an ingler, a bounetter, a scrounging sharpshooter, and in other terms not to be repeated in the presence of youth. Give them back their five dollars or they would have the law on him, they said. He paid the money and demanded an explanation, which they were only too ready to give.

The effect of the powerful fumes, it appeared, had been but temporary. At the end of twenty-four hours, all the varied insect life of the canalboat had stirred again. The bugs, sallying forth with appetites refreshed by the interval, had resumed operations. Other boats, with which the Le Moynes had exchanged experiences, had suffered likewise.

"You keep away from the towpath, young man," Mrs. Le Moyne warned Grandfather, "if you don't want Judge Lynch's court sitting on you."

"That," said Grandfather, with a side glance at my father, "was my just reward for associating with cameramen."

It was the first time, he went on, that his commercial responsibility had ever been impugned. Of course, there was nothing to do but to make good on every operation of the discredited Eliminator. He drew six hundred dollars from the bank, and with this sum in his pocket and a stout, nail-studded club in hand, he set forth on the unhappiest journey of his career.

Every boat he met, it seemed to him, greeted him with execrations. Several of the captains wished to fight him. Others threatened to jail him. Some indicated a preference for throwing him into Erie Water, and a few tried to do it. He completed that violent trip bruised in body and spirit but with his commercial honor restored. One remnant continued to haunt him.

"It was a full three years," he told us, "before I convinced the Canal that nobody could call me Bedbug Adams without peril to his front teeth."

"Did you ever hear of those wicked men again?" Jenny asked.

"I did," the old gentleman said. "At Cincinnati. They turned up there in the cholera scare of 1832-33 with their precious Eliminator and a lecture, which the rascally Quimby had composed, proving that insects were bearers of the disease. For their stench-powder he and Carr had substituted Genet's Patent Illuminating Gas. The machine blew up, burning an emergency pesthouse shed and two tents, and scaring half a dozen sick folk out of their wits. Both operators were deservedly jailed. I know nothing further of their nefarious careers." He paused and turned to my father. "Now that I reflect," he said, "I recall that the Carr scoundrel bore some resemblance to your friend with the patent box."

Father shook his head in mild deprecation. "Young Eastman is a very respectable character," he said.

"What did he call the thing?" Grandfather asked.

"The name escapes me," Father answered. "It was a rather

grotesque, Eskimo-sounding word, something like 'Kayak.' "

"Under any name you are well out of it, and your hundred dollars saved," Grandfather said. "No Adams money for such chimeras."

"I suppose you're right, sir," Father said.

The Adams money, as it happened, eventually went into another, and larger, box called the Myers Voting Machine, a forerunner of the voting machine of the present day. It worked well enough, but the politicians disliked it, so it vanished into the limbo of profitless products, leaving not so much as a dividend behind.

Grandfather did not live to witness that denouncement or to see the success of George Eastman's clicking box. One of his last intelligible observations was a warning to my father against catchpenny inventors—a caution but for which, and for two cameramen ill-met on a canal berm in the hot summer of 1828, my generation of Adamses might be Kodak millionaire-men, as Grandfather would have said.

CIRCUS DAYS FOR

GRANDFATHER

A gray norther from Lake Ontario drenched Rochester and ruined Decoration Day for three of my cousins and me. There would be no parade, no bands, no saluting cannon, no ceremony in Mt. Hope Cemetery, no patriotic harangues —nothing but rain. There was only one thing that could usefully be done. We could make our weekly duty call on our Grandfather Adams. Accordingly, we presented ourselves at the South Union Street cottage where we found him in his sitting room, glowering from his armchair. He was wrapped in blankets, a strip of red flannel swathed his throat, and an unguarded expanse of his chest glistened with goose grease. A pannikin on the nearby stove exhaled a faintly unpleasant odor. Two pill-boxes and the Hop Bitters bottle were within reach.

We four cousins advanced in order of age—John, I, Sireno and young Charlie—to pay our respects and ask about Grandfather's ailing health before seating ourselves.

"I am dying," he said in an annoyed voice.

We expressed polite concern.

"So the Widow Beebe would have me believe," he continued. This was what he called our step-grandmother when out of sorts with her. It had been her condition and name before she married him.

The kitchen door opened and her mild, bespectacled face appeared.

"It will do your quinsy no good to ramp and roar, Mr. Adams," she admonished him. "You must not stay long, children. Your grandfather has a rheum and, I fear, a fever."

"Nothing of the sort," Grandfather protested in what began as a bellow and ended in a croak.

"You see," his wife said placidly as a fit of coughing followed. She rubbed the sufferer's lips with camphor ice and went out, followed by his hoarse defiance.

"They shall stay as long as I choose," he said. He eyed young Charlie, who was fidgeting, and asked, "What ails the lad?"

"Charlie's fixing to go Indian hunting if the rain lets up," Reno answered with a touch of malice.

The tradition of plains warfare was still strong in the 1880's. My young cousin was, by turns, Buffalo Bill, Sitting Bull and General Nelson A. Miles. In whatever impersonation, he was equally sensitive to ridicule from us older boys.

"Over the left!" he retorted, an expression that was currently the extreme of repudiation.

Grandfather pounced upon it. "What is this vulgarism?" he snapped.

John came to the rescue. "It means over the left shoulder," he said. "Professor Glenn told our class that it comes from the Greek."

"Hmm!" the old gentleman rumbled. "Over the left, eh? Thunder on the left, regarded by the Athenians as an unfavorable or negative portent. Why not, indeed?" He nodded benignly.

Heartened by having escaped reproof, Charlie said boldly, "I bet *you* used to shoot Indians when you were young, Grandpa."

"Certainly not," said Grandfather. "Why should I?"

"Weren't there any around here?"

"Many," Grandfather answered. "They even followed the circus."

The word "circus" brought us to closer attention. It was one of enchantment. All of us were "canvasbacks," as youthful circus enthusiasts were called, and got out of bed at 4 A.M. whenever Barnum's came to town, in the fond hope of carrying a water bucket and earning a free pass.

"What circus was that, sir?" John asked with an effort at casualness.

"The one with which I was temporarily connected," Grandfather said.

Young Charlie bounced in his chair. "Grandpa," he said, "were you honest and truly in a circus when you were a boy?"

"I was not, so to say, a boy," Grandfather replied. "Nor was I active in exhibition. I was there in a fiduciary capacity."

John failed to get this. "To keep the Indians away?" he asked.

"To the contrary," Grandfather said. "They were profitable patrons. They frequented our penny shock machine. No Indian can resist the charm of electricity. They would shriek and whoop and squirm when the current was turned on, but they always came back for more."

"Why did they like it if it made them squirm?" Charlie asked.

"I don't know," said the old gentleman. "Nobody knows. Indians are Indians. When I raised the price to twopence, they still stood in line."

"*You* raised the price, sir?" Reno asked. "Did you own the circus?"

Grandfather hesitated. "I held a modest per centum," he admitted.

"Was it a big circus?" Charlie asked. "Were there lions?"

"One," Grandfather said. "Until it died."

"Did you put your head in its mouth?" asked Charlie.

"No," said Grandfather.

A puff of wind and rain had blown in Jenny, our pretty and spirited eldest cousin. She shook hands with the invalid, whose favorite she was, and inquired solicitously after his symptoms.

"Maybe you were a clown, Grandfather," said Charlie hopefully. "I'd admire to be a clown and paint my nose. Wouldn't you, Jenny?"

"No, I wouldn't," Jenny said decisively. "I'd rather be Miss Nettie Roblee and ride a milk-white steed standing up."

"She rode a dapple-gray," Grandfather said in a tone of reverie, "on one foot."

Jenny leaned toward him. "Who rode a dapple-gray?" she asked. "Not Miss Nettie. Where was this?"

"In Whitsey's Mammoth Symposium," Grandfather said. There was a pause. "*Eheu, fugaces!*" the old gentleman murmured. "How many long years! That rascal Jesse!"

The name electrified us. Our dead and distant relative Jesse Church was a combination of mystery, clan hero, and blot on the scutcheon. The occupant of every chair hunched forward.

"You've heard little good of him, I daresay," Grandfather continued.

"Wasn't he"—Reno hesitated, gulped, and went on—"illegal, sorta?"

Grandfather frowned. "He was not 'illegal,' as you ignorantly put it, Sireno. He was a truebred Church, but a wild young wastrel. His evasion from college to accompany the circus was only one of many escapades."

"We thought it was you that joined the circus, sir," John said.

"Eh? That was later," said Grandfather. "Jesse had been

with them a good two months before I was sent by the family to rescue him, lest he disgrace us further."

I inquired hopefully as to the nature of the disgrace. It appeared that Jesse had hired on with the circus as a hostler.

"Did he run away from college to look after a horse?" Jenny asked incredulously.

"Horses have riders," replied Grandfather sententiously. "To be near the horse was to be near the rider."

"Oh!" said Jenny. "The one on the dapple-gray. Was she pretty?"

"She had a temptational eye," Grandfather said, and hurried on with his narrative. "The show pitched in Palmyra. It was Muster Day, I recall, mortal hot and dusty, and the militia were parading down Main Street. I drove the gig over from our home, in East Bloomfield. I arrived very moist and distempered, and found young Jesse perched on the tailboard of a conny-wagon, cool as you please, inditing a poem to his inamorata. I never saw a young fool worse enslaved. He had been paying three dollars a week into the show's money box."

This shocked Reno's sense of business propriety, he being the commercial mind among us. "D'you mean to say, sir, that he paid out cash to be allowed to take care of the horse?" he asked.

Grandfather explained that it was the practice among the local Corinthians—by which he meant the gilded youth—to take the road with theatrical traveling troupes, paying a fee for the privilege and playing small parts or performing minor services. Jesse had applied the principle to the circus.

"He immediately tried to borrow ten dollars from me," Grandfather went on.

"Did you let him have it?" Reno asked. "I wouldn't."

"Nor did I," said Grandfather. "I made it clear that none of my avails were going to be dissipated upon a sawdust siren. Jesse replied that anyone who called the lady that was a maggoty liar and was liable to have his head caved in with a tent peg. Jesse," Grandfather added reflectively, "was a youth of unbridled speech."

"I think he was grand," said Jenny.

"So did not the object of his affections when she learned that he could no longer pay his scot," Grandfather said.

"Did *you* tell her, Grandfather?" Jenny cried. "How mean!"

"She asked me pretty roundly what I was doing there," the old gentleman said, "and I made my purpose clear. 'All very hoity-toity,' she said, 'but suppose he chooses not to leave?' 'He will go if you send him,' I told her. 'Why should I?' she said. I urged that by so doing she would bring comfort and relief to an anxious fireside, and she said, 'I don't care a brass pistareen about your anxious fireside. I'm thinking of the show. The lad is ready money.' 'No longer,' I told her. 'He's strappado,' and I made the gesture of turning out an empty pocket. She was painfully affected by it. And that," said Grandfather, "is how I became the money man of a circus."

"What happened to Jesse?" John asked.

A dim chuckle came from Grandfather, followed by a brief fit of coughing. "He drove the gig back to East Bloomfield with a flea in his young ear."

"Just like that?" I asked. "Didn't he make a fuss?"

"Without financial avails, he was of no further concern to the lady," said Grandfather.

"He died young, didn't he, Grandfather?" Jenny asked. "Did he waste away?"

"He did not. He joined a troupe of traveling thespians and played inconsiderable parts—Indians, soldiers and the like—in 'Metamora' and other dramas. He later died of a surfeit of raw turnips and iced punch."

"So when Jesse left, you took over the accounts," Reno said.

"Not immediately," said Grandfather. "The Mammoth

Symposium was exhibiting in adjacent towns—Newark, Phelps, Watercure. After some days, Floretta—"

"Was that her name?" Jenny asked eagerly. "How old was she? I bet she was pretty. Was she tall and dark and stately? Or slender and fair and languorous?" The works of Laura Jean Libbey were then just becoming popular among young ladies.

Throughout this spate of questions, Grandfather had been flapping an impatient hand. "Finance, not personal appearance, is the subject under discussion," he said. "Floretta asked me whether I was experienced in commercial dealings."

"What made her think that?" Jenny asked.

"My demeanor was mature and grave beyond my years," Grandfather replied.

"How old were you, Grandfather?" Jenny asked insinuatingly.

The old gentleman figured back and said, "A ripened thirty. While in my twenties I had already conducted several minor operations with profit, and I so informed her. She replied that she would deal aboveboard with me, that the Old Man, as she called Whitsey, had done a burk (I am repeating the language of the show folk), casting the little company upon its own resources, which were nil, and bidding her take charge. She then volunteered to show me the money box."

The circus's treasury, Grandfather explained, was in a sad state. Available cash consisted of ten bungtown coppers (old British pence), a dubious pistareen, which, if good, would have been worth no more than seventeen cents, and several bank notes so painfully uncurrent that, as Floretta remarked to him, a one-eyed taproom barkeep would not have accepted the lot in payment for a glass of cold tea. The rest of the assets were in trade.

"What kind of trade?" asked Reno.

"*Inter alia,* twenty-odd eggs and five pounds of cheese,"

the old gentleman answered. "I shall explain this phase later. I could readily see that commerce was a matter on which the lady had no docity, and she frankly sought to enlist my services. However, she warned me that it was a risky venture. When I replied that I was not born in the woods to be scared by an owl, she laughed and said that as the affairs of the company could not worsen, I might take over on a per centum basis and see if I could better them, which I accordingly did."

Small circuses, he went on to say, operated on a very narrow margin and were expected to accept anything that was offered at the ticket window. Such staples as gunpowder, plug tobacco, flaxseed, muskrat pelts and rum were practically legal tender, but other offerings—turnips, potatoes, eggs, fowls and home-woven fabrics—were less stable, and, in the case of Whitsey's Mammoth Symposium, presented recurrent problems to the new money man.

"Emperor Nicholas Biddle himself could not have balanced accounts with butter fetching ten cents a pound in Skaneateles and eight and a half at Oaks Corners," he told us with conviction.

What finally disgusted Grandfather was a misadventure with a Union Springs woodsman who brought a family of six to the show and tendered a well-cured Tuscarora scalp as payment for admission, arguing that it was worth eight bits of any man's money. Thereafter, Grandfather hung out a sign, in large lettering:

"SOUND COIN OR CURRENT NOTES ONLY."

It was a hard job to convert a rural populace, accustomed to trading in goods, to a legal-tender basis, but the new money man stuck to his rule: No shilling, no show. There was a riot over it at Phelps, Grandfather told us, where everyone wanted to pay in cabbage, a medium sharply depressed because of an overcrop.

Expenses of lodging were a constant bugbear. To avoid

them, members of the company, who traveled in wagons or on beastback, slept in the vehicles. He himself was quartered in the snake box, he said.

Charlie, who had been bored by all this economic detail, came to with a start.

"Snake?" he said. "Was there a snake? What kind, sir?"

"The Wreathing, Writhing Man-Eating Python from the Headwaters of the Wild Orinoco," said Grandfather. "It was one of our foremost attractions."

"Weren't you scared it would bite you?" Charlie asked.

"Pythons are constrictors," John put in. "They don't bite." John stood high in his classes at the Rochester Free Academy and tended to be oracular.

"It was stuffed," the old gentleman said.

Charlie's lip drooped. "I thought you said it writhed."

"It did writhe when I pulled the proper strings."

"Oh, *Grandfather!*" Jenny cried reproachfully. "Was that honest?"

The Moody & Sankey Revival had just been to Rochester, leaving local morality on a temporarily lofty plane. Jenny had attended every service.

"No," the old gentleman said, without perceptible contrition. "Nor was the Ferocious Jaguar of the Andean Jungles. She was a tamed wood lynx painted with spots and curves, and she kept licking the paint off and getting sick. I never saw a queasier animal. We used the same yellow for the Wild Cannibal's stripes. There must have been something wrong with it, for it itched him cruelly. I had to scrape him with coal oil after every performance."

"I think it was disgraceful," Jenny said.

"Circus business is not a camp meeting," the old gentleman retorted. "We were no worse than others. There were many genuine features in our exhibit. The lion was real, and the two monkeys. The tail feathers of the Beauteous Bird of Paradise were authentic. Whitsey had given an intoxicated captain in the China trade four dollars for them. Our dancing bear was an accomplished performer, and there was never a more risible clown than ours, when sober. The customers had their shilling's worth."

Charlie sighed enviously and said, "I don't see how you could ever have given up such a wonderful life, Grandpa."

"Whitsey came back," the old gentleman said, after some hesitation.

"Who was Whitsey?"

"The owner. Whitsey's Mammoth Symposium."

"Did he fire you, sir?" John asked.

"Not exactly, but he preferred to be his own treasurer. There was no place for two money men in the show."

"Where had he been, sir?" I asked.

"In jail."

"What for?" asked Charlie.

"He was a coniacker."

"Does that mean a thief, sir?" John asked.

"Would you understand better if I said that he operated a bogus?"

"I know," Reno said brightly. "False coinage."

"A mortal poor article," Grandfather said. "A fip from his mold fell into the sheriff's hands and he was jailed."

"Grandfather." Jenny spoke with wheedling urgency. "Won't you *please* tell me what she looked like?"

"Who?" asked Grandfather innocently.

Feet sounded upon the porch, and Dr. Ely entered. He was a trim, handsome middle-aged man, who wore his short beard accurately parted and was respected by all and feared by the young for his potent purges.

"Shoo, chickens!" he commanded, and we fled into the small parlor.

Jenny sat down on the melodeon seat and lost herself in musings. From them came a series of ejaculations.

"Think of it! Grandfather! In love!"

The suggestion seemed to offend Reno. "Who? Grandpa?" he asked. "Ah, go *West!*"

"Over the left!" young Charlie added.

"Well, I bet he was," she said. "I bet he was handsome, too. I bet he looked like—like—" She floundered for a moment, seeking the acme of glamour. "Like Fritz Emmet!" she concluded triumphantly.

We shouted her down. Nobody, in our estimation, could possibly be comparable to the composer and singer of the famous "Fritz Emmet's Lullaby." We were still arguing over it when our step-grandmother opened the sitting-room door. "You may come back for three minutes, children," she said.

Grandfather had been moved to a straight chair, where he sat staring disconsolately down at his thin, bare shanks. They protruded from a washtub of steaming water, sicklied o'er with a pale cast of powdered mustard. Facing a time limit, we concentrated upon the patient with brisk, competitive questions.

"Grandfather, did you leave as soon as Mr. Whitsey came back?" I asked.

"I waited until I collected my per centum," the old gentleman replied.

"I'll betcha!" said Reno with enthusiasm.

"Did you never see her more?" sighed Jenny poetically.

"Who?" Grandfather asked again.

"You know perfectly well who. The lady with the temptational eye."

Grandfather lifted a parboiled foot from the mustard bath, looked at it, and replaced it. "I returned to East Bloomfield and joined the Congregational Church," he said.

"What for?" Jenny blurted.

For a moment, the old gentleman looked startled. "I also married your grandmother," he continued.

"Oh, dear!" Jenny said.

"That is a most improper observation," he said not too sharply.

No rebuke could stop Jenny. She leaned forward to his near ear. "What *did* she look like, Grandfather?" she whispered.

"Your grandmother? She was tall and—"

"Not Grandmother," Jenny broke in. "You know. The other."

"Oh!" the invalid said. He closed his eyes, a smile on his usually firm mouth. "I have quite forgotten," he said clearly. "Dr. Ely prescribes a nap. Good day to you all."

GRANDFATHER'S
CRIMINAL CAREER

Little that went on in the city of Rochester escaped the notice of Grandfather Adams. His sources of information were a perennial mystery to my cousins and me, and our duty calls at his cottage, on Union Street, were shadowed by the probability that any recent misdeeds of ours would be known to him already. Thus it was with dismay rather than surprise that, on an October afternoon of 1882, we heard his bearded lips pronounce the word "muskmelon." Were any of us partial to that delicacy, he asked.

Jenny looked blank. Charlie looked virtuous. John, Sireno and I tried to look innocent.

Grandfather said, "It may or may not be news to you that the Hooker Nurseries were raided last night."

It was not news. We waited.

"Several of the miscreants were observed but have not yet been apprehended by the authorities," Grandfather proceeded. His phraseology, closely following the style of the Rochester *Democrat & Chronicle's* police reports, was not reassuring.

He surveyed us with chilling disfavor, and his long and gnarly index finger rose slowly until it pointed to John.

"Did you participate in this felony?" he demanded.

"Yes, sir," John said.

The finger swung in imperative demand first upon me, then upon Reno. Each of us muttered an affirmative. One did not lie to Grandfather Adams. John, our recognized spokesman, spoke up.

"Everybody hooks muskmelons in October, Grandpa. Hooking isn't stealing."

Reno and I nodded. It was, to our minds, a valid defense. This sort of minor pilfering was a seasonal ritual among Rochester's youth, like today's Halloween mischiefs. To hear it called felony shocked us.

"The police may take a different view," Grandfather said. "A member of the force called here this morning."

Jenny clasped her hands. "Oh, Grandpa!" she cried. "Must they languish in jail?" (Miss Laura Jean Libbey's impassioned sensibilities often echoed in her speech.)

"No," said Grandfather. "They will not, as you put it, languish, this time. The policemen came to interview me about a lost dog. Though, indeed," he added, "a term of incarceration might prove a needed correctional to their criminal tendencies. Prison can be an ennobling experience to a receptive soul. Many of the world's great have gone to prison and been none the worse for it—John Bunyan, Saint Paul, Sir Walter Raleigh."

"Sam Patch," Charlie contributed, naming the cataract jumper who had met his end at our own Falls of the Genesee, and so had become a local godling.

Charlie's intent was to be helpful, but his suggestion was not well received. "Sam Patch was a befuddled victim of his own inebriety," the old gentleman said tartly.

"Yes, sir," said Charlie meekly.

"Thus you children will observe," our mentor said, taking

up his theme again, "being in jail does not necessarily imply depravity."

Charlie's next utterance was delivered with an air of naïve candor. "Grandpa, were you ever in jail?" he inquired simply.

"Yes, Charles," Grandfather said.

We sat dumfounded. Jenny was the first to rally. "Whatever they said you did, I know you didn't do it," she said loyally.

"Oh, yes, I did," said the old gentleman, quite blithely.

Through the half-open window sounded the distant whistle of a steam canalboat crossing the Genesee River aqueduct. The old gentleman's eyes grew dreamy, and he launched into a lament for the old Erie—the Grand Western Canal, as he called it—a dull utility now, but a teeming world of activity, licit and illicit, sixty years before. He drew a word picture of canalside life as it was when Clinton's Ditch was the mainway of traffic in the expanding nation.

What a moving marvel of humanity was the old towpath, he said. There were gyppos in slinking squads—bright-kerchiefed folk, following the route in pursuance of their dubious trades. There were wandering tenkers, pikies, swing-kettles and blanketeers, hedgerow camping as they fared; bands of runaway apprentices, the pests of the countryside because of their henroost pilfering; road-runners and soap-locks, wastrels of the towns; and by night, the furtive procession of fugitive slaves, in constant dread of capture and return.

In the 1820's, slavery within the state had long been abolished. However, warrants from the Southern states were still honored, and a standard reward of a hundred dollars a head for colored fugitives stimulated the slave-hunting trade. Any rascal could get a local warrant for slave-catching. The practitioners of it were a scoundrelly lot, mainly suspected horse-thieves from Nine Mile Swamp or semi-outlaws from the Montezuma Marshes, contemned by decent folk. One of the most notorious slave hunters was Tib Mason, from Howland's Island, in the Marshes. He was so poison-mean that the marsh mosquitoes forbore to bite him.

"It was Tib who got me into jail," Grandfather told us. And this was the way of it, he said.

Grandfather was sitting, fare-paid, on the afterdeck of the line boat *Dawn Star*, chatting with his friend Artemas Bowman, who owned and captained her. Below decks, a dark, nonpaying passenger, named Pompey, lurked between bales of hay. Captain Bowman did not call himself an Abolitionist, which was a name of ill repute, but he had a confirmed ambition—a grudge—against man-hunters who operated in the free State of New York. The cowering slave in the hold was by no means the first fugitive to find haven on board the *Dawn Star* from the dogs and guns of his pursuers.

Beyond Port Byron, a lone horseman cut across from a nearby shunpike and urged his mount up on the canal's towpath. He had a horn at his belt, a coil of rope over his shoulders, and a musket across his saddlebow. Captain Bowman recognized him as Tib Mason. The horseman hailed the line boat unceremoniously: "Ahoy, *Dawn Star!* Head in."

"I can't dwell," Captain Bowman called back. "Fast deliverable freight."

"I got a warrant for that freight," Tib Mason said. He flourished a paper with an embossed seal. "Good anywhere in New York State."

"This ain't York State. It's Erie Water," the Captain replied.

This was a disputable point. Some authorities held that since the Erie gave access to Hudson's River and thence to the sea, it was open water under the rules of navigation. On the other hand, the Canal Commission, a state body, claimed control of it.

Tib Mason, impatient of such hair-drawn distinctions, called Captain Bowman a poxy sea-lawyer and demanded to be taken aboard. Captain Bowman, still prudently polite, said that he was not required to embark passengers except at regulation wharves. Thereupon Tib Mason cursed him vilely, booted the horse back to the shunpike, and vanished.

"Good riddance to bad rubbish," Grandfather said.

"We're not rid of *him*," the Captain replied gloomily. "He's a wily-pie, some trick always up his sleeve. Two to one, we'll find him dangling his legs from the next occupation bridge we come to."

The Captain was right. Tib was waiting at Farmer Sayre's bridge, a span that connected the two parts into which the canal, cutting through the countryside, had split the Sayre farmstead. The Canal Commission had built the bridge at its own cost, so that the farmer might carry on his occupation unhindered.

Tib Mason had abandoned his horse but not his gun. As the *Dawn Star* passed under the bridge, he dropped lightly to her deck. Once there, he proceeded with impressive deliberation. He detached his powder horn from his belt and, with his unpleasing buck teeth, worried the pledget from the mouth of the horn. Carefully and liberally, he sprinkled gunpowder upon the flashpan of his musket. Having made these preparations, he walked aft and addressed the Captain.

"Gimme my blackamoor," he said.

"What blackamoor?" asked Captain Bowman.

"The one you took on at Weedsport."

"Weedsport?" Captain Bowman said, playing for time.

"Yes, Weedsport," said the swamper. "And don't parley with me. The lock keeper saw you haul him aboard. Fetch him up and no more gafooh, or I'll blow a hole in you."

At this point, Jenny's feelings got the better of her. "I should think you might have done *something*, Grandpa," she said indignantly.

"It was no affair of mine," the old gentleman replied with a mildness that struck me as being not quite in character. "This I made clear to Tib Mason, at the same time stepping into the shelter of the water butt. 'Look you, Tib Mason,' I said to him. 'I am but a farepaid passenger. Any freightage is between you and Captain Bowman. I wash my hands of it.'"

"Oh, *Grandpa!*" Jenny was near to tears.

"As I have already indicated," Grandfather said, "Tib was brandishing a loaded and primed firearm. He also had the law on his side, no light consideration to a law-abiding citizen like myself. What was I to do? Of course, the charge that I attempted to thrust out Tib's eye with an ironshod fending pole was perjurious nonsense."

"Did you *have* a fending pole?" Jenny asked.

"Not ironshod," the old gentleman said. "They are forbidden by the Commission's rules. They do great damage to the banks."

"You had a pole," Reno said, "and he had a gun—"

"To be sure," Grandfather broke in. "The gun. The swamper dropped it on the deck, and pranced upon the berm like a cold with a bur in its tail. He was using calumnious language."

"Look, Grandpa," John said earnestly. "The last we heard of him, he was holding a gun on Captain Bowman and you were behind the water butt. How did he get to the berm?"

"Waded," Grandfather answered. He rubbed his forehead reflectively. "I appear to have omitted some details."

"Yes, sir," John said.

"Then let us retrace our steps to the point where I tactfully addressed Tib Mason, disclaiming all responsibility," said Grandfather. "A weakness of mine was a minor but persistent irritation in my throat. This weakness afflicted me at the precise moment when Tib Mason was rudely prodding my friend the Captain with the muzzle of his musket. I bent over and took a deep draught from the water butt. It went down my throat the wrong way. In a fit of strangling, I staggered toward the gunwale. A convulsion seized and mastered me. I retched violently, and my mouthful of water was vented upon the pan of Tib Mason's musket."

"So it wouldn't go off!" Reno cried.

"Wet powder, it is true, will not fulminate," Grandfather said. "When next I observed Tib Mason, he was floundering and splashing in the water."

"How did he fall into the canal, Grandpa?" Charlie inquired.

"His sworn testimony in court was that Captain Bowman butted him unfairly in the stomach," said the old gentleman. "As to that, I cannot testify, as I was still racked with my cough. That he went overside suddenly, I can confidently state."

"And you rescued him from drowning with the fending pole," said Jenny.

"He whanged him in the eye with the fending pole," Reno corrected her.

"Neither statement is altogether accurate," Grandfather said. "A six-foot man cannot well drown in four feet of water. Nor did I employ more force than was needful to discourage Tib Mason from boarding us again. Presently he climbed the berm, crossed the bridge, mounted his horse, and was off westward riding the towpath, which was illegal. But what swamper ever respected the law?"

Grandfather and Captain Bowman knew that, though lawless himself, Tib Mason would not hesitate to invoke the law. They expected to be intercepted, but they did not know where. While they were debating what to do, a boat, the

Ploughboy of Brockport, overhauled them. Captain Bowman and Captain Orson Greene, of the *Ploughboy,* held a conference. There was a transfer of some cargo, which Grandfather ignored. Then the *Ploughboy* passed the slower *Dawn Star* and continued on its way.

At the edge of the Montezuma Marshes, there was a lock. Here a constable was awaiting the *Dawn Star.* He arrested Myron Adams for attempted mayhem and resisting the execution of a legal warrant, and Artemas Bowman for harboring a fugitive. They were taken before the magistrate at Cayuga and ordered incarcerated for trial in the morning.

The jails of the eighteen-twenties were, in Grandfather's opinion, unfit for human occupancy. The one in which he and Captain Bowman were confined, on the brink of the great marshes, was worse than most. It was a makeshift. When the Cayuga Bridge, the longest in the world, was built, quicksands had been encountered and caissons sunk. Several of these caissons had since been abandoned, and one of them had been put to use as a temporary jail when the official establishment burned down. It was twelve feet deep and the sides were unscalable. Prisoners were lowered into it and brought up again by rope.

Here the two captives found themselves in full possession except for a horde of bloodthirsty marsh mosquitoes. In this unpleasant predicament Grandfather bethought himself of his membership in the Wayne County Horse-thief Society. It was one of many such groups across the state, made up largely of young Corinthians of the towns, whose official purpose was to discourage—by proclamation, advertising, and sometimes night riding—the flourishing traffic in stolen horseflesh, but whose social activities were fraternal, catholic and festive.

"It was a Friday," Grandfather said, "and there was an excellent chance that some of the brethren might be passing within earshot on their way to weekly meeting. I supposed they might even have the rope with them."

"The rope?" Jenny interrupted. "*What* rope?"

Grandfather smiled. "You may have heard unfounded tales about us," he said. "Our rope was merely a symbol, never put to practical use. Looped conspicuously above the chairman's platform at our meetings, it inspired salutary alarm in the hearts of the miscreants whom we unofficially, and perhaps even illegally, haled before us. So, on the chance of attracting the notice of a fellow-Horse-thief, I whistled, at intervals, a certain lay. It was presently answered in kind. Faces appeared at the mouth of our pit. The Society's identification query was put. I responded in form. A rope was lowered, and we were free."

"But you had to show up in court, didn't you, sir?" John asked.

"The Society took our case under advisement in its own court that very night," Grandfather said. "It unanimously resolved that we should be restored forthwith to the *Dawn Star* and dispatched on our way westward. An escort, equipped with jackeroos, was provided to see us safe aboard. There is great virtue in a properly leaded jackeroo in the hands of one habituated to its use, as all good Horse-thieves were.

"When we got back to canalside, Tib Mason, with several other swampers, was engaged in searching the *Dawn Star*. Fruitlessly, of course. Pompey was no longer there. A bit of a bobbery took place between the Society members and the swampers, and some of the swampers fell into the canal. Tib Mason was subsequently arrested and sentenced to thirty days' imprisonment on a charge of public riot."

"And where was Pompey?" Jenny asked.

"On his way to be delivered aboard a Canada-bound owler owned and manned by a responsible smuggler," Grandfather answered. An owler was a sailing craft engaged in contraband trade on Lake Ontario.

Reno asked how Pompey got aboard the owler.

"Goose-down," said Grandfather promptly. "Down, from

geese. Goose feathers—a staple of commerce in those days."
We might have been an infant class, so mildly instructive was
his tone. "The *Ploughboy of Brockport,* to which we had
transferred Pompey from the *Dawn Star,* had a consignment
of down, in sacks, for Rochester. Captain Greene, of the
Ploughboy, had stowed him in a sack with a couple of holes
cut for breathing. He passed the Rochester tolls at a shilling
a hundredweight, with an extra dollar for the collector. There
was," Grandfather remarked after a pause, "a prevalent sym-
pathy for fugitive slaves all along canalside."

"Didn't you ever go back to Cayuga?" Reno asked.

"Not often, and then very privately and by night, until the
six-year statute of limitations was up," Grandfather said.

Jenny's conscience was still troubled. "But you *did* break
the law, Grandpa," she said.

"True," he admitted. "And I have often regretted it. At
least," he amended, "I have often felt that I *ought* to regret
it. But the vision of Tib Mason at the end of my fending pole
intervenes and ruins my compunctions." He looked about
our circle with an amiable smile. "Some of you may recall
the pious saying of the sainted John Bradford when the con-
demned criminal passed on his way to the scaffold."

"No, sir," John answered, speaking for our collective ignorance.

"Even after fifty years," the old gentleman said, "when I
pass a jail yard, I paraphrase the old-time Bishop, and say
prayerfully, 'There, but for the grace of God and the statute
of limitations, goes Myron Adams.' "

MRS. MONTAGUE'S
COLLAR

How our grandfather would react to any innovation was a matter of anxious guesswork on the part of his family. Consequently John and I were in an uncertain state of mind that Saturday evening as we trudged through the snow of South Union Street on our way to the major junior social event of the season, the Grand Annual Soirée of the Pi Phi (Perfect Friendship) Fraternity, most secret and choice of the Rochester Free Academy cliques. Would we be able to conceal our destination from the old gentleman? And, if he did find out, what would be his attitude toward our entree into R.F.A. society via a formal dance? Our one concern was to get through the call, which we had ill-advisedly postponed until evening, and be on our festive way.

Seven o'clock found us scraping our feet on the cottage doorstep. We entered the overheated sitting room with polite hopes for Grandfather's good health and with our overcoat collars turned up and snugged close to our necks. This was precaution. We hoped to conceal our sartorial elegance from those still observant old eyes, lest it provoke undesirable inquiry.

"Good evening, John. Good evening, Samuel," our host greeted us. "Lay aside your coats."

"We've only got a minute, Grandpa," John said nervously.

"I'm not a bit warm, sir," I added, swabbing at the perspiration that oozed from my forehead.

"Take off your coats and sit down," Grandfather said in a measured and commanding voice.

We obeyed.

Grandfather surveyed our grandeur with disfavor.

"Why are you both dressed up like Mudge the Undertaker?" he asked.

There was something in the comparison. John had on a long-roll cutaway he had borrowed from Irv Plum's collegiate brother. I wore a black Prince Albert of a modish, if shiny, diagonal weave. It had been more hard come by than John's attire. For the use of it, I had contracted to do Lish Taylor's sidewalk shoveling for the next three snowstorms. (Lish had the mumps and couldn't go to the Soirée.) Each of us wore a made-up bow tie of cream-colored satin and a lapel badge with the legend:

R.F.A.———Pi Phi.

Grandfather was waiting for an answer.

John mumbled, "We're going to the Pi Phi dance, sir."

He gave it the Neo-Grecian pronunciation which was de rigueur in our Free Academic circle. Grandfather appeared thunderstruck.

"What kind of Choctaw is that?" he demanded. He turned to me. "*What* did he call it, Samuel?"

"Pee Phee, sir," I said stoutly. "Everybody in our set calls it that."

"Everybody, eh?" Grandfather rasped. "Pee Phee, eh? Your set, forsooth! Overgrown abecedarians! And I pay taxes for this." He leveled a finger at me. "You will regret such corruptions when you enter the classic shades of Hamilton College."

John had begun fidgeting and, with his fingers, easing the pressure of his collar, a high batwing of the newest style, trade-named, as I recall, the Ianthe. This uneasy gesture attracted Grandfather's attention.

"What's that thing?" he asked, leaning forward to peer at it. "Looks like a splay-winged duck. What did it cost you?"

"Fifteen cents, sir," John said, and added, in mitigation of his extravagance, "Two for a quarter."

"My first collar cost me a shilling," Grandfather told him. "It lasted me three years." His manner became dreamy, pensive. "Well do I remember," he said.

John and I telegraphed our dismay to one another. On the occasions when our grandfather well-remembered, he was good for an hour's discourse. Normally, we would have welcomed the prospect of an excursion into the past, for his reminiscences were often picturesque and sometimes spicy. But it was already seven-twenty. The Rochester Free Academy was still a mile away. The Mystic March of Pi Phi was scheduled for eight o'clock sharp. There would be Dosenbach's Harmonious Orchestra and Teal's Refined Refreshments.

"It was an Orlando Montague prime quality double," grandfather said. "I don't suppose either of you ever heard of Orlando Montague."

"No, sir," John said dully.

"Yes, sir," I said. It was now past hope that he could be halted, but there was a chance that a show of interest might speed the story up. "Wasn't he the mayor of Troy that you met on your first railroad ride?"

"Not mayor, my boy," Grandfather said with unexpected geniality, pleased that I had remembered another of his stories, "but a very respectable citizen." (By this time we had learned to identify "respectable" from Grandfather's lips as synonymous with "estimable" or even "eminent.")

"I do believe," he went on reflectively, "that I was the pioneer wearer of a Montague this far west. How the young ruffle shirts of the Third Ward stared! Their most dandified wear was a paper neck-frill pressed with a hot iron."

"*Our* Third Ward?" I asked. This section, across the river from Union Street, was still the habitat of Rochester's old-time aristocracy. "Did you bring the collar all the way from Troy?"

"Ah, Troy!" Grandfather murmured. "The most up-and-coming town in all York State when I was traveling the Erie Canal in the early days. The Collar City. History will so know and honor it. While man wears clothes, he will wear collars. Stop fumbling with your neck, John!" Grandfather glared at my unhappy cousin, who lapsed back in his chair. "When I wore *my* collar to the First Church social, the excitement was intense. The report of the newfangled dido had preceded me. I was the cynosure of all eyes. Later, it received favorable mention in the press by Obadiah Dogbery. This Dogbery . . ." Grandfather paused and seemed to lose himself in an effort to remember something.

Alarmed, John rushed into the breach and asked if the pioneer collar had been Mr. Montague's personal handiwork.

"He didn't make it," Grandfather answered. "He didn't even invent it. His wife did, though he always took the credit. Stop looking sidelong at the clock and I will tell you how it happened."

Grandfather had the account, he said, straight from the lips of Timothy Freegle, the mackerel inspector of Troy, "a respectable man but smelly," who was present at the original showing of the collar.

None of Troy's seven thousand residents was more esteemed than Orlando Montague, the ironmonger. Everybody in town knew that he changed his shirt daily. It was incumbent upon him to do so if he was to maintain his social reputation. For,

though already ageing—he would never see thirty-five again—
Mr. Montague was an approved macaroni, and his apparel set
a pattern for the imitation of the younger bloods.

The Montagues lived in style on River Street, in a house
with a number on the door, like a business concern. Mrs.
Montague, of comely person and well thought of for piety
and thrift, was known to have a mind of her own and a
tongue quite ready to speak it. It was her pride and com-
plaint that she must always be at her tub, since her husband
would allow no hand less skilled than hers upon his linen.

On a crisp autumn afternoon, Mr. Montague walked home
from the ironmongery humming a cheerful tune. He had hit
the Literary Lottery, so called because part of the proceeds
went to foster college education, for twenty-five dollars and
was meditating a new waistcoat. Doffing his broadcloth coat
in his hallway, he inspected it for wrinkles, gave it a shake
and a pat, and hung it on its peg.

"Wife!" he called. "Where are you?"

"Where would you expect me to be? At my washboard,"
his wife replied.

Passing through the kitchen to the rear of the hall and into
the washroom, Mr. Montague observed with benign approval
the trim, personable woman busy above the steaming washtub.

"My shirt, wife," he said.

Mrs. Montague straightened her back and dried her arms.
"What is it tonight, Orlando?"

"Harmonia Society practice," said Mr. Montague. He contributed a resonant basso to the local choral group.

"Can't you sing through the neckwear you have on?"

"My linen must befit a man of my condition and calling,"
he said.

"Then change your calling and follow a cleanly trade."

"Change!" Mr. Montague repeated, scandalized. "Change
my trade? Me, the best ironmonger in York State!"

"Ironmonger, indeed! A sooty smith!" said his wife.

"What ails the woman?" Mr. Montague regarded her sternly, but she was not easily awed.

"Fresh shirt," she said. "A fresh shirt he must have, day upon day, and another for the Sabbath. Wash, wash, wash! Nothing but wash, day in, day out. It's beyond reason. Must you always be gawking over your forge? Could you not snug a towel about your neck?"

"Tut, woman!" Mr. Montague said without rancor. "Set a hot sadiron to that"—he indicated the shirt on the washboard —"and they'll give me éclat at the meeting for having a proper wife."

"You and your ale-guzzling, catch-singing cronies!" she said, though her eyes were not unkindly. "See to it that you wash your neck well with soap."

"Is that my best red cambric?" He scuffed into a pile of shirts on the floor with his foot. "I shall be needing it, come Saturday evening."

"And what's my fine Mister up to Saturday evening?"

"We entertain the Harmanus Bleecker choral, from Albany, at a singdown."

"And a drink-down, I doubt not," Mrs. Montague said. "Have no concern. You shall look as dicty as the best of 'em."

Supper over and her husband departed, Mrs. Montague returned to her unending stint and found herself suddenly loathing the tousled heap of fabric before her. Every shirt would have been wearable at least a second time but for its sullied collar. She must wash and starch and iron a whole shirt because of a few unsightly smudges. In her father's day, it had been different. She conjured up a picture of that respectable malster, his thick, red neck protruding from a high circle of frilled paper that, at a cost of sixpence the dozen, could be worn once or twice and thrown away without undue infringement of economy.

A thought dawned in her active brain. If a detachable circlet of paper was feasible, why not a detachable circlet of cloth? How much labor would be saved if she had to wash but a strip of linen instead of a whole garment! She dashed to her workbasket, caught up her shears, and advanced to the attack.

Mrs. Montague was soon surrounded by decollated shirts. Next she darted upstairs, scooped the reserves out of her husband's highboy, and brought them down, resolved to make a clean sweep. Saturday was to be the showdown, and she set aside two garments for the intervening days. Then let the heavens fall. She would present the scheme to her husband in its revolutionary entirety, and if he raised too much of a whoobub, what had been done could be undone; she could always restore the wreckage with needle and thread.

For two days, she toiled unremittingly with the aid of a sewing-hussy solemnly sworn to secrecy, whom she had in at two shillings a day and found. Saturday came, and at five o'clock her husband appeared with the usual daggled smears on the white surface and the usual demand for fresh apparel.

"Wash yourself well, dear," his wife said, with a sweetness that might have struck him as excessive had he not been absorbed in planning his toilet for the evening's festivities.

He went upstairs humming the humorous ditty, "Tiddle-fridgets." His wife waited at the stair foot. Presently she heard his plaint:

"Can't find a b'dashed shirt!"

"They're all down here," she called.

"Then fetch 'em up and be spry."

"Come down and get 'em yourself. I've got a little surprise for you," said Mrs. Montague, still sweetly but with an undertone of decisiveness. When that note sounded, time was saved, as her husband had long since discovered, by meeting her wishes. He descended and found her with a freshly laundered shirt in her hands.

"The red cambric, you wanted," Mrs. Montague said. "Here it is." She held out the shirt. "Arms."

Bowing his head and stretching out his arms, Mr. Montague felt the garment slip into place. Then his fingers fumbled at the neckband.

"What the old scratch is this?" he demanded.

"Don't curse, dear," said his wife.

"There's no collar."

"All ready." She held up the starched ring before his eyes.

"What happened to it?"

"I cut it off," she said.

"Cut it? B'dashed and b'damned! What for, woman?"

"To make the wash easier."

"Then you b'damned well sew it back on again!" Mr. Montague cried.

"It doesn't need to be sewed. Tie it."

"Tie it to what, you—you puttering Jezabeel?"

The time had come for assertion and defiance. "Tie it to your ass's ears, for all I care!" said Mrs. Montague. "And please not to use ignominious language to your lawfully wedded wife."

Her husband snatched off the shirt, flung it into a corner, and kicked the collar after it. "Fetch me another," he said.

"Go into the washery and pick out one. They're all the same," she answered.

Mr. Montague uttered the roar of a goaded bull. "You've gone zany!"

"If you let your gorge rise like that, you'll have a cachexy, and I shall call Dr. Armitage to bleed you," said his wife.

Retrieving the garment, she smoothed out two strips of tape fixed to the back of the neckband, and deftly attached the collar by passing one tape through a corresponding slit in it, then knotting the two tapes together.

"What's that contraption?" her husband demanded suspiciously.

"To hold everything snug," she explained. "See, here are two more strips for the front."

"Never saw such a thing in my born days," he snapped.

"Just let me try it on," she coaxed. Mr. Montague sidled and stamped and spluttered. "It won't do a bit of good to prance," she went on placidly. "Stand still!"

She slipped the shirt back on him and affixed the collar at the front, tying it to the neckband with a neat bow. "Look at yourself." She propelled him gently to the wall glass. "There! Isn't that dicty?"

"Um-mm-mm!" he grunted, craning. "Hah!" He waggled his head like a duck, easing his Adam's apple into place with a careful forefinger.

"Don't you like it?" she asked.

Inwardly, her husband was filled with admiration for her ingenuity, but, reflecting that too much praise was likely to set a woman above herself, he merely said, "I guess it'll do for this evening."

Mr. Montague set out for the Mansion House, where he had an appointment for a preliminary drink in the private elegance of a parlor. Franklin Wrench, the lottery agent; Isaac Leroy, the whitesmith; Miles Tiggett, the Learned Tailor, so called because of his pride in his own erudition, and Timothy Freegle, the mackerel inspector—all Harmonia members and all men of fashion—awaited him. To his disappointment, none remarked his neckwear, which, as far as they could see, was the normal apparel.

Mr. Montague choked upon his first swallow of flip. (His doing this, grandfather explained, was artifice.) He plucked wildly at his throat in an apparent agony of strangulation while his solicitous friends pumped his arms and hammered his ribs until he subsided. By that time, his collar lay upon the floor.

"You've torn your shirt," Mr. Wrench said sympathetically.

"Step around into Elbow Street," the mackerel inspector said, "and I shall be pleased to supply you with a fresh one."

"What's this?" Isaac Leroy asked, goggling at the circlet, which he picked up.

"Oblige me," Mr. Montague said, took it from him, and tied it aptly to the neckband of his shirt. To fix the rear bow cost him some contortions, but the one in front was simple. He adjusted his neckcloth, patted it into place, set it with a handsome intaglio, and flirted a delicate bandanna handkerchief across the achieved masterpiece with a fine assumption of unself-consciousness. Mr. Wrench, goggling, asked,

"What is it?"

"A little device of my own," the ironmonger replied.

" *'Omne ignotum pro magnifico,'* " Tailor Tiggett said. He never missed an opportunity to air his classics. "*Mirabile dictu*, but dotch me if I quite twig it."

"Mortal simple," Mr. Montague said, and obligingly repeated the whole operation.

"Bunkum! Very bunkum!" the mackerel inspector exclaimed in admiration. "It'll become a fashion, I shouldn't be at all surprised. The Albany gentlemen must see this new example of Trojan enterprise."

Song was secondary at the musical meeting to interest in Mr. Montague's exhibit. The visitors made drawings of the collar to take back to Albany. One of them said, "You should introduce this into commerce, Mr. Montague."

"I will," Mr. Montague said, struck with the idea.

"And *that*," said Grandfather, "was fifty years ago and more. Today there isn't a dollar-a-day workingman in the country but what puts on his clean collar for Sunday. Thousands of 'em. Millions of 'em. All because Mrs. Montague had a tantrum of temper. It made Troy the collar center of the world."

"Right away?" John asked.

"Not right away. At first, there was opposition, as there always is to any innovation, even in as affording a community as Troy. It was the Troiades who saw the labor-saving virtues of the collar and advanced its adoption. I suppose," he added witheringly, "that your Pee Phee Greek would not include a knowledge of the 'Troiades.' "

John and I looked blank. Grandfather condescended to enlighten us. " 'The Trojan Women,' " he said. "Euripides gave that title to a tragedy over which, Samuel, you will one day struggle."

He went on to explain that when the new collar began to show signs of languishing, the matrons of Troy, New York, banded together and threatened a strike—he called it a turn-out—against the old-style shirt. "No slavery to the washtub" was their slogan. They waged so successful a campaign that within two years Mr. Montague had taken a partner and was exporting collars by the gross.

John rose hopefully. "Thank you for an instructive and entertaining evening, Grandfather," he said.

"Sit down," Grandfather said. "I have not finished."

John sat down. The old gentleman continued. "Others imitated the Montague collars—Independence Stark, Lyman Bennett, the ex-Reverend Ebenezer Brown, a Methodist parson turned storekeeper. I don't think they made much profit at first, but the fashion spread. Mr. Brown had a clerk named Jones, George Jones. A restless young man. Came from Vermont. He ambitioned to go to New York and try his luck at the printing trade. Mr. Brown offered him a partnership in the collars, but young Jones was set in his ways. Nothing would do but he must be a printer. Off he went, and the solid men of Troy all said that a fool and his money are soon parted, and that Jones would rue the day he quit a promising commerce to set up a paltry printery in New York."

There was a pause. This was the crucial moment. I ventured what I hoped might be the terminal question.

"Did he?" I asked.

John looked at the clock and moaned softly. Grandfather followed his glance with a frosty smile.

"Fifteen minutes fast," he said. "Begone to your hybrid-Greek revels. Did you put a question to me, Samuel?"

I eased my damp form into my overcoat. "*Did* Mr. Jones rue the day, sir?" I asked.

"If he did," Grandfather said, "Troy never heard of it. The paltry printery that he set up became the New York *Times*."

PIETY AND PIE

Savory odors seeped through the kitchen-door cracks of the South Union Street cottage into the adjoining room, where five of us grandchildren sat in prim attendance upon the head of the family. Grandfather Adams' second wife could be heard, moving about upon her proper duties, which were unmistakable to anyone with a nose. It was said locally that Mr. Myron Adams had married the Widow Beebe because she had the lightest hand with a piecrust in the city of Rochester.

For us guests to have evinced any interest in those provocative emanations would have been highly injudicious. It might be that the product was for home consumption only. On the other hand, if Grandfather intended us to have pie, pie we should have. But any request to that effect would have blasted our hopes. The head of the Adamses was something of a Puritan and believed in mortifying the flesh, particularly that of his descendants. Consequently, Jenny, John, Reno and I bent angry glances upon seven-year-old Charlie when he sniffed the air and emitted a mouth-watery "Mm-mm-mm-mm!" of yearning.

"If you must drool and dribble, Charles," Grandfather said, "employ your handkerchief."

Jenny reached out her small, feminine square of mignonette-embroidered cloth, but Charlie had already utilized his coat sleeve.

The old gentleman, whose temper was edgy because his feet were paining him, glared at his youngest grandchild for a long moment before resuming his reminiscences of the zero spell of 1827, which started his chilblains.

"That," he recalled, "was the winter of Sister Sophia's success in the piety contest."

Reno burst into a loud guffaw, which met with a look of chill disfavor from Grandfather.

"Perhaps you will explain, Sireno, what you find so risible in your great-aunt's winning of a piety contest?"

"Piety?" Reno repeated, somewhat dashed. "I thought you said 'pie-eating,' sir."

"I did not say 'pie-eating,'" the old gentleman retorted with asperity. "There is a difference, which should be patent to the veriest dummock, between an exercise in Biblical lore and a test of athletic prowess."

"Athletics like base——" young Charlie began.

But Jenny overbore him with her tactfully eager, "What's a piety contest like, Grandpa?"

Grandfather was mollified. "You are all familiar with spelling bees."

"Reno spelled down the first grade in Conesus School last term," Charlie said, full of family pride. "He won a nice book."

"*Gospel Gleanings*," Reno said bitterly. "Yah!"

Jenny rebuked him. "What did you expect? A Jack Hazzard adventure?"

Grandfather ignored the interruption. "A piety contest **and** a spelling bee are not dissimilar. Sides are chosen. The leader of one faction propounds a text from Holy Writ. The opposing team must then either cap the text or assign it to its proper context. And so on, until all but one participant are eliminated by error. Sophia, having survived every test, was adjudged the individual victor, besting not only two members of the Bible Christians, a vegetarian sect notorious for scriptural erudition, but also the learned pastor of the First Peculiar Baptist Church of Troy, New York."

"My!" Jenny exclaimed, gratifyingly impressed.

Charlie's mind was on more secular matters. "Didn't they used to have pie-eating matches, too, Grandpa?" he asked.

"We did. It was a recognized branch of sports."

Encouraged by that "we," I took a calculated risk. "Did you ever get into one, sir?"

"Betcha you licked 'em if you did," Reno, our sporting character, said in swift follow-up.

A confirmation from the old gentleman would not have surprised us. His past, as we had come to learn through casual revelations, was as various as his talents were versatile. This time he disappointed us.

"No, I never competed in that arena," he said, "though I once officiated. Samuel, fetch me my ort-book."

I placed in his hands the repository. He riffled the pages, found his place, and inserted a gnarled finger to keep it. "Ahem!" he coughed in preliminary. We settled back expectantly.

A matter of flaxseed, snuff and muskrat pelts in an intricate pattern of barter had taken that shrewd and experienced road trader, Myron Adams, to Syracuse shortly before November canal-close. His business affair having been satisfactorily concluded, he found himself with an empty evening on his hands. Above the inn-yard pump, at which he was washing up before supper, he noticed a broadside affixed to the wall.

It announced a challenge to be determined that evening between two self-styled champion pie-eaters, in the second-floor
assembly room. Nothing loath for harmless diversion, the
traveler ate a leisurely meal, climbed the stairway, and paid
his scot at the door with a measure of gunpowder, which was
acceptable, though not legal, tender.

Though he was late, the proceedings had not yet started.
There had been a pucker over the selection of an official to
conduct the event. A group of canal-boat captains, present
in full fig—flare pantaloons, brass-buttoned jackets, hand-
painted castors cocked on their heads, and loaded canes in
readiness—were loud in debate. They were men of consequence, the aristocracy of the Erie, willing fighters, bibbers,
gamesters; contentious fellows, Grandfather said, quite capable of cleaning out the hall if their wishes were ignored.

Matters were at a deadlock when Captain Argus Sharp of
the packet *Gallant Sea Mew* spied the new arrival. He at
once bellowed for silence and attention.

"Gentlemen and fellow mariners," he shouted, seizing and
raising Grandfather's hand, "here is a man we can all approbate, Mr. Myron Adams, the well- and respectably known
commercialist of East Bloomfield. Though not a brother-chip
of our nautical fraternity, he is equally notorious through all
the locks of Erie, from Albany to Buffalo, for his probity and
his sportsmanship. I propose him as chairman."

It was carried *viva voce*. The people's choice was led forward and the gavel placed in his hands.

"Did you *want* to do it, Grandpa?" Jenny said.

He stroked his beard reflectively. "One must oblige one's
friends," he said. "I had a profitable relationship with the
canal folk. Moreover, I was naturally of an affording and officious nature, and it was a signal honor to be selected for a
post of responsibility and hazard."

"Hazard?" Reno hopefully repeated.

Grandfather explained that, though the athletic sports of

that day were not so scandal-riddled as at present, one still had to be on the lookout for sharpshooting and skulduggery.

As chairman, his first concern was to inform himself of the terms of the contest. It was to be not the usual "feast to a finish," which continued until one of the competitors was glutted to the point of quitting, but a time race for fifty dollars a side of twenty "hard" or double-crust pies. ("Soft" pastry, such as squash, custard and lemon meringue, was, he stated, in a lower category.) Each entrant was to start at the end of a row of pies and eat toward the center, the one who first finished his twentieth pie to be declared the winner.

The chairman inspected the pastry, which was ranged in tins on two plank trestles broadwise of the stage. At the ends were seated the rivals, waiting hungrily. They had fasted for twelve hours.

The busiest spot in the room was the betting stand at a corner of the stage but on the main floor. Here operated the stakeholder, a man of venerable aspect, with flowing hair, a white beard, and a clerical broadcoat, all of which failed to inspire the slightest degree of confidence in Grandfather.

"Seldom," he informed his intent audience, "have I encountered a personality which less pleased my mind. The stakeholder was a very theologaster for false respectability."

"Theolo—" John began on a note of inquiry, but got no farther. Jenny had slipped a swift hand over his mouth. It was obviously not the time for further interruptions.

The stakeholder's functions, our narrator set forth, were onerous. He must be familiar at sight with the worth of paper money, which was extremely fluctuant. Banks issued their own notes at will, the discounts upon which shifted unpredictably from day to day. "Niagara money," for example, at par on Saturday, might be in the "broken" category by Monday sundown and worth precisely nothing.

Observing from the corner of his eye, Grandfather noted that the theologaster's work was prompt and decisive. The canallers were laying hard coin. The townsfolk leaned to bank issues, while the rural people, less pecunious, wagered among themselves in kind: goose feathers, flaxseed, duck shot and garden produce.

"Detrimental though this was to public morality," Grandfather told us, "I was powerless to stop it. I did, however, warn the gamesters that they betted at their own risk and advisement, and without official guarantee. It was now my office to introduce the two contestants." He opened the ort-book and refreshed his memory from a newspaper clipping. "As I thought," he said. "The Pennsylvanian was the challenger."

This was a stocky, florid fellow, very cock-a-hoop in his manners, to use Grandfather's own term. Though his proper name was Purtweiler, he ate under the professional pseudonym of the Great Alexander. His rival, Forty-Pie Hoskins, claimed both New England championships, soft and hard. He was an ill-favored, lantern-jawed six-footer with a squint in his near eye. Grandfather, as he performed the introductions, noted the rancor with which the principals glared at each other, shared by the seconds standing back of them. It seemed out of character. Meetings of this kind were usually conducted in a spirit of urbanity.

For the information of the audience, Grandfather announced that the challenger was a straight apple man, while his opponent would alternate apple with rhubarb. By mutual consent this would be a "wet" match; water, lemonade, or cider could be taken at will. Tins must be cleaned; dropped crumbs or filling would count against the offender. Emesis would be visited by instant disqualification.

"Agreed, gentlemen?"

Both replied in the affirmative.

"Prepare."

At the word, the seconds whipped out knives and stepped forward.

"Ready, Great Alexander?"

The Pennsylvanian filled his mouth from a water ewer, gargled deeply, and projected a solid stream against a wall five yards away. It was an impressive exhibition of labial virtuosity. "Ready," he growled.

"Ready, Forty-Pie Hoskins?"

The Yankee gnashed his formidable jaws, gleaming with teeth which had been newly stopped with the mineral succedaneum. "Let 'er go!" he shouted.

"Cut!" ordered Grandfather.

The seconds strode from pie to pie, neatly dividing each into quarters, and returned to their posts.

"Eat!"

The test was on. Expert observers noted at once the difference in technique of the two entrants. Hoskins made the most of his cavernous jaw by attacking his pastry at the base, champing and chawing through with a noise like a straw-chopper.

"Gulch-and-gobble," Grandfather characterized his style. "Uncomely, but it covered a deal of pie."

The Great Alexander, on the other hand, was a steady muncher. Starting at the apex of the triangle, he pursued his rodent way through crust and filling in persistent swallows.

In no time Hoskins led by nearly a pie. Odds were freely offered upon him and as freely taken. Six pies along and now leading by a full tin, Hoskins lost the rhythm of his breathing, inhaled a flake of crust, and fell into a fit of coughing. His second restored him with a series of thumps between the shoulders, but not before his rival had caught up with him. There were loud cheers when the challenger coolly paused for a draught of cider. The betting speeded up at even money.

"As the *Wayne Sentinel* so justly put it," Grandfather said, "the excitement was intense."

The pair was bite-for-bite on Pie Number 12 when the

New Englander clapped his hand to his mouth and yelled, "Time!" Between thumb and finger he drew forth a slender, metallic object, which Grandfather identified as a silver-eyed blunt. A clamor of protest against the interruption rose from the opposition. It was within the chairman's official competency to halt the proceedings, which he did by wrenching away the tin upon which the Great Alexander was industriously working.

Hoskins brandished the needle. "Foul!" he clamored. "He put it there."

"You're a liar!" the other vociferated, advancing upon him.

"Order! Order!" Grandfather commanded.

They paid no heed to him, but embarked upon an exchange of insults with a wealth of invective that attracted the favorable notice of the experienced canal captains.

"The most copious hoggee on the tow-path," Grandfather commented, "could not have been more vituperous."

From words to action was but a short step. Seizing upon the nearest pie, the Great Alexander obliterated his enemy's features in a welter of apple pulp. Hoskins flew at his throat. The seconds joined in. Several backers took a hand. The canallers surged forward, uttering nautical war cries. Presently everybody was fighting.

"You, too, Grandpa?" young Charlie asked eagerly.

Not Grandfather. His suspicions had already been aroused by the pretentious hostility which the rivals exhibited toward one another. It was just a little overdone. Now he noted that, while there was a great whoobub, with much flailing of fists and stamping of feet, little if any physical damage was being done to the pie-eaters or their assistants. It was a mock battle that they were waging.

With what purpose, the chairman asked himself. Obviously to divert public attention. The money! Grandfather whirled about to look at the betting table. It was bare. The snowy-whiskered stakeholder, his pockets bulging, was already astride a windowsill.

"Halt! Stop, thief!" Grandfather thundered.

The man filliped his fingers toward his accuser, in jaunty farewell.

"Important business in the next county. I can't dwell," he responded, and vanished.

Sense of responsibility, as the old gentleman frequently impressed upon his respectful descendants, was an Adams trait. As chairman, he was obligated to a trust. He fulfilled it instinctively by following through the window just after the stakeholder had removed the ladder planted there for his advantage.

"I took a severe hyst," Grandfather said, with the ingenuous expression that frequently accompanied his deliberate archaisms.

But John remembered that one. "It must have been a bad fall, sir," he said sympathetically.

"It wrenched my ankle sorely," the old gentleman said. "But for that I should have overtaken my quarry before he reached the berm and launched forward in a mighty effort."

"Did he jump the canal?" Reno asked breathlessly.

"No man," the old gentleman answered, "ever spanned that forty-foot breadth. But the money-heavy theologaster made a creditable attempt. He landed, knee-deep in mire, floundered through to terra firma, and so away. Owing to my injury, I could follow no further."

"I bet he was in cahoots with the pie-eaters," Reno said.

"It was unquestionably a collusive plan. When I returned to make my report, the canallers were still fighting, but the principals and their seconds were gone," Grandfather replied.

"Didn't you ever see them again, sir?" I asked.

"The contestants, but not the theologaster," Grandfather said.

John's craving for knowledge could be stifled no longer. "What *is* a theologaster, Grandpa?" he demanded.

Before his curiosity could be satisfied, the kitchen door swung partly open. A gush of warm and spiced richness exuded. Our step-grandmother's kindly voice announced:

"Pieplant, mince and pandowdy. Who will have which?"

With one motion we got to our feet.

"Sit *down*," Grandfather thundered in a tone that loosened the hinges of our knees. His voice was lower but no less imperious as he addressed his wife. "I have not yet concluded, madam."

"I ask your pardon, Mr. Adams," she responded, with the irrefragable placidity that was the preservative of peace in that household.

He resumed the saga. "Yes, I encountered those two rapscallions a week later in this very city. The theatrically bitter enemies were sharing a repast in great amity at Bement's Recess near the Four Corners. They changed color when they saw me."

"What did you say to them, Grandpa?" Jenny put the question in an apprehensive voice.

"I made it abundantly clear to them," the old gentleman answered grimly, "what would happen if ever they attempted to operate canalside again. They had no further bulimy for . . ." He broke off and looked at us with an insinuating half-smile. "What would you suppose they were eating?"

That was too easy. "Pie!" five unanimous voices guessed in chorus.

The half-smile became a smile. "The obvious is not invariably the accurate," said Grandfather urbanely. "The precious pair was sharing a cut of hog's harslet at sixpence the order. You may now withdraw to the kitchen."

MUNK BIRGO AND THE CARCAGNE

Against the admonitions of his wife, Grandfather had gone out walking in the March slush. In consequence—though he would never have given our step-grandmother the satisfaction of admitting it—he came down with a hard cold.

"Let me send for Dr. Ely, Mr. Adams," she urged.

"No such a thing," the old gentleman retorted. "It is no more than a pesky rheum. Hand me my antifogmatic."

Throughout the day he treated himself to frequent sips from the amber-hued bottle containing his favorite home remedy, Hop Bitters. He was still dosing when, the next afternoon, Jenny, John, Reno, Charles and I found him basking in the glow of his lyre-shaped Franklin stove. To the cheering, alcoholic influence of the Bitters we owed, I am sure, the one story of the supernatural that we ever heard from his lips.

A Lake Ontario gale had been blowing for two days. A specially savage blast rocked the frame cottage, filling the dark afternoon with unearthly voices. Grandfather cocked an ear.

"Howls like the carcagne," he observed.

"What's that, sir?" I asked.

He put on his look of pretended incredulity. "You don't know what a carcagne is?" He swept the circle of our faces with his glance. "Not any of you?"

"No, sir," John answered.

The rest of us shook our heads in expectant agreement.

"Just as well, perhaps," said Grandfather. "Superstitions are not for the young."

"I don't mind ghosts," Charlie averred valiantly.

"Was it a ghost, Grandpa?" Jenny asked. "The carcagne, I mean."

"She, not it," he corrected. "No, not a ghost. You must understand that there is no such thing as a carcagne any more than there are ghosts."

"If there had been, what would it be like?" Charlie inquired insinuatingly.

"She was supposed to be a storm-hag with a wolf's head, a vampire's mouth, and a bat's wings."

"Oo-oo-oo!" said Charlie enjoyably and shrank perceptively as the wind echoed him.

"None but the lakers believed in her," the old gentleman continued. "They were a witch-ridden lot alongshore."

"Our lakers?" John asked. "Lake Ontario?"

Grandfather nodded. "Stout enough fellows in a storm or a ruckus," he said, "but scared of an owl in the dark. Say 'carcagne' to any one of them and he would spin you a tale to make a woodcat's whiskers bristle. All fahdoodle, as I have warned you. And yet—and yet"—his voice dropped to a ruminative murmur— "I have often wished that Munk Birgo could have lived to tell what he saw and heard that foul night of gale off Oswego Harbor."

Jenny's breath oozed forth in a softly tremulous sigh. "I don't think you ever spoke of Mr. Birgo before, Grandpa. Was he a friend of yours?"

"Of no man's," replied Grandfather.

"It's a funny name," John said. "Was he baptized that way, sir?"

"Baptismal water never touched him," said Grandfather. "It would have sizzled."

Everybody on the lake and ashore knew Munk Birgo for a man of evil in word and deed, Grandfather continued. He was part French, part Indian, and part (if loose talk was to be believed) something worse than either. When in liquor, he would scutter up a tree like a squirrel and shout, "I am Munk Birgo! There is fire in my blood and breath, and I can spit brimstone!"

"Could he, Grandpa?" Charlie asked in awe.

"I never saw him do so," was the cautious reply, "but many accredited him with strange potencies derived from his parentage."

Munk, by common report, had been born in a feverous hag's nest on a reed-encircled islet of the great Montezuma Marshes, Grandfather told us. It was said that his mother was not a broom-witch but a fork-witch, which is one degree worse. Who Munk's father was, nobody inquired with too much particularity. Some said the Devil.

Munk's first commercial activity was as an owler out of Ogdensburg. No great harm in that, Grandfather said. Most Lake Ontario small craft did a bit in the contraband line— woollens, powder, rum and whatnot. But how Munk came by his sloop was a darker matter. He claimed to have sighted her from a low point off Sodus, unmanned, unrigged, and drifting toward a lee shore, but there was plenty of piracy on the lakes in those days, and few to put factious questions. At any rate when Munk turned up with his new sloop, her stern board had been scoured clean and bore the legend, in fresh-painted red-and-blue lettering:

Munk Birgo
His Fancy.

She was a sweet craft, in Grandfather's opinion, a bit walt perhaps, but trim, staunch and clover to handle, and could show her heels to the fastest revenuer between York State and Canada Shore.

"Then you saw her, sir?" John said.

"Once only," Grandfather replied. "She was pelting into Genesee mouth, full sail and both sheets made fast before fifty miles of gale, as foolhardy seamanship as ever I saw in my life. There stood Munk, tall and spare, black-a-vised and jaunty—well favored, too, in his dark way—with the tiller between his knees, singing the Devil's Anthem and beating time with a cemetery bone."

Having held the sheet of a sharpie's mainsail in Owasco Lake races, I deemed myself a nautical expert. "Do you mean he steered with his legs, sir?" I asked incredulously.

"Always," Grandfather said. "It was his special sea-trick. He had built a low steering platform aft, so that he could hold the tiller with his knees. It left his hands free to manipulate the sheets when a revenuer was to windward of him and he had to rely on sharp maneuvering. And," he added darkly, "he had need of all his trickery if half of what was said of him was true."

"What's a cemetery bone, sir?" Charlie asked.

The old gentleman hesitated. "Birgo was in a way of business that was spoken of under men's breath," he said.

"What was it? What business?" all four of us wanted to know.

"Anatomy," said Grandfather.

We others looked at John, who was our recognized expert in the often designedly obscure references of our grandfather. John blinked. "Did he teach it, sir?"

The old gentleman shook his head. "He practiced it. He was a resurrectioner, as the word went in those days."

"I know," John interpreted. "Body snatchers. They dug up dead people."

"What for?" Jenny asked, horrified.

"To sell," Grandfather answered. "It was a regular commerce."

The College of Physicians and Surgeons of Fairfield Seminary, in Herkimer County, needed cadavers for its students, Grandfather went on. There was another market in Albany, and a steady demand from New York City, where a subject in prime condition would fetch as high as fifty dollars. There was developed a nocturnal trade operated by bands of desperadoes who raided village churchyards and carted the bodies away. However, the countryside became aroused, and nightly patrols guarded both the shunpikes and the highroads against the "cad-wagons." It was when the roads had become hazardous for the operators of the business that Munk Birgo, so gossip ran, took up transporting their secret freight for them in his sloop.

The Fancy harbored in Oswego River mouth. Munk's avowed cargoes were salt from the Syracuse beds, grain, and now and again a run of fish.

"But when he sailed by night," the old gentleman said, "there was no manifest to tell what the sloop carried."

"Wasn't he ever caught, sir?" John asked.

Again the old gentleman hesitated. "Not by the law," he said.

"By—by the carcagne?" Jenny asked in a whisper.

A fit of coughing racked Grandfather's bent but still powerful frame. John poured a draught from the amber bottle, which the patient swallowed slowly and with appreciation. The paroxysm was appeased and the narrative was resumed.

"I will recount the story to you as it was told to me by a gypsy crone who was camped on the rocky point opposite the Oswego lighthouse on the night Munk Birgo was last seen," said Grandfather.

From then on, the narrator did not detract from his tale by warning us to disbelieve it. With a touch of histrionics, Grandfather gave himself over to the legend, which he told in the style and parlance of the gypsy herself.

All lake dwellers, so he prefaced the story, remember the great gale of 1829 that swept down one night out of a cloudless northeast. In local phraseology, it was fit to blow a bespoken boot off a wooden leg. Though it was mid-August, a wintry chill was in the air. "Cold as Presbyterian charity," the gypsy woman had described it to her interested hearer.

The spears of an aurora were stabbing upward to the zenith. There was a wild whoobub of wind alow and aloft. The crested breakers that boomed upon the rocks spat electrons like thunderheads. All boats known to be out had come into harbor except one fishing smack, and a crowd stood on the slope above the docks, every eye watchful for her. At last she rounded the point, reefed down to the thirds, scuttering like a mink out of a henhouse, and fetched to against Saunders' dock. Her captain couldn't make the leap to the planking too soon; he craved solidity beneath his feet. His knees were shaking as he walked toward the people, and he looked like the Devil convicted of murder.

"Everybody safe inshore?" the captain asked, and when they told him that he was the last, he uncovered and said "God be thanked!"

The carcagne was out, he told the hushed crowd. Had he seen her, they asked fearfully. Nobody ever really sees her, he said—nobody that comes back in the flesh to tell of it—but he had glimpsed a dark patch swooping overhead, lighted by gleams of fox-fire redder than the aurora glow, and had heard a flutter of thick wings and smelled a whiff of corruption tainting the clean air. If it wasn't the carcagne . . .

Some of the crowd retreated toward their homes, but that was the ignorance of hoi polloi, Grandfather said, because, as all informed folk knew, the creature could not range overland, and they were safe enough on the hillside. Then, as the rumor spread, more inhabitants of the village came out, until all the slopes around the harbor were black with people. From the distant church tower came the strokes of twelve, Methodist time.

It was then that the citizens saw Munk Birgo strolling down the roadway that led to the small wharf where his *Fancy* was moored. He had been going from tap to tavern, and was unsteady on his pins. The Presbyterian preacher halted him.

"Surely you are not going out this night, Birgo?" he said.

Birgo cocked his chin. "Who says it?"

"For the sake of your sinful soul—" the minister began, but Munk Birgo stopped him with a spate of oaths.

"Do you know how much I value your spoopsy counsels?" Munk asked, and answered himself, "Not by the gizzard of a trifle. Not by the product of a quarter-cipher. Back to your humbox, parson!"

"You go to your damnation," the clergyman warned him.

"If all Hell yawned beyond the first line of breakers, go I would just the same," Munk said. "I have my own occasions, and I follow them."

"I know those godless occasions," the minister said, looking him in the eye.

"Then mind your own occasions, Reverend," Birgo said with a laugh. "I'll see you at sunup."

He swaggered down the wharf, jumped aboard, cast off, and, mounting the steering platform, took the tiller in his customary knee-grip. He was mouthing some broken rhythm. Most of those near enough to hear it stopped their ears. It was the Lord's Prayer backward, the gypsy woman had told Grandfather, and he went through it without hitch, gulp, or stutter.

"I am a Romany out of the true Egypt," she had said, "but those words would have burnt my throat to a cinder."

Settled into position, Munk touched neither sheet nor halyard to make sail. Nevertheless, the sloop veered smartly from the dock and set course for the open, missing the guardian rock at the river mouth by a thin hair.

At this, my nautical soul was stirred to protest. "How could she sail upwind under bare poles?" I demanded.

"I don't know," the old gentleman said. "Nobody knows. I am passing on to you the account as it came to me from the gypsy."

A small mist oozed out of nowhere and cloaked the sloop from human sight.

Oswego had little sleep that night. Some said that Munk Birgo had sailed out to keep tryst with the carcagne. Soberer opinion had it that he was transferring a shipment of anatomy for the resurrectioners, three of whom had lately been seen in the locality. The crowd on the hillsides settled down to wait the night out. They watched the northern lights shooting up and falling away. Strange sounds were heard from the upper air that were not of the storm, a high, mad wailing that had laughter in it, too.

With the first paling of the east, the gale turned gusty, then diminished and steadied to a fisherman's breeze. From the lighthouse, a voice shouted, "Sail ho!" All eyes swung to the north.

The sloop was coming in, moving faster than any man there had seen human craft move before. Mainsail, foresail and jib were trim and taut. Above and ahead, as if pointing the course, sped a thick, small cloud that at one moment took a hideous shape, and again became a formless blackness outrunning the breeze. The boat yawed, and shot between the lighthouse and the storm beacon, its deck so tilted that the crowds ashore could see the platform aft.

At that sight a shriek went up to split the moon. Those whose legs would serve them scrambled up the hillside and ran for the dear life and reason. Others cowered close to the ground with their cloaks over their heads. The minister thrust out his hands against the portent on the boat and prayed lustily.

Grandfather paused to cough, and John asked in a determined and manly voice. "What did they—I mean, what was in the boat?"

"The gypsy crone was too frozen with fright to look away," Grandfather resumed. "She recognized the—er—figure on the steering platform as Munk Birgo, but only because of the familiar attitude; it held the tiller between its knees." He took a slow swallow of the Invalid's Friend & Hope. "It was Munk Birgo's skeleton, picked bone-white," he said.

"Oh, my goodness!" Jenny quavered, ladylike even in shock.

Charlie's curiosity overbore his terrors. "Was it the carcagne that ate up Mr. Burgo?" he asked fearfully.

Grandfather's answer was to go on with the tale. The sloop, so the gypsy had told him, struck the guardian rock at the river mouth head-on with a splintering crash, slid off into the depths, and was nevermore seen, plank, strake, or gunnel. A mad hoot of triumph sounded through the air. There was the whirr of a strong wing-beat, and a trail of fox-fire and stinkstone sparks died away in the distance.

"So ended an evil life," Grandfather said solemnly.

Jenny rallied. "Grandpa, dear," she said, "you don't *believe* it was the carcagne, do you?"

"Certainly not," the old gentleman replied, all briskness now. "An idle tale, such as passes, lip to ear, wherever gypsies, tenkers, and other folk of the road gather over a fire-log. Discharge your minds of it."

"Yes, sir," said John. He stared out into the gloom which was deepening with uncomfortable rapidity. "I think we ought to be starting home."

Another violent blast shook the walls, tortured the thrashing boughs of the lilacs beyond the window, and passed on with a whistling wail. Grandfather tilted his head to listen with a frightening intentness.

"All huncamunca and fahdoodle," he mused. Then, with a sly insinuation he added, "Yet there are times, with a wildness such as this outside, when I find myself wondering *what* it was that piloted Munk Birgo's *Fancy* straight and true into Oswego Harbor on that night, fifty years and more past and gone."

A FINGER LAKES
BOYHOOD

Summertimes I exchanged canalside life in Rochester for lake shore adventure in Cayuga County. This came about by the fortunate circumstance of my maternal grandfather, Samuel Miles Hopkins, D.D., buying a point on the east side of Owasco Lake, smallest of the five aquatic "fingers" which form a chain of beauty through the heart of Central New York. There I spent joyous vacation days with my Hopkins relatives and our friends from Auburn, the nearby city which assumed social proprietorship of the locality.

With the coming of summer to the lakes, the youth of the vicinity underwent a radical change of nature. We, who had been land animals, became not only lacustrine, but amphibian. When a new boy came among us he was subjected to an inquisition. The object was to determine his nautical status. The neophyte who could not handle himself as well on or in the water as on land, was out of luck. For, the length and breadth of the Finger Lakes, in the 1880's, aquatics were less a sport than a necessity.

Motor boats were, of course, far in the undreamed future.

Steam launches were for millionaires; there were not a dozen on the five lakes. Oar and sail were the standard motive power. No road led to my Grandfather's place. The lake was our sole highway. A mile and a half away, on the opposite shore, the Southern Central Railroad was our medium of supplies and connecting link with the outer world.

The ordeal of a newcomer of the younger generation started with the key question:

"Can you swim?"

If he answered "No," he was sternly bidden to learn, it being indicated that this was not only a measure of self-preservation but also a preliminary to social recognition. The unfortunate ignoramus would be banished from boat and dock until he had learned the art. Once he had qualified in this respect he was examined as to his seamanship.

How would he handle a canoe in a storm? (This was a catch-question, the answer being, "Nobody but a darn fool takes a canoe out in a storm.") Would a flat-bottomed or a round-bottomed boat be safer in a seaway? (A "greeny" was likely to declare for the flat, because of its appearance of superior stability.) Did he row loose-oar or thole-pin? Could he feather? Was a smoothboard or a clinker-built slicker in the water? Then the final test: what did he know about sailing?

Rash, indeed, was the novice who based his pretensions on book-knowledge alone. (*The Boy's Book of Seamanship*; *How To Sail a Boat in Six Easy Lessons; 25 Cents.*) He might be able to identify a cleat, to distinguish between a halyard and a backstay, to tell how to reef, and to state glibly which tack had the right of way. But, unless he had actually handled tiller and sheet in a blow, he might better go inland and climb a tree than abide our test. For he would be cast adrift in our own private school-ship, appropriately called the *Tub*, and the result was invariably an inglorious grounding on the shore.

The pride of the Hopkins family was an eighteen-foot

Sandusky sharpie. She was a lovely, lively little craft, two-masted, high-prowed, drawing less than a foot of water amidships, and stabilized by a deep centerboard. In the hands of experience, this is a safe type for the treacherous Finger Lakes weather, where vicious little gusts come sweeping down from the steep-hilled banks to undo any but the most vigilant expert. Our *Undine* was fast, too, and could show her wake to any competitor in the weekly races.

The sharpie was not for us Hopkins grandchildren, though we might ship as hands and haul the centerboard, or hold a sheet in light weather. Our personal navigation was limited to the rowboats and the *Tub*. This latter was a lumbering, snubnosed, flat-bottomed scow with a leg-of-mutton sail shaped out of one of Grandmother's discarded counterpanes, home-made leeboards, and a sawed-off oar for tiller. We learned about sailing from her.

As the senior of the male grandchildren, I was captain. By the time I was twelve and had handled the *Tub* for two seasons, I deemed myself capable of circumnavigating the globe. My confidence was not shared by my elders, and my control of the *Undine* was limited to a brief handling of the tiller while whatever senior was in charge was lighting his pipe. But the *Tub* had taught me much, and I picked up the rest by attentive observation, which proved to be fortunate. The great gale of 1883 gave me my opportunity.

This July storm was one of the worst three-day blows I have ever known. Owing to unexpected visitors over the week end, our camp larder had run low. Our natural emergency food supply was cut off: no fish would bite in that turmoil. We children brought in some mushrooms from the woods, and Grandfather shot a woodchuck, the fresh meat of which is preferable to starvation, but not greatly. On the fourth day of short rations, Grandmother addressed her husband.

"Samuel, we need bread."

"Yes, my dear."

"We are out of eggs, coffee, milk, bacon and other things that are spoiling in Ensenore station."

Grandfather held up a finger to the whistling gale and looked out across the mile of white spume between us and the far shore.

"It is blowing," he said conservatively.

"I didn't know that a Hopkins would stop for a little wind," she said.

"Quite so, my dear," he answered. He opened the door to the side room. "Come, my sons," he called. "Ensenore."

Uncle Jack and Uncle Woolsey rose from the cribbage board and reached for their caps.

I trailed along to the dock, in the vain hope of being allowed to ship. Grandfather merely remarked that it was no weather for small boys. I watched the *Undine* put out under a handkerchief of canvas on the foremast and rather less aft.

Two hours later she came in, yawing madly under mainsail alone. The foremast had carried away, a foot above the deck, in a wild squall that caught her before the sail could be dropped. The nearest shipyard was on Cayuga Lake, thirty miles away.

Back of the shore was the forest. With hatchet and saw we went mast-hunting. A hemlock of suitable girth and height was located, chopped down and trimmed. In less than two hours we had our improvised mast stepped, stayed and rigged. To the expert eye it appeared serviceable, but there was a flaw somewhere. It held on the next trip over to Ensenore and brought the *Undine* almost in on the return when, crack! And it was overside.

Tamarack has the favored local timber for masts in the lake country. A five-mile tramp to a tamarack bog yielded a likely-looking spar. It did not live up to its looks. Securely stepped and stayed, it bent with supple promise to several gusts—then snapped in two. Again the *Undine* was a semi-wreck.

"If soft wood won't serve, hard wood may," Grandfather said.

He picked out a shagbark hickory sapling which was tough to fell and trim. It stood up.

Three days is the supposed limit for this type of storm. On the fourth morning the wind dropped, the sun came out, the gale was spent. That's what we thought, who should have known better the treacheries of Finger Lakes weather. Grandfather and Uncle Jack decided to take the morning train for Auburn, so Uncle Woolsey and I sailed them across before as sweet a breeze as a sailor's heart could wish. Having discharged our passengers and taken on cargo, we set out on the return trip. A cloud-bank formed with formidable swiftness in the north. The breeze whipped around and became a gale. Halfway home, my uncle handed me the tiller.

"I don't feel well," he said.

I have always thought that it was the aftermath of the woodchuck, though it may have been an over-age mushroom. In either case, my companion was reduced to total helplessness. The boat was mine to command, with two sails and a rudder to handle in the face of gusts which were rising to fifty-mile-an-hour velocity.

In a long lifetime, I doubt that I have ever felt an equally exhilarating sense of responsibility. For a long half hour I juggled the *Undine* up to windward. I coaxed her, I babied her, I eased her, and between squalls I drove her into the leaping assault of the head-waves.

Open navigation, I decided, was simple, but it could not be kept up indefinitely. My business was to bring my command into port. The problem was a tricky one. I had to put in as near shore as possible without smashing my centerboard upon the rocky bottom, then spin the boat about and nose her into the dock under her own momentum.

Looking up to estimate my distance, I beheld with dismay my grandmother advancing to the narrow and fragile planking which formed the outer span, followed by a bevy of female grandchildren. Now, if I misreckoned and bumped the dock too hard, the whole lot would be in the lake and I in disgrace forever.

I yelled to them to go back, but my voice must have been drowned by the wind. At that desperate moment I felt a grinding beneath my feet. Bottom!

To jam my tiller hard over was instinctive. The sharpie came up gallantly, but a cross-gust caught her and she made for the dock, head on, like a runaway freight car. I gave one last, despairing yelp, one last despairing shove to my tiller, and the prow swerved, missing the woodwork by a mouse's whisker.

When I came about, the dock was empty. The family had seen all they needed of my seamanship. Relieved of the anxiety of a wholesale immersion, I made a respectable landing at my second effort. The female contingent were too busy reviving my uncle to offer any comment at the time. The report must have been favorable, however, for a few days later, my grandfather said quite casually: "Samuel, suppose you and Winthrop (my younger cousin) take the sharpie over for the mail."

I can still see the astonished and envious faces of my contemporaries, gathered at Ensenore pier for the afternoon ceremony of meeting the 5:02, as I nonchalantly threaded the shipping (all manned by adults) and ordered my crew to "make her fast."

A week later I lost my hard-won reputation. Without informing any of us, Grandfather had rigged aloft from foremast to mainmast some sort of contraption which he called a vang. We were returning from Ensenore, I at the helm and Grandfather amidships when we were hit by a gust from the port quarter. It was the merest catspaw and should have made no trouble for the experienced mariner that I deemed myself. But when I eased up on the foresail it stuck. The interfering and unnoticed vang had caught and held the gaff. Over we went, a quarter of a mile from shore, in 150 feet of water.

Notwithstanding his seventy-odd years, the old gentleman, nimble as a spider, skittered up over the side of the slowly capsizing craft, and perched on the bottom, where I miserably joined him by swimming. Some carpenters, working on a barn roof, saw the mishap, came out in a flat, and we were ingloriously rescued. The *Undine* drifted ashore.

When next I showed my shamed face at Ensenore, the whole lake was aware of my disgrace. I was greeted by raucous hoots, saluted as "Captain Tipsytottle," treated to cries of "All hands stand by to abandon ship," and called by the fighting name of "landlubber." I was prepared to regret that I had not gone to the bottom, when Grandfather, like the fine gentleman he was, came to the rescue.

"I wish to hear no more contumelious remarks addressed to my grandson," he thundered in those tones which had made him a noted pulpit orator. "The accident was due entirely to my own carelessness. I have now to inform you all that Samuel will captain the *Undine* in next Saturday's regatta."

It was my day of restored glory. Alas! I did not live up to it. I misread the direction of an offshore puff, lost a twenty-rod advantage, and came in third. But, at least, my nautical status was established on a firm foundation.

Nowadays a score of cars come daily to the place that was my grandfather's and is now mine, bringing all the appurtenances of modern existence. Motor boats whizz past my dock. An occasional amphibian plane churns to a stop off my point. It is all very convenient. Life is far easier than in the old days. But it isn't half as much fun.

BASEBALL IN MUMFORD'S PASTURE LOT

A smart single rig drew up to the hitching post of No. 52 South Union Street as we three boys approached. Out of it stepped a short, red-faced, dapper man who secured his horse and then addressed us.

"Does Mr. Myron Adams live here?"

"Yes, sir," John said.

"We're just going in to see him," Sireno added. "He's our grandfather."

"Well, you can wait," the stranger said. "I've got private business with him."

"If you're trying to sell him a colored enlargement of a photograph . . ." John began but got no further.

"I ain't," the caller interrupted. "My name is Phillips and I represent the Rochester Baseball Club."

"There isn't any," I said glumly.

It was cause for humiliation to every right-thinking inhabitant of the city, young and old, that in the spring of the baseball-mad year of 1879, Rochester was represented by no professional team whatever.

"There will be if I can sell fifty of these here tickets, good

for the whole season and only ten dollars," Mr. Phillips said.
"D'you think he'll pony up? How's he on baseball?"

"He wouldn't know a Dollar Dead from a Young America
if it hit him in the snoot," Reno answered. The Dollar Dead
was the standard amateur ball, the Young America the
twenty-five-cent junior favorite.

"I'll have a crack at him anyway," Mr. Phillips decided. He
vanished into the cottage, and in a few minutes we heard
Grandfather, in his deep and resonant voice, putting an end
to the interview. "What?" he cried. "Money? To witness what
should be a *gentleman's* pastime? Nonsense! Fustian! Good
day to you!"

The crestfallen visitor came out, silently climbed into his
buggy, and drove away. We went in to pay our duty call.

A week later, the three of us ran upon Mr. Phillips again,
this time in Livingston Park, and heard from him tidings of
great joy. In spite of Grandfather's recalcitrance, Rochester
was to have its team. Mr. Asa T. Soule, the patent-medicine
magnate, had just come forward with an offer to finance a
club out of his private pocket, provided it should bear the
name of Hop Bitters, the cure-all he manufactured.

The news spread fast and, as the opening of the season
drew near, Rochester glowed with restored pride. In its first
game the new club swamped an amateur nine, fourteen to
six.

Next, an exhibition game was scheduled against Rochester's ancient and bitter rival, the Buffalos, who were in the
National League and therefore supposedly a cut above us. It
was to be the event of the year, and the admission was fifty
cents. John, being ten years old and our senior member, put
the painful question to Reno and me.

"Where are we going to get half a dollar apiece?"

"Grandpa Adams," I suggested doubtfully.

"In your mind, baby mine!" Reno said, using the most emphatic negation of the time.

"What other chance have we got?" I asked. Nobody had an answer. Fifty cents was unthinkably hard for a small boy to come by in those days. Grandfather was our only hope.

In preparation for the desperate attempt upon his purse, we all three devoted the next week or so to attending him with great assiduity. We mowed his lawn. We weeded the vegetable patch. We suffered errands gladly. When but two days remained before the game, we decided the time had come. We washed our hands and brushed our hair, and since none of us coveted the honor of putting the momentous question, I plucked three timothy heads for the purpose of drawing lots.

"Shortest straw pulls the skunk's tail," I said. This was formula; no disrespect was intended.

John drew the short one, and, led by him, we went to face our grandfather. John opened cautiously, speaking of the importance of the coming event to Rochester and the Hop Bitters Club. "You know, Grandpa, our team's named for the medicine," he said brightly.

The old gentleman glanced at the mantel, where stood a dark-amber bottle containing the spirituous and inspiriting "Invalid's Friend & Hope."

"Why, yes," he said. "A superior restorative. Very comforting to the system," a sentiment shared by thousands of the old gentleman's fellow-teetotallers.

"It's a dandy ball team," Reno gloated.

"I assume that you refer to its costume?" Grandfather said coldly. He did not countenance slang on our lips.

"Yes, sir," Reno agreed hastily. "You ought to see their uniforms."

"I am willing to believe that they present a macaroni appearance," the old gentleman said. "But what is the precise connection between this remedy and the projected contest?"

"Mr. Soule is giving the money for the club," John explained.

"Mr. Asa T. Soule? I was not aware that he had sportive proclivities."

"Oh, he's not really a sporting man," John hastened to disclaim. "No, sir! He—he's quite religious. Why, he won't have a player on his team who ever played on Sunday."

I saw that Grandfather, a strict Sabbatarian, was impressed. "They've got a rule against Sunday games in the National League," I said, opportunely recalling an item in the *Democrat & Chronicle*.

"Baseball is a very Christian game, sir," John added.

"I daresay, I daresay," the old gentleman conceded. "But it is not, by all accounts, what it was in my day. When I first came here, the Rochester Baseball Club met four afternoons a week. We had fifty members. That was in 1827."

"I play first base on the Livonia Young Eagles," Reno said eagerly. "Where did you play, sir?"

"In Mumford's pasture lot, off Lake Avenue."

"Reno means what position, Grandpa," I explained.

"Batter, for choice," said the old gentleman.

"You couldn't bat all the time," Reno demurred.

"No," Grandfather said. "But I preferred to. I frequently hit the ball over the fence."

"When your side was in the field, where did you play?" John asked.

"Wherever I thought the ball most likely to be batted, naturally," the alumnus of Mumford's pasture lot replied, manifestly annoyed at the stupidity of the question.

"That's a funny kind of a game," Reno muttered.

"I see nothing humorous in it," Grandfather retorted. "The cream of Rochester's Third Ward ruffleshirts participated in the pastime."

"Lots of the nicest boys in town go to baseball games now," I said hopefully.

"Well, well. " Our grandfather's deep accents were benevolent. "I see no reason why you should not attend. You are old enough to go by yourselves, I suppose."

"It isn't that exactly, Grandpa," John said. "You see, sir—"

"It costs money to get in," Reno blurted.

"So I was informed by the person with the inflamed nose," said Grandfather dryly.

"Only fifty cents," John said with admirable casualness; then he added, "We thought, sir, that perhaps you would like to come along with us and see how they play it now, just for once."

There was a breathless pause. Then Grandfather said, "Fetch me the emergency cashbox from the desk."

Hardly able to believe our ears, we fell over one another to obey.

During the next forty-eight hours, John, Reno and I debated long and seriously as to whether we should brief Grandfather on modern baseball, which he was about to see for the first time. All of us were, of course, experts, although we had never seen a professional game. We knew the rules and the etiquette of the diamond and could have passed perfect examinations on the quality and record of every wearer of a Hop Bitters uniform. Reno and I were for giving Grandfather the benefit of our erudition, but John outargued us. Older generations, he pointed out, did not take kindly to instruction from younger.

"He'd just tell us that he played the game before we were born," he said.

On the great day, Grandfather and the three of us arrived early at Hop Bitters Park and found good places in the fifth row directly back of the plate. Before our enchanted eyes there stretched the greensward of the diamond, bounded by the base paths. It was close-cut, but the outfield was practically in a state of nature, its grasses waving gently in the breeze. We had heard that the Buffalo manager had entered a protest against the outfield's unmown state, complaining that he had not brought his players all the way to Rochester to have them turned out to pasture.

The stand filled up promptly. There must have been as many as three hundred people present, mostly of the prosperous classes. Mr. Mudge, the undertaker, and Mr. Whittlesey, the Assistant Postmaster, took seats in front of us and were presently joined by Mr. Toogood, the Troup Street livery-stable man. Two clerks from Glenny's China Emporium crowded past us, while on the aisle side the manager of Reynolds Arcade took his place, accompanied by Professor Cook, the principal and terror of No. 3 School. Back of us sat a red-necked, hoarse-voiced canalman. Mr. Mudge addressed our grandfather.

"A pleasure and a surprise to see you here, Mr. Adams."

"The young must have their day," Grandfather replied amiably. "*Maxima debetur puero reverentia*, you know."

"Yes, sir; I don't doubt it for a minute," the liveryman said earnestly. "I hear those Buffalos are tough."

"We can lick 'em," I said loyally.

"Rochester boasted a superior club in my day, also," Grandfather said.

"Did you play on it, Mr. Adams?" inquired Professor Cook.

"I did, sir, for two seasons."

"I assume that the game as then played differs from the present form."

"You are justified in your assumption, sir," said Grandfather, who then entered upon an informative discourse regarding the baseball of 1827.

The play at Mumford's pasture lot, he set forth, was open to all fifty active members of the club. The pitchers, who were ex officio the captains, chose up sides. Twelve to a team was considered a convenient number, but there might be as many as fifteen. A full turnout of members would sometimes put three teams in the field. Mr. Mudge expressed the belief that this must result in overcrowding. Where did they all play?

Pitcher, catcher and basemen, Grandfather said, remained in their positions. The basemen stood touching their bases with at least one foot until the ball was hit. The remainder of the out team formed a mobile defense, each man stationing himself where he foresaw the best opportunity of making catches. Mr. Toogood wished to know what the third team did while two were in the field. It waited, the veteran explained. At the close of each inning, when three batters had been put out—whether on flies, fouls, or by being touched or hit with the ball—the runs were totted up and the side with the lower score was supplanted by the third team. This continued until the hour agreed upon for stopping, which was usually sunset. Then the team with the largest total was adjudged the winner.

"Sounds like three-old-cat gone crazy," Reno muttered in my ear.

Further elucidation of the baseball of Grandfather's day was cut short by a shout of "Here they come!," as, amidst loyal clamor, the home team strode forth in neat gray uniforms, the name of the sponsoring nostrum scarlet across their breasts. They were a terrifically masculine lot, with bulging muscles and heavy whiskers. Eagerly we boys identified our special heroes, having often trailed them through the streets to the ballpark entrance. "That's Meyerle, the first base," John said. "He can jump six feet in the air and catch the ball with his left hand."

"The little, dumpy one is Burke," said Mr. Toogood. "He's shortstop. You oughta see him handle daisy-cutters! Oh, my!"

"McGunnigle, our right fielder, batted pretty near three hundred with Buffalo last year," Mr. Mudge told Grandfather proudly.

"Three hundred runs?" Grandfather asked with evident skepticism.

The reply was drowned by the loudest shout of all. "There he comes! Tinker! Tinker!" A hundred voices chorused, "What's the matter with Tinker!" and three hundred antiphonal howls responded, "HE'S ALL RIGHT!"

The canaller leaned over and spoke confidentially in Grandfather's ear. "You watch that fellow Tinker, Mister. If a high fly goes out to left field, he'll git under it and do the prettiest back flip ever you seen before he catches it. You wouldn't see nothing like that in the League. Used to be a circus man."

"I shall make it a point to observe him," Grandfather said.

Out came the enemy at a carefree trot. They were even more muscular-looking than our heroes and sported whiskers at least as luxuriant. They lined up near the plate, faced the stand, and saluted the crowd grimly, fingers to the peaks of their green caps. We boys joined lustily in the chorus of opprobrious hoots that was the response. A man in street clothes appeared and took a stand a yard behind the catcher, who stood five yards back of the plate.

"On which side does that person play?" Grandfather asked.

"He doesn't play," Mr. Mudge answered. "He's the umpire. He makes the decisions."

"In our game, we had no need of such intervention," Grandfather said. "If a point of dispute arose, the captains consulted and came to a composition."

"Suppose they disagreed?" Professor Cook suggested.

"Then, sir, they skied a copper for heads or tails and abode by arbitrament of the coin, like gentlemen and Corinthians," Grandfather replied. He turned his attention to the scene below. "Why is the tall man throwing the ball at the short man?" he inquired.

"That's our pitcher, Critchley, sooppling his arm up," Mr. Toogood said.

Grandfather frowned. "That is *throwing*, not pitching," he said. "He should keep his arm down."

"He's only got to keep it as low as his waist," Reno said.

The old gentleman shook his head obstinately. "Knuckles should be below the knee, not the waist. A highly improper procedure."

The Hop Bitters team had now taken their positions and were standing, crouched forward, hands upon knees, in the classic posture. A burly Buffalo player stalked to the plate, rang his bat upon it, and described threatening arcs in the air.

"High ball," he barked at the umpire.

The umpire shouted to the pitcher, "The batsman calls for a high ball."

Grandfather addressed the universe. "What in Tophet is this?"

We boys were glad to enlighten him. "He wants a pitch between his shoulder and his belt," John said.

"If he'd called for a low ball, it'd have to be between his belt and his knee," Reno added.

"Do you mean to say that he can choose where the pitch is to come?" Grandfather asked incredulously.

"Yes, sir. And if it doesn't come there, it's a ball, and if he gets eight balls, he can take his base," I said.

"I should admire to bat in such circumstances," said Grandfather.

"Maybe it wouldn't be so easy," Reno said. "Critchley's got a jim-dandy curve."

"Curve?" asked the old gentleman. "What may that be?"

"Outcurve or incurve," Reno told him. "It starts like this, then it goes like this or like this—sorta bends in the air— and whiff! One strike!"

"Bends in the air!" An indulgent smile appeared on Grand-

father's visage. "These young folk will accept any absurdity,"
he said to Professor Cook.

"Some do hold it to be an optical illusion," the principal
said diplomatically.

"Certainly," Grandfather said. "Anything else would be
contrary to the laws of God and nature. Let me hear no more
of such fahdoodle," he concluded sternly, turning his back
upon Reno.

The first inning was uneventful, as were the second and
third. Pitcher Critchley's optical illusions and those of the
opposing pitcher were uniformly and dully successful. Grandfather fidgeted and commented sharply upon the torpor of
the proceedings.

"Lackadaisy-dido!" he said. "Why does not someone hit
the ball?"

"A couple of goose eggs is nothing, Grandpa," John said.
"Just let our team once get a start and you'll see."

The last of the fourth inning supplied a momentary stir. A
high foul came down just in front of us, and the Buffalo
catcher raced after it. The ball slithered from his outstretched
fingers. We boys shrieked with delight. He glared at us and
Grandfather addressed him kindly.

"Young man, that was ill-judged. You would have been
well-advised to wait and take it on the first bounce."

We held our collective breaths, but the wrath died out of
the upturned face.

"Look, Mister," the catcher said, earnestly argumentative,
"that ball was a twister. How'd I know where it would
bound?"

The canaller back of us raised a jeering voice. "Butter-
fingers! Whyncha catch it in your cap?"

"You can't catch a ball in your cap any more," John said
to the canaller. "It's in this year's rules."

"Back to the berm, fathead!" the catcher added.

The umpire walked up, lifting an authoritative hand. "No conversation between players and spectators," he snapped, and the game was resumed.

Later, there was a considerable delay when a foul sailed over the fence. Both teams went outside to search for the ball, and Grandfather took the occasion to expatiate upon the superiority of the old-time game.

"Our Saturdays," he said, "were very gala affairs. Ladies frequently attended and refreshments were served."

"Did you have uniforms, Grandpa?" I asked.

"Uniforms? We had no need of them. We removed our broadcoats, hitched our braces, and were prepared."

John said, "Our nine has militia caps with brass buttons."

"Fabricius Reynolds played catcher in a canaller's tall castor," Grandfather recalled. "It was of silky beaver, gray, with a picture of the *Myron Holley* passing through Lock Twenty-three painted on the front. Very bunkum."

"I've got a fifteen-cent Willow Wand with 'Home Run' on it in red letters," Reno said proudly.

"Hamlet Scrantom's bat was of polished black walnut with his initials on a silver plate," the old gentleman went on. "He was a notorious batsman."

The quest for the lost ball was eventually abandoned, Mr. Soule reluctantly tossed out a new one, the umpire called "Play ball, gents!," and the dull succession of runless innings continued. Then, in the opening half of the sixth, with two Buffalos out and two on base, a break came. A towering fly to left field brought a yelp of anticipatory delight from the admirers of the accomplished Tinker. Fleet of foot, he got beneath the ball while it was still high in air. His back flip was a model of grace and exactitude. Down came the ball into his cupped and ready hands—and broke through. Amid howls of dismay, he chased it, scooped it up, and threw it home. It went four feet above the catcher's reach, and the Buffalo runners galloped merrily in.

"Boggle-de-botch!" Grandfather exclaimed.

John plucked at his sleeve. "I want to go home," he said brokenly.

"Do not show yourself such a milksop," the old gentleman said. "How far is our own club behind?"

"Three runs," John groaned.

"And there's another," I added, almost in tears, as the Buffalo shortstop sent the ball over the left-field fence.

"Pooh!" said Grandfather. "Four runs is not an insuperable advantage. Why, I once saw Hamlet Scrantom bat in more than that at one stroke."

We stared at him. "How could he, Grandpa?" John asked. "Even if there were three men on base—"

"There were. I was one of them."

"—that would be only four runs."

"Seven, in this instance," the old gentleman said cheerfully. "Hamlet knocked the ball into a sumac thicket, and we continued to run the bases until it was found and returned."

From then on, the Hop Bitters were a sad spectacle. They stumbled and bumbled in the field, and at bat, as the embittered Reno said, they couldn't have hit a rotten punkin with the thill of a four-horse bob. On their side, the enemy fell upon Pitcher Critchley's offerings with dire effect. They dropped short flies over the basemen's heads. They slashed swift daisy-cutters through the impotent infield. They whacked out two-baggers and three-baggers with the nonchalance of assured victory. Grandfather assayed the situation.

"The Buffalos appear to have the faculty of placing their strokes where the Rochesters are not," he said sagely, a comment later paralleled by Willie Keeler's classic recipe, "Hit 'em where they ain't."

We boys and the Rochester rooters around us became silent with gloom. Only Grandfather maintained any show of interest in the proceedings. He produced a notebook from the pocket of his ceremonial Prince Albert coat and, during what was left of the game, wrote in it busily. We were too depressed even to be curious. It was a relief when the agony ended, with a pop fly to the pitcher.

"Three out, all out," the umpire announced. "The score is Buffalos eleven, Hop Bitters nothing. A game will be played in this park . . ."

But we had no heart in us to listen.

We went back to Grandfather's cottage, and over a consolatory pitcher of raspberry shrub in the sitting room he delivered his verdict.

"The game is not without merit," he said thoughtfully, "but I believe it to be susceptible of improvement."

Surprisingly, the Hop Bitters nine beat both Worcester and Washington in the following fortnight. On the strength of their improvement, a return game with Buffalo was scheduled for August, and we boys resumed what Grandfather would have called our "officiousness" at Union Street; we were sedulous in offers to mow, to weed, to fetch and carry. On the last Saturday in July, when a less important game, with Syracuse, was on the card, we found the front door locked and our step-grandmother out back, tending her hollyhocks.

"Where's Grandpa?" I asked.

"You'd never guess," the old lady said with a twinkle.

"Gone canalling," John surmised.

"Mr. Adams is attending the baseball game, if you please," his wife said, "and no more thought of the fifty cents expense than if it was so many peppercorns. This is the second time since he took you boys. I do believe he has ideas."

Grandfather did, indeed, have ideas. We learned of them later. The notes made while the Buffalos were swamping the wretched Hop Bitters were the groundwork of a comprehensive plan which turned up among his papers after his death. It was a design for the betterment of baseball and was addressed to Mr. Soule, the Hop Bitters Baseball Club and the Citizens of Rochester, New York. A prologue, which still seems to me to have its points, introduced it.

The purport and intent of the game of baseball, as I apprehend, is to afford healthful exercise to the participants and harmless entertainment to the spectators. In its present apathetic and supine form it fulfills neither desideratum. A scant dozen runs for an afternoon's effort is a paltry result, indeed. I have seen twice that number achieved in a single inning when the game was in its prime. I therefore have the honor, sir, to lay before you a prospectus for the rejuvenescence of the pastime and its reclamation from the slough of inertia and monotony wherein it is engulfed as practiced in your ballpark.

The plan provided for an extra shortstop between first and second bases and two additional outfielders to take care of long flies. But the really revolutionary proposal dealt with the pitching. The expert of Mumford's pasture lot approved of one innovation he had witnessed, the right of the batter to call his ball. But this did not go far enough. Grandfather's rule proscribed the pitcher from "any motion or pretense delusive of or intended to delude the eye of the batter."

"Such practice," he wrote, "savors of chicanery and is subversive of true, Corinthian sportsmanship." So much for curves!

Whether Mr. Soule ever received the memorial I don't know. Certainly he did not act upon it. A Rochester team took the field in the following spring with the usual complement of nine players and Grandfather never went to another ball game.

MARCIA AND THE
CELEBRITY

Only the rigorous family rule constrained the four of us to attendance upon our grandfather, that September Saturday. Our hearts were downtown where scandalous proceedings impended. The outcaste Dr. Mary Walker, in PANTS, if the capitals in the morning paper were to be believed, supported by Rochester's own revolutionary daughter, Susan B. Anthony, was to deliver an inflammatory address in favor of that devil's doctrine, Female Suffrage.

We were four, not five, because young Charlie had played hooky and headed for Corinthian Hall with his putty-blower up his trouser leg. As the rest of us climbed the cottage steps, Grandfather's formidable voice met us halfway.

"Why shouldn't she wear 'em if she's a mind to?"

Dr. Ely, our family physician, appeared in the partly opened door. He turned to issue a warning.

"Stop waggling that foot or I'll come back and amputate it."

We entered, Jenny in the lead. "What ails your foot, Grandpa?" she asked politely.

"Poor man's gout," he snapped. By this he meant an in-grown toenail.

He tossed aside the issue of the *Democrat & Chronicle* over which he and Dr. Ely had been holding high debate. Jenny peeked at a crumpled headline.

"Does she really wear you-know-whats?" she inquired decorously.

"What if she does?" the old gentleman retorted.

"It isn't very ladylike," Jenny said.

"Why should it be? There never yet was a women's rights speechifier that wasn't more cock than hen. Let 'em dress accordingly." He shifted his leg to a more comfortable position. "Except one," he added in a milder tone. His eyes strayed to the secretary desk against the wall.

"Who was she, sir?" Jenny asked.

"None of you has so much as heard of that brilliant, if wrong-headed exponent of Equality for the Sexes, Miss Frances Wright, I suppose," he replied.

"Did she wear 'em, sir?" Reno asked.

"She did *not*," was the emphatic answer.

"Anyway, I've heard of her," Jenny said brightly. "I've heard Grandma say that she was not a nice person."

"Then you had better not remain to hear more about her," the old gentleman growled in a tone that he seldom employed toward his favorite. "Go out to the kitchen and help your grandmother with her pin-money pickles." The spicy odor was oozing through the crack of the door. "And close the door after you."

"Oh, *Grand*-pa!" Jenny wailed, and withdrew, close to tears.

"Miss Frances Wright," said the scholarly John in a musing tone. "Didn't she write a book?"

"She did. Several. One of them is on the second shelf yonder. At the right end. You may fetch it."

He handed John the key. John opened the glass doors and took down the volume. A twinge in the afflicted toe distracted Grandfather's attention so that he failed to notice his grandson opening to the fly-leaf and holding it up for our inspection. There was an inscription in spidery handwriting.

> *To an Impudent Young Yankee Blade,*
> *whom may Heaven undeservedly pardon,*
> *this Memorial, with the Obliged*
> *Recognizances of the Author.*
>
> F.W.
> *London, England. Oct. 26, 1821.*

We stared at one another. Our austere and dignified forebear thus characterized!

John said hesitantly, "Is the book yours, sir?"

"A gift from the gifted authoress, as you see."

"Then you're the imp—the young blade?" I ventured.

"Eh? What? Give me that book, John." A slow, reminiscent smile appeared upon the bearded lips. "Ah, yes," he murmured. "A very tongue-free lady. A clement disposition. This" —he tapped the cover—"is an earnest of her lenity."

"Why did she want Heaven to pardon you, sir?" John asked.

"My conduct," said Grandfather, "was in a measure reprehensible. I cannot look back upon it without contrition." Reno winked at me. The old gentleman's expression was anything but contrite. "She brought it upon her own fair head, however," he pursued, "by an attitude which could not but be irritant to one's sentiments of patriotism as an American. We were all powerfully patriotic in those days."

John, who had been dipping into the book, looked puzzled. "She says some pretty nice things about us here," he remarked.

"Nice! Over-nice. And she was worse on the lecture plat-

form before the book came out. Praise to the face is open
disgrace, as the rhymster puts it. She dispensed encomiums
until the stomach turned. Toosey-woosey and honey-fuggle,
as one might say. One might suppose that she had discovered
the United States of America and could not find words ful-
some enough in which to approbate her own discovery.
Doubtless she meant well by us, but, for my youthful taste,
she was intolerably—how shall I put it?"

"Condescending," I suggested.

He frowned at me. "You are ignorant of the meaning of the
word, Samuel."

John came to the rescue. "Doesn't it mean patronizing, sir?"

"A corrupt and deteriorate attribution. When we speak of
affable and condescending manners do we indicate patronage, *de haut en bas*? No; no," he answered himself. "The
proper significance of condescending is the attitude of fellowship on a basis of equality."

Having thus set us aright etymologically, he took Miss
Wright's opus from John's hands.

"What was it you did to her, sir?" John asked.

The smile returned to Grandfather's lips and became mo-
mentarily a grin. "I fixed *her* flint," he said. Though critical
of slang in the mouths of our generation, he occasionally
came out with a phrase of ancient cant. "That is," he qualified,
"I would have if my better nature and Squire Grainger had
not intervened. Do any of you remember your distant kins-
woman, Marcia Everingham, born Dillard?"

We did. The primmest, prissiest portrait in the family
connection was that of the ringletted old lady, a very pattern
of piety. Grandfather's next words somewhat mitigated that
impression.

"Marcia was the town terror. Not yet eleven years of age,
she was already the most accomplished liar in Ontario County.
She lied to everybody; to her doting parents, to her teachers,
to the parson himself. And," he added, "to Miss Frances

Wright." He glanced at the kitchen door to make sure of its being tight closed. "No ladies being present, I can recite to you the circumstances," he said.

Canandaigua, New York, Grandfather began, was all of a feeze over the visit of the distinguished Miss Wright. Young Myron Adams, then just past his majority, drove from his home in East Bloomfield to attend the afternoon reception given in her honor. Passing along Main Street, he caught sight of little Marcia Dillard engaged in a study of the court-house wall. He pulled up his high-wheeled suicide gig and mounted the steps to see what was holding her attention. It was a roster of legal actions.

At his greeting, she turned with a bright and innocent smile. "Oh, how-d'ye-do, Cousin Myron! I think crime is cruel interesting, don't you?"

"That depends," said the young man.

"What's arson?"

"Never mind," Grandfather said, foreseeing that further research into the annals of malfeasance might inspire more embarrassing questions. That list was hardly appropriate reading matter for a ten-year-old female.

"People always say that when I ask questions," she complained. She shifted an all-day sucket from one cheek-pouch to the other and turned admiring eyes upon the elegance of his velvet coat, flowered waistcoat and cameo-secured neck-cloth. "Where are you going, all dressed up so dicty?" she demanded.

"To the gala for Miss Frances Wright."

"I know. At Squire Grainger's. It'll be mortal bunkum, won't it, Cousin Myron?"

He replied that the Grainger entertainments were usually quite superior. "Would you like to go, Marcy?" he asked.

Her mouth drooped. "I can't. I'm disinvited." Dolorously she explained that all the other girls in the dame-school which she attended were going. "It's that meanie, Miss Gillespie," she said.

"Your teacher? I suppose you have been doing or saying something specially pernickety," said Grandfather who was conversant with her reputation.

"I never," she disclaimed. With hands piously folded before her she intoned:

> Pinky, pinky bow-bell.
> If I should tell a lie,
> I'd go down to the bad place.
> Cross my heart and die!

"Now will you believe me, Cousin Myron?"

"No," said Grandfather. "But never mind that."

"She said I was an *enfant terrible* and would disgrace the school," said the afflicted Marcia in a rush of words. "*Enfant terrible* is French. It means a bad child." She brightened a little. "I'm not very apt at the Rule of Three and I'm a downright ignorama at Gains and Losses, but nobody can say that I ain't a dab at French. I suppose there'll be raspberry lemonade," she quavered, and wept.

"See here," Grandfather said, "do you very much want to go?"

"How can I? It's scambling to go where you're disinvited. I'd never be a scambler," she declared virtuously.

"It won't be scambling if I escort you," he assured her. "Wipe your nose, smooth down your frock, and disgorge that sweetmeat."

"Oh, Cousin Myron!" she cried. "I do love you. Shall I be presented to the English lady? Will she be very proud and huffish? Is it true that she's writing a book? I ambition to write a book when I grow up."

He replied that Miss Wright was gathering data for publication.

Marcia's bright eyes became dreamy. "I could tell her things," she murmured.

That was the exact moment, said Grandfather, when Satan took over the proceedings.

The fiesta was well under way when they arrived. They made their manners to the Squire and his lady-wife and were ushered into the back parlor where a representation of Canandaigua's schools was exhibiting its best behavior.

A small, pretty Englishwoman, very finified in a silk gown, a Paisley shawl, and earbobs as big as plums, sat on a dais, gazing out over the assemblage with an air of resolute amiability. The spatulate arm of her high-backed chair held a notebook, a pewter well of briar-root ink, two fresh goose-quills, a sandbox and a shot-bowl. A file of children, solemn, starched and suffering, was being conducted to the presence. Each recited a verse or exhibited a carefully memorized compliment. The lady smiled brightly.

Her wandering regard centered upon the newcomer from East Bloomfield, who must then have been a personable young man, as he stepped up to present her with a cluster of artificial flowers delicately sprayed with scent. (Natural blooms would have been inelegant for so formal an occasion.) They exchanged appropriate observations on the weather after which he introduced his young kinswoman, Marcia Happalonia Dillard.

"Marcia aspires to woo the muse of literature," he said, adding in a sharp aside, "Drop a curtsy, ninnywit!"

"Happalonia," the lady repeated. "What interesting names the North Americans choose for their children! Do they call you 'Happy' in the home circle, my dear?"

"No, ma'am," Marcia said. "I'm not."

"Not happy? Surely you should be. Why not?"

"My folks don't understand me," Marcia said sadly.

Miss Wright smiled at Grandfather. "*La femme incomprise.*" She turned to the girl. "How old are you, child?"

"Fifteen."

"What! You do not look it."

Marcia reached for a long word. "I'm precocious."

Miss Wright looked skeptical. Marcia was disappointed. Had not Cousin Myron assured her that the traveling English would believe anything that was told them?

The lady asked, "Do you live here in Canandaigua?"

"No, ma'am. I just school here. We live in Palmyra."

"Palmyra? Palmyra! Classics in the wilderness."

"We aren't wilderness," the Palmyran said. Half closing her eyes, she recited: "Palmyra is destined to become the metropolis of this region. With our advantageous situation on beautiful Ganargwa Creek, we cannot fail . . ."

"Yes, yes," the lady interrupted. "Ganargwa. That is an aboriginal name, is it not? I am interested in the aborigines. Do you have Indians in Palmyra?"

"Oh, yes, ma'am. Lots."

"Are they wild?"

"Awf'ly wild. Pa shot one last week."

"Shot an aborigine? What for?"

Marcia recalled the list on the courthouse wall. Arson she rejected—Cousin Myron had refused to tell her what it meant. She passed from A to B.

"Bastardy," she said.

Miss Wright gasped. "Do you know what you are saying, my child?"

"Oh, yes, ma'am," Marcia replied. "He weltered in his gore."

The visitor turned to Grandfather. "Can this be true?" she asked.

Grandfather was saved from the necessity of thinking up a suitable reply by the arrival of the Lady President of the Hepzibah Sewing Circle, who had elbowed her way to the dais, dragging a reluctant child with her.

"Oh, Miss Wright, ma'am," she gushed. "Such an honor to

our humble village! This is my little Mirabella. Make your manners, dear."

The visitor regarded the lank and simpering maiden without enthusiasm. "How do you do?" she said. "Will you excuse me if I continue my conversation with this other little girl?" Mother and daughter passed on.

"That's Mirabella Upcraft," Marcia volunteered. "She has a tetter. It wouldn't be mannerly for me to tell you where."

"Never mind her. Tell me of yourself. You attend school, one supposes."

"Yes, ma'am."

"Do you like it?"

"No, ma'am."

"Not like your school? All these other children love it."

"So they tell *you*, ma'am. They're saucy little liars," said Marcia mournfully. "If they love it so, why do they play hooky?"

"They play hooky?" said the authoress, making a note. "And you do not?"

"No, ma'am. I would not so diminish myself."

"What are your favorite amusements?"

"Attendance upon church and Sunday school," was the prim reply.

"Hunca-munca!" retorted the lady, who prided herself on her Yankee colloquialisms. "Church is a duty. I wish to know how you and your young companions disport yourselves. Do you play with dolls?"

"Not any more."

"What do you play with?"

"Oh, wildcats and foxes, and bats and snakes and owls," Marcia replied.

"Creatures of forest and darkness," the authoress commented. "Do you, then, frequent the woodland at night?"

Marcia had once made a nocturnal excursion with a bevy

of her mates, and had been soundly spanked for it. She now expanded this adventure. "Yes, ma'am," she replied. " 'Most every night."

"Doubtless with your parents. Supplying meat for your larder." Miss Wright had a vision of a frontier family creeping forth in the darkness to stalk a deer or a squirrel for the morning's meal.

"No, ma'am. We get our meat from the Stone Front Store."

"What, then, is the purpose of these excursions?"

"Gold," Marcia said in a whisper.

"I was not aware that the precious metal is found in this vicinity."

"Oh, yes, ma'am! Bushels and barrels of it."

Another entry went into the ledger. "Have you, yourself, discovered any?"

"Not yet, ma'am. But Tip says we will. He's got a hazel cunjur-wand."

"Indeed!" Miss Wright turned a page and took a fresh goose-quill. "And who may Tip be?"

"The gypsy boy I go gold-hunting with. He can charm birds, too."

Miss Wright's eyebrows went up. "A gypsy? You go night-faring with a gypsy? I have already set down some reflections upon the innocent freedom enjoyed by the youth of this great nation, but really!"

At this point, Grandfather interrupted the story to read a passage aloud to us:

The youth of both sexes enjoy a freedom of intercourse un-known in the older and more formal nations of Europe. They dance, sing and "run in sleighs" together by sunshine and moon-shine, without the occurrence or even the apprehension of any impropriety.

"This was written before the encounter with my little kins-woman," Grandfather told us. "I believe that, after the interview, it was deleted from the manuscript, but later restored. However, to resume."

"Am I then to apprehend," asked Miss Wright, "that parents permit their progeny of opposite sexes to rove the forest by night?"

"They don't know," the girl said. "We lie awake and wait, and when Presbyterian time strikes the mystic hour, we make our evasion out the window."

"This is most extraordinary," the lady said. She appealed to Marcia's escort. "Is this child truly representative of American family standards?"

"Best old York State stock," Grandfather assured her.

Gratified by the impression she was making, Marcia now recited a couplet:

> " 'Oft have we passed the guilty night
> In revellings and frantic mirth.' "

The British authoress' stock in trade was broad-mindedness. But there were limits. This time, she was honestly shocked. Such libertinism from a maid of tender years! Such innocence of face! It was hardly credible. In the interests of truth, as embodied in her forthcoming book, she put the question direct.

"I trust that you will take my meaning, my dear. Surely you have, yourself, remained virtuous," she said.

Marcia was puzzled, but not for worlds would she have admitted it. Memory came to her aid again. In that good old household standby, *The Temperance Almanach*, under the heading "Maxims of Conduct for Young Females," she had read that "A Virtuous Child is she who is Docile and Pious and Keeps her Face and Hands as Clean as her Soul." Her soul was all right; she had no misgivings on that score. But her hands! Why had she not stopped by the town horse trough and washed? Now it was too late. She could not qualify.

"No, ma'am," she said in a shamed quaver.

Miss Wright's fashionable earbobs oscillated. "I think it is dreadful," she exclaimed. "What sort of upbringing can the unfortunate child have had!"

"I am an ex-cept-u-ally well-brought-up girl," said Marcia. "Whoever is without sin among you, let him squale the first rock at her."

Miss Wright was not too scandalized to note a new Yankee-ism. "Squale?" she repeated. "Squale a rock?"

She entered it in the margin of her ledger. "This child," she said to Squire Grainger, who now came forward to suggest that the guest of honor take some refreshment, "is quite the most extraordinary example of youth that I have yet been privileged to meet. Will you permit me a few moments to put my notes in order?"

"Well, my dear," the host said to Marcia as his guest withdrew, "and how did you come on with our celebrity?"

Marcia's smile was complacent. "Slick as Zillikoffer's wheel," she said, lapsing into a vernacular which the absent note-taker would have appreciated. "She asked a mortal lot of questions, but I answered 'em all. Didn't I, Cousin Myron?"

"You did, indeed!" Grandfather replied.

"I'm not sure, though, that she understood everything I told her," she continued reflectively. "I'm not sure I understood it quite all, myself," she added with charming candor. She turned to the Squire. "You're a knowledgeable gentleman, Mr. Grainger," she said. "What *is* bastardy?"

"Great God of Israel!" Squire Grainger ejaculated.

Grandfather dandled the slight volume upon his knee. "So," he remarked to us, "the Squire went into the inner sanctum where his guest was busily writing up her notes. When he returned his face was purple as a plum. Miss Wright's projected chapter on 'Morals of Adolescence in a New York State Community' had, I fear, stirred his bile. Marcia and I were dismissed from the premises with undeserved contumely."

We all stared avidly at the book. "I'd like to read that chapter, sir," Reno said.

The old gentleman shook his head. "You never will, Sireno."

"Aren't you going to tell us what's in it?"

"I don't know. Nobody knows. It never appeared."

"Never appeared?" John repeated. "Why? What did Miss Wright say to you?"

"I was not permitted to see the lady again. Upon Squire Grainger's insistence I wrote her a letter of explanation, as the result of which she deemed it advisable to elide the chapter. Rather a pity, too. It might have relieved the cloying amenity of the treatment."

There was a sharp knock on the door and Jenny thrust her face, still wearing an expression of lofty resentment, in from the kitchen.

"Grandma wishes her cookery book," she said, "if you have quite finished your private conversation."

"We have," Grandfather answered, "and you may restore this to its proper shelf." He handed her Miss Wright's *Views.*

I have always suspected that Jenny did her pin-money pickling close to the door. It is, at least, significant that she at once opened the book to the fly-leaf and read the inscription.

"How funny!" she commented. "Impudent young Yankee blade. Oh, no! It couldn't possibly be." Her prim, little laugh tinkled in the air.

Grandfather frowned. "What is so risible about it?" he demanded.

"An impudent young blade? You, Grandpa, dear? Nobody would ever believe it of you."

"Hm!" the old gentleman said. *"Tempora mutant et nos in illis mutantur."*

"You must have changed a lot," she said a little cruelly. Then, with sweet insinuation, "Grandpa?"

"Well?"

"Did *she* have a temptational eye?"

"That," said Grandfather, his dignity restored, "is a wholly irrelevant question."

THE SAGA OF
FOUR-SKATE PILKINGTON

With the coming of November, Archie Cossett's father leased
a stretch of the winter-closed Erie Canal at the Exchange
Street swing bridge and opened his skating rink. Junior season
tickets, which Archie peddled to his schoolmates, cost two
dollars and a half. For a boy to amass so great a sum involved arduous labor at small pay, coupled with various pri-
vations; walking to school, rain or shine, instead of squandering
three cents on the horse-car; shunning the drugstore's nickel
soda-water, eschewing the corner bakery's cream puffs.

We juvenile Adamses prayed for November snow, which
would mean sidewalks to be shoveled at a dime an hour.
Winter did set in obligingly early, that year of 1882. By
Thanksgiving our hands were blistered to a pulp, but we
had a common fund sufficient for four brick-red Cossett Skating Rink pasteboards which set forth in bold type that they
were good for the season, gala nights excepted, were non-
transferable, and were revocable for "ill, disobliging, or unruly conduct on the ice."

Having made so favorable a start, winter now dawdled. Temperatures hung tantalizingly in the thirties. Soggy day succeeded soggy night. Archie Cossett's father sat on the official platform he had planted in the canal bed, and glared across a surface of unprofitable, water-streaked ice with the silent and savage patience of his Scotch Presbyterian nature.

Two days after Christmas, the four of us—John, Sireno, Charles and I—slung our skates over our shoulders and, as we had done a dozen times before, trotted down to the canal, only to be greeted by the grim legend "NO SKATING."

"May as well go and thank Grandpa for our Christmas presents," John said.

Dejectedly the rest of us agreed. We followed him across the Genesee River aqueduct and through the tainted slush of Union Street to our grandfather's small, snug cottage. There, we presented ourselves to the old gentleman and, with mechanical politeness, acknowledged the gifts he had given us, all of which had been selected with an eye to economy and utility.

He received us with his usual austere amenity, and then remarked on our depressed demeanor.

"This is the yuletide season of bright and cheery faces," he reminded us.

John set forth our grievances against the weather. "Isn't it *ever* going to freeze up, Grandpa?" he asked.

"*Nil desperandum,*" Grandfather said, "if I make myself clear."

"Yes, sir," John returned briskly. " 'Never say die.' It's our class motto."

The old gentleman frowned. "A free—in fact, a licentious—rendering," he said. "Today's youth has no Latinity." And he bade us present our skates for his inspection.

John's and mine, I recall, were Barney & Berry All-Clamp. They were put on with a key, and were death on the soles and heels of shoes. Reno's were an older type, handed down to him by his father; they had a single screw clamp for the heel, and a strap that could be double-wrapped across the instep and around the ankle for firm support. As befitted a learner, Charlie had skates with box supports—low-set blades, like a sled's runners—fore and aft. Every blade of every skate was highly polished and fresh-ground. Our host approved them all except Charlie's.

"Too sharp in front," he declared. "The blade will bite the ice."

"There's no ice to bite," Charlie mourned.

"Patience, patience," the old gentleman said benignly. "I can remember one season when there was a thunderstorm on New Year's Day, and the next noon three of us skated all the way from Palmyra to the Wide Waters of the Erie, so sharp and swift was the freeze."

"You must have been a wonderful skater, Grandpa," John said.

"It is true," Grandfather said, "that I could perform many evolutions not inelegantly. On Erie Water, Ganargwa Creek, or even Canandaigua Lake there were few if any to surpass me. Had I remained at home, I might have preserved a fine conceit of myself. Ah, well! One lives and learns."

Charlie asked what in particular Grandfather had learned, and received a surprising answer.

"The dark duplicity of man," the old gentleman said. He lost himself in gloomy retrospection, then spoke again. "And what a man!" he said dreamily. "Pitted against him I was as a barnyard fowl challenging a soaring eagle. He could do the outside edge, or the inside edge, forward, backward and crossfoot. He could skate spread-eagle, toe-to-heel, double spinner. The like of him is born but once in a generation."

Grandfather closed his eyes—a propitious sign, provided he did not fall asleep. We waited in hopeful silence, and after a few moments' recollection, he opened them again and set out upon his narrative.

"That was the iron-hard winter of 1826, when the black ice
held on all waters from Lake Ontario to Chesapeake Bay,"
Grandfather said. "I had gone on an official mission of the
Wayne County Horse-thief Society, down to Pennsylvania
where the local farmsteaders were sorely plagued by the running of stolen stock across the York State border. In Owego, I
encountered a former Hamilton College crony named Lathrop, who, being footloose at the moment, readily agreed to
accompany me to my destination, the flourishing town of
Tioga. We arrived on a Saturday evening, when a winter
gala was in progress on a broad reach of the Susquehanna
River at the town's edge.

We went first to the inn. There our host suggested that we
participate in the festivities, which we were not loath to do.
Happily we had our skates with us. Sagacious winter trav-
elers went thus equipped, for rivers or lakes or canals often
afforded better facilities than the rough turnpikes."

Warming to his subject, the old gentleman pictured the
scene he and his companion found. A huge bonfire near the
riverbank was kept at a high blaze by brush from an adjoining wood lot. It lighted up the figures of men and women,
gliding, darting, and swooping upon the glass-smooth ice.
Bedded in embers from the fire, a large iron kettle simmered
and steamed with water to be used to prepare the hot,
buttered rum which was the inspiration and support of such
occasions.

There Grandfather and young Lathrop were welcomed by
Squire Maurice of the iron works, and invited to partake. Being teetotal in principle and practice, Grandfather politely
lifted his palm in refusal. Young Lathrop was of another mind.
In college, he had been known as one who, as Grandfather
put it, frequently bowed his manly form to the killing cup.
Presently, under the stimulus of several potations, he began
to diminish the skill of the local skaters and to vaunt the

repute of his companion as the most accomplished iceman in York State.

Grandfather protested in vain. Nothing would do but that he must display his prowess. Despite his modest disclaimers, the ice was cleared of the others, who now ranged themselves expectantly along the bank of the river. While he was making his preparations, Lathrop performed a grandiloquent introduction.

"Ladies and gentlemen!" he cried. "Mr. Myron Adams, Esquire, of East Bloomfield, New York, will exhibit for your kind approval some of those elegant evolutions which have famed him far and wide as the champion of the Grand Erie Canal and adjacent waters."

Thus presented, Grandfather could do no less than his best. He performed creditably, so he thought, and the generous applause of the Pennsylvanians spurred him to more daring experiments, one of which broke a strap and brought him down, fortunately unharmed. Expressions of admiration and approval accompanied him as he limped to the fire to repair the damage.

"They gave me more éclat than my efforts merited," Grandfather told us. "But it was not unanimous. As the applause died down, a loud and scornful gardaloo offended the peaceful night."

"I know what a gardaloo is," John said quickly, and delivered what, in modern parlance, would be called a Bronx cheer.

"Precisely," Grandfather replied, though he was not too well pleased. He enjoyed puzzling us with his archaisms. "The unmannerly interruption came from near the fire, where a worm fence enclosed a sorrow of stones."

He paused, and we three others turned to the knowledgeable John.

"A sorrow of stones?" John repeated.

"Yes," Grandfather said. "A sorrow of stones."

"What sort of stones?"

"Headstones and footstones."

"Oh! A graveyard," said John.

"Farmer Fergus's family burying ground," Grandfather said. "The perpetrator of the gardaloo sat on the fence surrounding the graves, and an unpleasing sneer was upon his face."

Getting down from the fence, and stepping forth into the full light, the stranger revealed himself as the possessor of a broad and bestial face with squint eyes and protuberant cheekbones, a squat and powerful form, arms whose hands dangled to the knees, and bow legs. He wore a coonskin cap, a gay linsey-woolsey jacket, morocco boots, and gold earhoops like a gyppo.

"Altogether a prodigious apparition," Grandfather told us. "His aspect was that of the ferocious African gorilla."

The stranger advanced, shivering ostentatiously. The Squire poured a tot of rum into a horn cup, filled the cup with smoking water, added a dollop of butter, and handed the confection to the man, who took it and nodded.

"Solomon Silliman's obediences to one and all," he said civilly.

"Solomon Silliman," Reno said with relish. "Was that really his name?"

"I don't know," Grandfather replied. "Nobody knows." And he resumed his story.

"What fetches you here, friend?" Squire Maurice asked the newcomer.

"I stopped to observe this young sprig," the man answered, jerking a thumb toward Grandfather. "A pawky exhibition."

Lathrop, indignant at the slur, ruffled up to the fellow. "Do you think you could better it?" he asked.

"With a skillet bound to one foot and my grandmother's sadiron to the other," the stranger said.

Lathrop turned and spoke to the crowd. "Who will loan this brag-hard a pair of skates?"

Several men responded. After consideration the stranger selected a pair belonging to B. Saunders, the white-smith. He affixed them with precision, rose to his feet, ambled to the river, and stamped on the ice several times as if to satisfy himself as to its texture. Then he gazed about him with a confident smile.

"A simple exercise to start with, good folk," he announced, with a wave of the hand.

Striking out quickly, Solomon Silliman spanned and respanned the river, shifting from the outer to the inner edge of his skates with the nonchalance of a pedestrian crossing a corner. Every stroke proclaimed the expert. Returning to a spot near the bonfire, the skater obliged with a swift succession of figures—the Dying Hawk, the Dutchman's Delight, the Double Buck and Wing, the Fairy Float, and the Rat-tat-too—all performed with an address and rhythm beyond emulation. Standing upon his toe points, he put his audience in stitches with a travesty of that popular though vulgar dance step, the Rutland Wriggle. They cheered him when he came to the fire for another draught of rum, which he swallowed, reeking hot, as if his gullet were a brass pipe.

There was a general demand that Solomon Silliman return to the ice. He looked to his straps, made some adjustments, and said, "Another pair of skates, if you please."

"What's amiss with mine?" the whitesmith asked.

"They serve well enough," the man replied, offhand, "but a single pair does not suffice for a man of my quality." He looked over the crowd and accosted the town baker, "Here, you! You're a big fellow," he said. "Yours will do. Off with them, if you want to see something that will bung out your eyes like warts on a toad."

"Aren't you going to take off the others first?" the baker asked.

"No," said Silliman. "I shall attach yours to my hands."

The dazed baker began to protest, but at an imperious gesture from the stranger, removed his skates and handed them over.

Solomon Silliman examined the blades and shook his head. Walking over to a sandbank on the river's brink, he hacked and picked at the frozen sand until he had dislodged several large chunks, which he pulverized. He rubbed sand gently upon one blade after another, and then filled both his side pockets with the residue, casually explaining that it would be useful ballast for the feat of delicate balancing he was about to perform. With the baker's help, he strapped the skates to his hands, swept out on the ice once more in an easy turn and addressed the spectators.

"My friends, you are about to be gratified by the presentment of a paragon which no other living man can equal. It has won the deserved plaudits of kings and emperors in the high courts of Europe, where I am known under my professional style as Four-Skate Pilkington. With your kind permission, I shall now withdraw a few rods upriver. There I shall turn and retrace my course at lightning speed, hand and foot, foot and hand"—his voice swelled to a booming basso—"in the unprecedented feat of *skating on all fours!*"

At that moment, the high, quavering neigh of a horse in distress floated through the air from the direction of the nearby pike. Several men left to investigate, and Silliman, who had seemed about to elaborate his speech, abruptly set off, though at an easy pace.

"I'm notional that there is something queer afoot," Squire Maurice said in Grandfather's ear, "and that our four-skating friend may have a hand in it. In my quality of J.P., I will have a word with him when he comes back."

The retreating skater's easy pace quickened at five rods. At ten rods, he was streaking for the bend, half a mile away.

In the clear moonlight, Grandfather and the Squire saw him shake the encumbering skates from his hands and begin to swing his arms in wide sweeping movements, like a farmer sowing seed. At the moment, nobody interpreted the evolution, but his pace made it clear that Four-Skate Pilkington— now Two-Skate Pilkington—was not coming back.

The Squire was first to realize it. He raised a shout.

"Tallyho! After him! He's evading for the border," he cried.

"With my skates!" the whitesmith wailed.

Grandfather plunged out on the ice in pursuit. Close behind him came Lathrop, Squire Maurice and the Methodist parson, who had a brisk foot. The rest of the crowd strung out back of them, leaving the skateless whitesmith and baker hopelessly out-distanced.

Fancy skating, Grandfather told himself as he settled into his swing, was one thing; the long pull to the state line, beyond which the Squire's magistracy would be impotent, might be quite another. He speeded up with a grim determination to overtake and capture the fleeing man.

"And so I might well have done," the old gentleman told us, "had my wits been as swift as my feet. As I rounded the curve and again sighted my quarry, both my feet checked with instant violence. Forward and upward I soared, and then came down in the most calamitous hyst of my existence. Hardly had I come to earth when Lathrop crashed upon me, and then the parson was entangled with both of us. Attempting to hurdle the heap, Squire Maurice tripped and broke a rib, and each following skater, as he reached the area of the disaster, went skittering across the ice on belly or back, for the rascally ingler, with his graceful gestures, had sown the surface with the sand from his pocket. My last sight of him was as he twisted his head about to cock a snook at the mass of us, helpless and far in his rear."

The thwarted pursuers limped and crawled back to the

fire, Grandfather said, proceeding with his story. In the meantime, one of the other men had found the horse that had
neighed. It was crippled, and, as was later established, had
been stolen earlier in good condition by Solomon Silliman or
Four-Skate Pilkington or whatever his name was from a farmer
in the next county. Apparently he had abandoned it after it
was hurt, and had seized the opportunity afforded by the
merrymakers to devise his ingenious escape.

"Then he didn't skate on all fours?" Charlie asked.

"Nobody ever skated on all fours," said Grandfather.

"And it wasn't true about the kings and emperors?"

"All folderol and fahdoodle," Grandfather replied. "He was
a vagabond, an ingler and a horse-thief, with a touch of immortal genius."

The old gentleman went on to outline the subsequent career of the champion. After pawning the whitesmith's skates
for the price of a night's lodging in Owego, the fugitive made
his way up and westward across New York State, reaching
Rochester before Grandfather got back to that part of the
country. There he gave an exhibition and made a successful
exit with two pairs of skates and nine dollars, which he had
collected in advance of his heralded performance on all fours.
Traveling canalside, he then struck eastward across the state.
At Syracuse, he had the impudence to go to the printer and
order, on credit, an issue of guttersnipes ("They would now
be called 'dodgers,'" Grandfather obligingly told us), ex-
ploiting his skill and citing personal testimonials from numer-
ous crowned heads. It was ruefully estimated that there must
have been nearly twenty dollars tucked beneath his flying
coattails when they were last seen, leveled out in the wake
of his departure.

The winter broke as he reached Utica. The ice rotted and
sank. His profitable kantikoy was over. He stole a sorrel mare,

and the Oneida Horse-thief Society chased him all the way to Lake Ontario without once coming within sight of him. At Oswego, he made a hasty sale of the mare and looked about him for passage to Canada.

The two-masted sloop *Fairaway* was readying to put out on the first voyage of the season. The escaping thief made a quick deal with Captain Asa Birdmaster, a man who asked no questions of money except how current the notes were, and shipped as passenger. He was never heard of in York State again.

"He was as rascally a man as ever I met in my life," Grandfather said, "and as great a genius in his own line. A virtuoso, a master, a nonpareil. Never shall I set eyes on his like again."

There followed a long silence, until Reno said, "I suppose they had *real* winters in those days, Grandpa."

"Times do not change. The old rule holds," the old gentleman said pleasantly and quoted a familiar line from the *Hop Bitters Almanac:*

> "As days do lengthen
> The frost doth strengthen."

He stood up, and took the *Almanac* from its shelf. Then he crossed the room and opened the door leading to the stoop. Our step-grandmother, in the kitchen, must have been listening.

"Mr. Adams! Mr. Adams! Muffle up your throat or you will catch your death of a rheum!" she cried.

"Don't pester me!" Grandfather called back to her. "I'll be only a moment."

He stepped outdoors, moistened a finger, and lifted it to test the rising wind. He came back, opened the *Almanac*, and studied it briefly.

"My respects to that worthy Scotsman, Mr. Cossett," Grandfather said. "Advise him from me that we shall have a month of ice."

Grandfather's forefinger, backed by the weather forecaster of the *Hop Bitters Almanac,* turned out to be correct. Solid winter set in that night.

MR. STUMPY'S PREVIEW

In 1893, the year my Grandfather Adams died, New York City blossomed with hundreds of forerunners of the motion picture. Fourteenth Street was the principal place of display for these devices; on it penny arcades, nickelodeons and peepshow booths offered kinetoscopes and their animated pictures, while curb venders vied with them and noisily thrust crude portable versions of the new art under the noses of passersby.

My cousin Sireno was visiting me in the city that fall, and one afternoon I took him to Union Square. We found Fourteenth Street in full blast, the air ringing with the vociferations of the shills. We walked along for a while, and as we hesitated before one tinselled booth, a seedy little peddler approached us, waving what looked like a pack of tiny playing cards bound together at the top. He held them up delicately, like a prestidigitator, and riffled them deftly with his thumb. As he did so, two miniature pugilists fought briefly before our astonished and gratified eyes.

"Just like life," the hawker said. "Anyone can work it."

I asked him how much he wanted for the cards, and he said confidentially that it would be a dollar, to me. I would have paid it, but before I could reach into my pocket, Reno, a shrewd bargainer, stopped me and offered the man a dime. They haggled for a while, and the vender became impatient.

"Look, brother," he said. "You can paste these things in a strip and whirl them over a sort of wheel—I'll sell you one cheap—and they'll do everything but *talk!*"

"A wheel?" Reno said. He turned to me, and repeated, in an awed voice, "Whirl on a wheel! Grandpa!"

"Mr. Stumpy!" I exclaimed.

"Who?" the peddler asked.

"You wouldn't know him," I said. "He must have died quite a long time ago."

On a December Saturday in 1883, my four cousins and I went to pay our weekly call upon our grandfather. Sometimes it was possible for us to forecast the character of a visit by taking an investigatory peek through the side window of the cottage before going in. If the stand in the sitting room displayed books on its marble top, we were in for a session of mental improvement at the hands of Mr. Carlyle, Mr. Tupper, or the Reverend T. DeWitt Talmadge. If the old gentleman's scrapbook was there, we might expect reminiscence. And if—as happened on rare occasions—a pitcher of raspberry shrub waited, pink and inviting, festivity was indicated.

This Saturday, Jenny did the spying. What she reported was startling. "He's playing with paper dolls," she whispered to us.

"I don't believe it," John said.

He tiptoed to the window, and Reno and I followed him. We looked into the sitting room, and there was Grandfather intent upon a scroll of white paper to which he had affixed small, bright-hued cutouts. His scrapbook was at his feet, and on the stand before him was a strange contraption, obviously homemade. My boyish understanding of the mechanism was vague, and my memory of the construction is more so. Two of our step-grandmother's rolling pins, set in improvised racks, appeared to be fundamental. Most of the paper scroll was wound on one cylinder, and the operator was in process of tacking the free end of the scroll to the other. This done, he gave it a twirl.

I tried for a clearer vision. "They *look* like paper dolls, all right," I whispered.

Young Charlie scrabbled up beside me. "They're decalcomanias," he whispered back. "I got a set at home."

Decalcomania was a juvenile fad of the period. But what was our dignified grandparent doing with such frivolities?

Reno plucked at my sleeve. "We have to go in even if he *has* gone loony," he said.

We did go in then, feeling awkward at catching the old gentleman, so to speak, off his base. He looked up and greeted us abstractedly but without embarrassment. Jenny stared at the bright figures on the scroll.

"Why, they're ducks!" she cried. "What ever are you doing with them, Grandpa?"

"Eh?" said Grandfather. "Oh! Pursuing a long-forgotten artifice—something of which I had not thought in years until I chanced upon an old clipping in my ort-book." He rotated the two pins and the scroll rolled rapidly from one to the other.

"They're flying!" Charlie cried, in great excitement, and, indeed, some effect of flight was achieved, though I thought it a poor and confused similitude.

So thought the old gentleman. "A feeble essay," he said, stopping the mechanism. "Never would it have roused the Wembley brothers to action. Mr. Stumpy would have flouted it with well-merited scorn."

"Who were the Wembley brothers?" Jenny and John asked in unison, and at the same time I inquired, "Who was Mr. Stumpy?"

"One at a time," Grandfather said. "One at a time." He pushed the apparatus aside and settled back.

Of all the human oddments that frequented Erie Water in the early days, Grandfather said, the queerest was Mr. Stumpy. Nobody knew his real name, his origin, his age, or anything much about him, except that he was foreign, and nobody cared. He minded his own occasions and was content to let other folk mind theirs. His line of trade was repairs, his place of business a roofed ark of two tons burden, in which he plied the canal. Sometimes he poled his ark; sometimes he hauled it at the end of a fifty-foot towrope. On the cabin was displayed a sign:

ODD JOBS & AMENDMENTS
SUITABLE & CHEAP.

There were few repair jobs beyond his capacity. He could expertly tinker pot, pan, or kettle, mend rigging, splice tackle, rig a crane, calk a leaky seam, and do a handy job of carpentry. A shelf in his cabin was supplied with home-confected medicaments with which he would make shift to treat any ill from snake bite to swamp shakes. He was a bit of an artist, too, and could produce a recognizable likeness on either the camera obscura or the camera lucida. He was well versed in penmanship, both round and florid, and at a modest charge would indite a persuasive cupidity for a lovelorn illiterate. Though he spoke with the thick accent of a foofoo, Grandfather said, his use of English showed a nice discrimination.

This was too much for John, as it was intended to be. "I know a cupidity is a love letter, sir," he said, "but what's a foofoo?"

"Good Erie lingo for a foreigner," the old gentleman replied. "Foofoos were not kindly regarded, canalside. Mr. Stumpy was an exception."

He was unfailingly officious, Grandfather said, always ready to do one a good turn gratis. For the rest, Grandfather went on, the ark man was small and meagre, frugal by habit, and meek of bearing. He would accept almost anything in trade, as a substitute for legal tender—an officiousness that insured his popularity with the canal wives. Flaxseed, goose down, mink skin, eggs, or homespun—or even a rare butterfly, moth, or spider, for he collected and preserved these, as well as herbs and simples—was legal enough tender for him.

"Today he would be termed a scientist," Grandfather said, "but there was no such word in the 1820's."

The ark man's favorite run, our narrator continued, was the Long Level, west of Rochester, where for sixty-two miles there was no lock, and hence no toll to pay. Like everyone else with business along Erie, Grandfather himself had a hail-fellow acquaintance with the industrious little man. Eventually the hazard of a sudden July storm improved the acquaintance to something like friendship.

Grandfather had been on an official inspection tour of the canal banks, which involved traveling afoot. Between Holley and Stillson's Basin, he passed the ark, whose owner had stopped on the towpath to ease his shoulder pad where the rope chafed him. A civil greeting passed between them. At that moment, there was a crackle of electrons, and the first shrewd gust of a storm pressed the craft against the bank. From its open starboard window whirled a number of sheets of paper. Mr. Stumpy uttered a wail and dropped his rope.

"Look for a post!" Grandfather shouted at him. "Look for a post, man! I'll gather your papers."

Too seasoned a canaller not to realize the impropriety of casting loose any craft in such a gale, the ark man snatched back his towrope. Happily, there was a mooring post a few rods downwind. Mr. Stumpy reached it, tossed two half hitches over it, and joined Grandfather, who was already off in a wild pursuit of the flying papers across the unfenced fields.

From the little man's distress, Grandfather assumed that
the papers would be something of value; manuscripts, or perhaps legal documents. To his surprise, he found, when most
of the sheets had been recovered, that they all bore the presentment of a man, drawn in bold strokes. Still stranger, the
figures were so nearly identical that it was difficult to distinguish between them. Scrutiny showed that they were the
same figure in slightly different postures. Mr. Stumpy, plainly
embarrassed, undertook to explain. He said the papers were
part of a private experiment, and he added, gratefully, that he
hoped someday to show Grandfather the results of it.

The two men went back to the ark, where Grandfather
helped his companion restore order to the wind-blown cabin.
A wheel of peculiar design stood at one end of the small
room, and at the opposite end was a wall mirror that seemed
to Grandfather disproportionately large and costly for so simple an interior. His host saw that he had remarked them.

"Please say nothing of all this, blessed Myron," Mr.
Stumpy asked. He belonged to an obscure religious sect that
used the form "blessed" as the Quakers used "friend."

"At your wish," Grandfather replied. "But it is a queer
kantikoy, Mr. Stumpy."

"It is no more a kantikoy than I am Mr. Stumpy," the little man said gravely.

"Who are you, then?" Grandfather asked, surprised.

"Pay no heed," the ark man said hastily. "Pay no heed,
blessed Myron. Stumpy is near enough."

As Grandfather was about to take his leave, Mr. Stumpy
presented him with a jar of basswood honey. "Are you a
friend to me, blessed Myron?" he asked, when Grandfather
had thanked him.

"Why, yes, I hope so," Grandfather replied.

"So are not the brothers Wembley," Mr. Stumpy said.
"Do you know the brothers Wembley?"

"Everybody canalside knows them," Grandfather said.

"They are good and pious folk. What have they against you, Mr. Stumpy?"

"I do not attend their worship," the little man answered. "Their Sabbaday is not my Sabbaday."

Nobody from Lake Erie to Hudson's River, Grandfather said, departing for the moment from his story of Mr. Stumpy, commanded more respect than the two Wembley brothers, and this in spite of the fact that they were rafters, a breed by no means popular on the canal. Their rafts were the longest and broadest allowed by the Honorables, the Canal Commissioners. For draft animals, the Wembleys had oxen. Two miles an hour was towpath speed for an ox-drawn raft, which was a sore exasperation to hurrying packets held up in its wake. Yet the hardiest captain hesitated to raise voice against the brothers, for they were godly men, and curses directed against such were prone to redound upon the maledictor.

"Witness," Grandfather said, "the case of Captain Skibo, of the line boat *Seafoam*, who, after being blocked at Lock Thirty-nine for an hour, damned the Wembleys' rafts and all their occupants, and that very evening choked on a perch bone, coughed himself into a cachexy, and burst a blood vessel."

Prayer meeting every evening and three Sabbath-day sermons were regular events aboard the Wembleys' lead raft, the old gentleman went on. It was known as the Gospel Raft, and for Sunday services the brothers moored it, when possible, in a basin where there would be room for other craft to gather. Large crowds often attended the meetings. Micajah Wembley was a notable performer on the lap-organ; Jonathan possessed a basso profundo that rolled like thunder among hills. Both were powerful exhorters, and their prophecies of doom sent shivers down the spines of the sinful. It was their theme that Satan held special sway along the Erie.

They firmly believed in a personal, earth-frequenting Devil
—Micajah proclaimed that he had once seen him in full pan-
oply of horns, fangs and switching tail—and in his familiar
spirits, the witches who were spawned from the slime of the
pathless Montezuma Marshes. Micajah, in particular, was
learned in the lore of darkness, and could distinguish between broom witches and fork witches by the reek of their
passage through the upper night.

To protect themselves from these powers, the brothers had
raised a Pennsylvania hex broom upon the prow of the lead
raft and had hung their cabin windows with witch balls,
blue, green, and amber, molded at the Mt. Vernon glass
factory, in the Oneida hills. Also, they were steady customers
of a store on Exchange Street in Auburn that specialized in
charms, amulets and silver bullets.

Always assiduous to swell their congregation, the pair had
several times approached Mr. Stumpy with friendly invita-
tions to join their Gospel Crew, which welcomed all Christian sects. His response had been invariably courteous: "Thank
you kindly, blessed Wembleys. You take your path to Heaven
and I will follow mine."

Their somber suggestion that his path might lead to a different and less desirable terminus failed to move him.

There came a Sunday evening in September, 1826, which
Grandfather fixed as about Muster Day, the day the militia
regularly turned out for its semiannual drill and inspection.
This was two months after the episode of the blowing papers. The Gospel Raft was moored in Parker's Basin, near
Brockport, and Mr. Stumpy was poling his ark westward toward it, looking for a post. The meeting then in session
aboard the raft had drawn a large crowd, for it was to deal
with a familiar and favorite topic, "The Licentious Evil of
the Public Dance." Grandfather, finding himself in the vicinity, had decided to attend.

Brother Jonathan was preaching. Brother Micajah sat beside him, the lap-organ ready on his knees. The sermon proceeded by formula. The preacher would deliver a long and titillating description of the supposedly demoniac orgies that had recently been held in some respectable enough neighboring tavern. Then the organist's elbow would pump, the reeds would give a squawk and a blare, and Brother Jonathan's mighty voice would lead the listeners in an appropriate refrain:

> "Gay! Gay! Gay!
> To be gay,
> Think on the dreadful Judgment Day!"

The sermon had reached the third or fourth repetition of this chorus when the repair ark came up. As Mr. Stumpy, poling, drew abreast of the preacher, the music died and Jonathan's formidable basso hailed him.

"Sabbathbreaker, ahoy!"

Mr. Stumpy leaned on his pole and looked at Jonathan, startled.

"Uncover in the presence of the Lord and His worshippers!" Jonathan cried.

The boatman obligingly took off his coonskin cap.

"Down on your knees and repent of your sins!" Jonathan commanded him.

The little man considered for a moment, shook his head, and thrust again with his pole.

"I look for a post," he said mildly, and a dozen or more rods along he headed to shore and moored for the night.

The congregation on the raft could see his light, unnaturally brilliant, as many afterward stated, and hear the sound of his tinkering, and they knew he was busy at profane pursuits on the Sabbath, an affront to piety. Grandfather, noting the angry looks cast toward the ark, and seeing the brothers counseling together, speculated uneasily upon what measures they might take against the harmless little ark man.

He lingered aboard after the benediction, and when the congregation had dispersed, saw Jonathan jump ashore and set out down the towpath toward Mr. Stumpy's ark. As he approached it, he dropped to all fours, and presently Grandfather could see his head outlined in the light of the window. It remained still for a few moments, and then was withdrawn. There was a startled, stifled cry, the cabin light of the ark went out, and Jonathan Wembley came plunging back along the path like one pursued. He scrambled aboard the raft and fell on his knees. Grandfather went to him and set a hand upon his shoulder. Jonathan was shaking from head to foot. When he could command his voice, he said tremulously, "This is matter for the Canal Commission."

"What is?" Grandfather asked.

"Witchcraft and devilry," said Jonathan.

Grandfather did not believe in witches and even had his heretical doubts about the Devil.

"What did you see?" he asked.

"Spawn of Satan! Spawn of Satan!" Jonathan cried, and would say no further. "My lips would shrivel," he muttered.

He was insistent that Grandfather, as a minor canal official, should present the case to the Commission and have Mr. Stumpy banned from the waterway. In Grandfather's opinion, there was no case for the high authorities, but he was disturbed for the safety of the ark man; the brothers were likely to stir up sentiment against him.

"An evil will befall because of this wickedness," said Jonathan as Grandfather left the raft.

Grandfather wondered if he should stop at the ark on his way to the inn where he was staying, and warn Mr. Stumpy. But the window of the ark still showed no light, and he decided to wait until morning.

The evil Jonathan had foretold befell that very night. Without ascertainable cause, the canal berm breached widely two miles west of Parker's Basin, the basin was sucked dry, and all the craft in it were hopelessly mudlarked by dawn. Word passed among the angry canallers that the slightly mysterious Mr. Stumpy was the agent of mischance, and Grandfather, who had heard the report, went after breakfast to see him.

On deck, Mr. Stumpy listened with his head sunk between his shoulders while Grandfather told him of Jonathan's spying the night before.

"Witchcraft?" he said. "Spawn of Satan? They are fools. Do you wish to see, blessed Myron?"

Grandfather very much wished to see, and he went with Mr. Stumpy into the cabin of the ark. There he noticed a mechanism that he took to be the newly invented Genet Patent Combustible Gas Generator for domestic illumination. Before it, mounted in a rack, stood a wooden cylinder a foot long and half that in diameter. It had a handle by which it could be turned, and the large mirror Grandfather had seen earlier faced it. Mounted above the cylinder was a scroll made of the papers the two men had pursued in the storm. These had been pasted together to form a strip, one end of which was attached to the cylinder.

Mr. Stumpy drew black curtains over the windows, almost completely darkening the room, and then took up his flint box and a hank of dried flax, which he ignited with a spark struck from the flint.

"Close your eyes, blessed Myron," he said.

Grandfather did so. He heard the plop of the combustible gas, and the whir of the cylinder as Mr. Stumpy spun it.

"Now look," Mr. Stumpy said. "Have no fear."

Grandfather opened his eyes. He gave a gasp. The hairs at the nape of his neck stiffened and stirred, and his muscles tautened as he strove to compose himself. There was no

sound in the room but the guttering gas and the whisper and
creak of the cylinder, but it seemed that there should be other
sounds, for there was life mirrored in the glass before his
eyes. The figure he saw there was no larger than a hawk
moth, but it was human. It was alive. It crawled, it reared itself up and brandished its arms and sprang into the air. It
pranced and danced. Grandfather felt inclined to pray.

The whirring ceased. The mirror darkened. "That is all,
blessed Myron," Mr. Stumpy said gently.

"What is it?" Grandfather asked feebly.

"Illusion," Mr. Stumpy answered. "The pictures supplant
one another so swiftly as to befool the eye with the illusion
of continuity. That is all. No witchcraft. No devilry, except
in the evil minds of men."

"Mr. Stumpy," Grandfather said earnestly, "go away from
here."

"How can I? The ark is mudded."

"The Wembleys are holding noon session to preach you
down as having caused the berm to breach by aid of Satan,"
Grandfather told him. "Go away while there is yet time."

"And abandon my home?" asked Mr. Stumpy.

"The repair gang is already at work on the breach," Grandfather said. "They will soon be reinforced by the Hurry-Up
Boat with its crew. The water will rise. You are shallow of
draft. The canal will be boatable for your ark while the others
are still mudfast. Take your advantage of it."

"Perhaps I had better," Mr. Stumpy said sadly. "I only
thought to make an innocent poppet-show for the pleasure of
children, and to touch a small profit for my pains. And for
this I am accused of commerce with the Evil One. Thank
you, blessed Myron. I will follow your advice."

Grandfather helped Mr. Stumpy to get the boat in readiness and then visited a few staunch spirits among the older
and more staid canallers, who could be relied upon to try

to maintain the peace on his mere say-so as a canal official. They promised to come to Mr. Stumpy's aid if they were needed.

Since traffic on the waterway was halted by the low water, a large congregation—upward of a hundred glum-faced men, Grandfather estimated—gathered that noon on the Gospel Raft. He did not go aboard himself but took his stand on the towpath where he could hear Brother Jonathan and at the same time see the ark. The men he had enlisted were waiting nearby on their own boats.

Jonathan opened the service by declaring that for some time he had harbored suspicions of Mr. Stumpy. These, he said, had been horridly confirmed by his visit to the ark the night before. Two witches, he asserted, had flown above him as he went there. (Grandfather had seen the pair and had taken them for owls.) There had been a stifling reek of stinkstone in the air. Peering through the cabin window, Jonathan had seen an infernal glow, by the light of which Mr. Stumpy was performing his unholy rites. Jonathan, his eyes straining and his teeth chattering, had seen the veritable Satan, in miniature, materialize upon a black mirror and perform a demoniac dance to the lewd mutterings of Mr. Stumpy. Terror had seized him, and he fled.

Everyone on the raft knew what had happened next, the preacher went on. The Grand Erie Canal had been blighted beneath their keels. Everyone knew, he continued with waxing fury, the author of the disaster. Let all good Christians unite to purge Erie Water of this malefactor, who, even now —his voice rose to a bellow—was making his evasion.

"Forward, hosts of righteousness!" Jonathan cried.

The water had risen somewhat, and the ark was, indeed, in sluggish motion. As the crowd surged off the raft and moved toward the ark, Grandfather blew his pathmaster's whistle, and the forces of order rallied to him. They made a valiant attempt to bar the towpath, but they were a scant dozen against a hundred. The first rush swept them aside like straws.

Fortunately, Mr. Stumpy had heard the whistle and the crowd's yells. He plunged from the ark into the canal, floundered through the shallow water, and disappeared into the forest back of the berm, unsuccessfully pursued by a small band of whooping religionists. Meanwhile, the other crusaders swarmed upon the ark, gutted it, smashed the devilish mechanism, and burned what remained. As for the ark man, Grandfather said, he was seen no more, nor hide nor hair.

"What do you think became of him, sir?" John asked.

"Some believed," the old gentleman said, "that Satan, his master, reclaimed him in a clap of fire from a prodigious thunderstorm that thwarted the last of his pursuers that night. Another version had it that he was devoured by bears, which were predatory in that region at the time. It is known, however, that a week later a two-masted owler, setting out from Genesee river mouth for Canada on a smuggling operation, was storm-beaten back to the American shore and there picked up a stranger, hungry and battered, whom it took across Lake Ontario to the haven of Canada. It may well have been Mr. Stumpy."

"Didn't you ever hear anything more of the poor man, Grandpa?" Jenny asked.

"I don't know," the old gentleman said slowly. "I have never been certain. However . . ."

Lifting his scrapbook from the floor, he spread it open on his knees and pointed to a newspaper clipping. "This is an excerpt from *Man*, of May 19, 1834," Grandfather said. "*Man* was a journal of high probity and scruple." We read:

THE PHENAKISTOSCOPE, invented by Prof. Stampke of Vienna, is so constructed that a series of figures, painted on a revolving card and reflected by a looking glass, are made to present to the eye a variety of motions which give to the figures the appearance of life.

Reno, who read the item with concentration a second time, broke out, "Stampke—Stumpke—Stumpy!"

"The similarity is suggestive," Grandfather said.

"I bet he was the fellow!" Reno cried.

"Didn't you try to find out, sir?" Jenny asked.

"I did," said Grandfather. "I went so far as to write a letter to Vienna and procured its carriage by brig. In the then state of European posts, its delivery was hazardous and a reply still less probable. I have never heard from, or of, Professor Stampke, nor have I had occasion to recall his strange device until today, when this item met my eye by chance."

On Fourteenth Street, nearly a dozen years later, Reno and the shill concluded their haggling at an agreed price of thirty-five cents. (Shortly thereafter, the market broke, and gladiators on a pack of cards could be had for a nickel.) Then Reno and I went on exploring Fourteenth Street, at a total cost of more than two dollars apiece. We saw all the nickelodeons and peered into all the kinetoscopes, and we bought what other peddlers had to offer in the line of "flip-pictures," as they were termed in the trade. It was worth every cent, because it seemed to us that our belief in Professor Stampke and Grandfather Adams had been confirmed.

However worthy or unworthy of the posthumous honor the Viennese savant may be, it is improbable that he will ever get an Oscar from Hollywood, nor will history assign him the place Reno and I gave him. He lives only in the faith of the Adams descendants, but we, at least, are firmly convinced that he is the true father of the motion picture, and that Grandfather was present at the first preview.

TREASURE HUNT

When the old frame station of the Southern Central Railroad, later the Lehigh Valley, at Ensenore, New York, was torn down a few years ago, a neatly hand-lettered extract from the prose writings of Sir Edwin Arnold, the author of *The Light of Asia*, was removed from one wall:

According to the Chinamen, Ginseng is the best and most potent of cordials, of stimulants, of tonics, of stomachics, cardiacs, febrifuges, and above all will renovate and reinvigorate failing forces. It fills the heart with hilarity, while its occasional use will, it is said, add a decade of years to ordinary human life. Can all these millions of Orientals, all these generations of men who have boiled Ginseng in silver kettles and have praised heaven for its many benefits, have been totally deceived?

This handsome testimonial, hung there by a station agent long since dead, was a memento of the ginseng craze that swept the Finger Lakes region in the latter part of the nineteenth century.

Three of us Adams boys were in on the start of it. My cousins John and Sireno had come from Rochester to visit me and spend the summer vacation of 1884 in the rough camp of my maternal grandfather, Dr. Hopkins, at Second Peacock's Point, on Owasco Lake. Besides us, there were some eleven adults in the family group staying at the camp at the time. Shortly after my cousins' arrival, one of those furious gales that rack the region blew up out of the northwest. For four days, no boat dared venture on the lake, and we were cut off from Ensenore, our base of supplies, on the opposite shore.

Provisions ran low. This was nothing new; we had lived on the country before and could do so again. The grown-up males set out with guns and fishing tackle to look for game and fish. A special mission was assigned to us boys. We were to bring in puffballs or, failing that, such other edible fungi as we could find. I was put in charge, as the one most familiar with fungi and the terrain.

A year before, a puffball four feet in circumference had been picked up in Duryea's Woods, a mile upshore. I led my forces there in the hope of finding a repeater. Starting from the summit of the ninety-foot cliff that overhangs the lake, we deployed and scouted the forest back of it. At first, nothing rewarded us but some greasecups too small to be worth gathering, but as we emerged into a clearing, Reno shouted, and John and I ran to him. He was standing at a spot where two large basswoods had fallen and rotted, studying a plant some eighteen inches tall with leaves of a lucent green, as if they had been fresh-washed by rain. At the top of the plant was a queer-looking, half-formed cluster of pale berries.

"What kind of a dingus do you call that?" Reno asked.

"Don't touch it," I said. In a countryside rank with poison ivy and stinging nettle, the rule for anything unfamiliar was "Hands off."

"I bet it's some kind of sassafras," Reno said.

"Let's dig it up," said John.

I agreed, doubtfully, and Reno got out his new I.X.L. knife and set to work. The root was firmly set. It was a lumpy, unsightly object when, at last, it lay on the ground. There was an unwritten rule of the camp that any unusual object found in the woods should be reported or, if possible, brought back, so I broke off a hemlock branch and, protecting my hands with basswood leaves, managed to fasten the plant to it.

We then carried it in gingerly fashion out into the clearing. The ground here was dotted with pink-gills, the flavorsome and meaty field mushrooms. We filled our baskets, circled through the woods, and reached the Lower Lake Road. A two-seated, open wagon of the type called democrat wagon was coming toward us. The driver, a boy named Sid Selover, pulled up his span of farm horses and asked us what we had there.

"It's a plant we found in the woods," I said.

"Scared it'll bite you?" Sid asked.

"How do we know but what it's poisonous?" John said.

"Rats!" said Sid genially. "That's brightweed. Give you a dime for it."

"Where's your dime?" Reno challenged him.

"You wouldn't expect a fella to have that much *on* him," Sid said.

"No trust, no bust," Reno retorted. "We'll keep it."

"Tell you what," Sid said. "Frank Clark, over to the Ensenore station, he'll buy it offen you."

"What's he want with it?" I asked.

"He sells it to the Chinese," Sid answered. "They make a powder of it and smoke it in their pipes and it drives 'em crazy." (Sid was a bit muddled, as we later learned.)

Back in camp, our pink-gills were received with approval. Uncle Woolsey had shot three rabbits and two squirrels. Uncle Jack had caught a mess of bullheads and one brown trout in Dutch Hollow Brook. My father, who had a gift for diplomacy, had talked a farm wife out of two loaves of bread and a dozen fresh eggs at the exorbitant price of half a dollar, take it or leave it and she didn't care which, summer folk not being popular with the country people.

The mysterious plant was discussed by our elders, who thought that it might be ginseng, and then again it might not. Frank Clark would know, they agreed; better take it to him when the lake was navigable again.

The four-day gale blew itself out and we three boys rowed the mile and a half to Ensenore to consult Frank. Being rather awed by him, I was not pleased when my cousins deputed to me the job of acting as spokesman. Although not yet of age, Frank displayed a sort of pedagogical austerity. He had a pair of keen eyes, set in a craggy and ascetic face. His loose-jointed form and shambling gait belied his considerable strength. He was the most feared batsman in the Owasco Lake Baseball League.

Frank already had a local reputation as a person of sagacity and authority. "Old head on young shoulders," the neighbors said of him. His taciturnity and abruptness of manner were largely defensive against a time-wasting public, for he was a busy man. He was station-master of the Southern Central at Ensenore, as well as freight, express and passenger agent, telegraph operator and postmaster. On the side, though in the same building, he ran a general store. The station was Frank's inviolable castle. So jealous was he of his feudal rights and prerogatives that one Christmas Eve when he surprised a burglar, who had been terrorizing the locality, in the act of looting the till, his sense of outrage overbore his instinct of self-preservation. Unarmed, he strode up to the intruder and, with no more parley than a gruff, "Gimme that gun," took away his .45, locked him in the mailcloset, and stood guard until the 5 A.M. milk train came in.

I approached this formidable person with respect and some misgiving. He was in his official position behind the post office window. Through it I opened negotiations.

"Mr. Clark," I began, "we've got something . . ."

"I'm busy," said Mr. Clark.

"Shall we wait?" I asked.

"You needn't to," he said.

"When'll you be through?" I persisted.

"Don't know. Quit pestering me."

John, a more resolute character than I, and not so familiar with Frank's reputation, took the stalk of the plant which I was dandling and thrust it beneath the grille of the window.

"All we want to know is, is this ginseng?" he said boldly.

At the word, Frank set down the claw hammer with which he was opening a box, and drew the plant inside. "Come in," he snapped, jerking his head toward a door, and we went inside.

"Where did you find it?" he demanded.

"Duryea's Woods," I answered.

"Want to sell it?"

"Yes, sir."

"How much?"

Reno spoke up. "Sid Selover offered us a dime," he said.

Frank Clark carefully scraped the earth from a bump on the root and scratched its surface. We could smell a delicate and aromatic odor.

"It's a good root," he said. "An old root. It'll fetch a price in New York." From his cash drawer he drew a shining object and held it up.

"A cartwheel!" Reno cried.

No less uplifted, I said, "Are you paying us a whole dollar for it?"

"We'd have taken a quarter and said thank you," John added.

Frank Clark said curtly, "I never cheated a customer yet, and I don't aim to start with you. Fetch me some more."

The interview was ended.

John and Reno and I promptly organized ourselves into the Gin Seng Tong, with oath and secret password. The valuable weed was by no means easy to find. It grew sparsely, often in difficult parts of the dangerously precipitous glens that cut through the lakeward slopes. But the sense of adventure, added to the profit motive, kept us at a high pitch of diligence.

Frank Clark told us he had a connection in New York with a reliable Chinatown exporter, who paid him a dollar and up for prime roots. In his dealings with us, he was scrupulously honest. He even laid aside his grouch to guide us on some of our expeditions.

Well-shaded ground sloping to the east, we learned from him, was the likeliest place to find ginseng. The plants were hard to discern, during the early summer, in the thick undergrowth. In the fall, when the berries turned crimson, identification was easier. For the present, our cicerone told us, he would accept only well-grown plants. The next year, he intended to start his own nursery, and then any stalk that could be transplanted would do.

The Gin Seng Tong had a good season. There was no week in which we did not make half a dozen marketable finds, and by the end of summer our treasury fund had reached an incredible twenty-odd dollars.

That autumn, after we boys had gone home to Rochester, a dire event befell. Ike Jump's nephew, an ignoramus who lived outside Ensenore and didn't know ginseng from skunk cabbage, chanced upon a well-aged ginseng plant in Ensenore Glen, where he was searching for a lost sow. The plant's root was of human form, with branching arms and legs and a spindly, headless neck, a perfect specimen of a rare type.

Frank Clark, to whom the boy took it, had heard of these "mandragons" and knew that they commanded a fancy price from the Chinese, who attributed to them desirable potencies beyond those of the usual root. He made a special shipment of this one to his New York correspondent and, when the payment came, handed over to the lucky finder a ten-dollar bill, which made his eyes pop.

Unfortunately, the boy bragged. Probably he lied. Rumor buzzed. The root had fetched a fabulous amount in Chinatown. Fifty dollars, said some. Nonsense, said others, not fifty, seventy-five. One hundred. One hundred and fifty. Two hundred. Two hundred and fifty. The sum was whatever came into the gossipmonger's head, but on one point the whole region was soon agreed: there were fortunes to be had in the woods. Everybody fell to root-grubbing. The ginseng craze was on, and only snowfall put a stop to it.

None of this, however, reached the ears of us three tong members, impatiently at school in Rochester. Out of our summer's earnings we bought two spades, a mattock, and a botany book, but it was the next July before we at last got back to Second Peacock's.

A scene of devastation awaited us. The countryside had been ravaged. Botanizing vandals from Auburn, Moravia, and even distant Syracuse had scarified the tender face of the earth. Nothing was spared. The demented prowlers had yanked out by the roots such innocent and useless vegetation as burdock, elderberry, tansy, joe-pye weed, mandrake, ox-heart, and pokeberry, and the furor still raged. The station platform at Ensenore was littered each day with plants, most of them trash, which Frank Clark had to burn.

New excitement was stimulated by a report from Skaneateles; a summer renter had found in his teasel field a mandragon root three feet long. It later turned out to be a counterfeit as gross as the neighboring and previous Cardiff giant, and we heard that the Skaneateles Chinaman to whom its sculptor had submitted it for verification chased the faker out of his laundry at the point of a flatiron.

But enough authentic finds of ginseng—"shang" to the trade—were made to keep the pitch of interest high, a two- or three-dollar specimen being not infrequent. The farmers caught the craze. They posted their woods and even stood guard at night with shotguns. Old Man Beardsley, over near Henpeck—a name now, alas, deleted from local nomenclature—attracted some attention with a sign that read:

ALL PERSONS ARE POSITIVELY FORBIDDEN
TO VEGETATE ON THESE PREMISES

His wood lot was worth guarding. It yielded enough plants to let him start quite a respectable nursery.

Many others decided to go in for ginseng culture, and for a time little, close-planted plots enriched with leaf mold and covered with roofs of laths three inches apart, in the prescribed fashion, became a familiar sight.

All this competition, and especially the posting, made the going tough for the Adams tong. How many copses and groves we were ignominiously chased from, I would not undertake to say. Where we were able to explore unmolested, others had been before us. The leavings were always meagre— a few scrawny stalks with spindling roots worth only a few cents. Our total takings in a month of woodmanship that would have taxed the endurance of Daniel Boone were under three dollars. The game was up. Our tong disbanded. We traded our botany book for a dime novel and our tools for fishing tackle, and turned our attention to the perch in Owasco Lake.

For the most part, the farmers had spoiled our sport and our prospect of becoming botanical millionaires without doing themselves much good. Lack of scientific knowledge was their trouble; ginseng culture is not a hit-or-miss activity.

Few of the cultivators knew how to protect their crops. Blight, root rot and mildew attacked the plants. Snails and eelworms preyed upon them. After a few years of this, most of the experimenters gave up.

More patient growers, however, became expert and did a profitable business. Willard R. Austin, of Moravia, who once dug a wild root weighing an even pound, and his fellow-Moravians, the Bowens, father and son, stuck to the trade for more than twenty years, marketing their product in Elmira and New York, for export to China. There was little demand for it in this country, though a patent-medicine stomachic called Garfield Tea was based upon ginseng. However, as these successful ginseng gardens expanded, a new risk developed. Professional night raiders from New York appeared upon the scene.

Frank Clark was a victim of these. Learning of raids on Seneca Lake, he fenced his patch with barbed wire and hung the wire with bells of loud tone and high sensitivity. He had not reckoned with wild creatures accustomed to wander at night. The belled wires proved disastrously responsive to their visits. A dozen times a night, poor Frank, roused by the clangor, would leap from his bed, seize his shotgun, and charge down the hill to his ginseng patch in time to see a rabbit scurry into the brush or a raccoon swarm up a tree trunk. Once, there was a wild carillon when a deer blundered into the wire. Frank shot the deer, which was some satisfaction to him.

Sturdy though Frank was, the strain told upon him. He lost ten pounds through lack of sleep. He discarded the bells and kept a dog tied inside the enclosure. But the dog had friends in the vicinity; it learned to slip its leash and crawl through the wire, causing Frank more sleeplessness. In the course of time, it died. Its owner did not replace it, since the depredations of the ginseng bandits had flagged. Several seasons went by without any local thefts.

Then, one December morning, Frank went out to find his plot ravished. There were broad wagon-tire marks in the soft roadway. Frank followed the trail as far as Cascade, at the head of the lake, but lost it there. Nearly twelve hundred dollars' worth of roots had been dug up. Frank quit the ginseng business in disgust.

There was encouragement for those who stuck to the ginseng trade in the steady rise in price. In the days of the Adams tong, average roots brought no more than two dollars a pound. By 1900, the price was six dollars and a half. In 1927, there was a shortage in the Orient, and the price reached a fabulous high of twenty-four dollars, but by that time the industry had been all but abandoned in the lakes district. Cultivated plants brought much less than the wild growth, the latter being credited with more powerful medicinal effects, and the forests had been pretty well denuded.

"The shang rustlers had got smart," says octogenarian Arthur J. Bowen, of Moravia. "They'd learned to wait till fall, when the berries turn bright red and you can spot a plant ten rods away through the shrubbery. Nowadays, I couldn't take you to a wild shang plant if I wanted to."

Mr. Bowen is the author of a poetic lament for the ravaged woodlands of his prime, entitled "Extermination" and copyrighted in 1903:

> The big forests with their timbers so tall
> Is where the Ginseng grew, both large and small:
> But soon came the men at a terrible rate
> And cleaned up the forest—which is the Ginseng's fate.
> But now the shang digger with his eye so keen
> Has hunted the woods, and there is not a plant to be seen.

The horticultural authorities at Cornell University confirm Mr. Bowen's pessimism, though they believe that the species is not wholly extinct in the Finger Lakes region. Certainly, however, it is very rare. It has not recovered from the pillage of the frenzied amateurs of the last century. Yet I never drive through the autumn woods that border my home on the shore of Owasco Lake without keeping an instinctively hopeful eye out for a glint of crimson topping a leafy green shaft. I cannot help feeling that I might chance upon a full-grown plant and exhume from beneath it that valuable symbolic vegetable and promoter of virility, a seven-year mandragon root.

THE INVALID'S FRIEND
AND HOPE

In Grandfather Adams's eyes, Mr. Asa T. Soule was a noble character. Many times I have heard the old gentleman refer to his fellow Rochesterian as "a very respectable citizen," a *summa cum laude* which represented the apex of encomium. We grandchildren heartily agreed. Had not Mr. Soule revived professional baseball in Rochester at a time when it seemed that all hope was lost? No honor could be too great for him.

This was a minor consideration to Grandfather. A more important one was the somewhat ostentatious Soule benefices to church and charity. Chiefly, however, the old gentleman's esteem derived from his appreciation of the widely exploited Soule nostrum, Hop Bitters, the Invalid's Friend & Hope. Any man, in Grandfather's grateful opinion, who could confer upon mankind so heart-and-stomach-warming a preparation as the Bitters, was a benefactor of the human race, and that is all there was to it.

Although disappointed in his efforts to reform the sport in the direction of greater liveliness, Grandfather retained enough interest in baseball to write Mr. Soule a warmly com-

plimentary letter about his stand on Sunday games, which
was rigidly sabbatarian. In return, the recipient sent around
to the South Union Street cottage a whole case of Hop
Bitters.

Many years later I had occasion to trace Asa T. Soule's activities, both medical and sportive. By this time Mr. Soule
was long dead. Grandfather, who had outlived him by a few
years, was long dead. Hop Bitters was no more than a faint,
alcoholic memory in the patent medicine industry. How
Grandfather would have regarded my findings had he lived
to learn of them, I can only conjecture. They would not, I
am sure, have shaken his faith in Mr. Soule or in his Invalid's
Friend & Hope, for his loyalties were rock-firm. And I suspect
that he would not have, to use his own word, "approbated"
my report.

Early in the 1870's there appeared upon hundreds of respectable sideboards, mantelpieces and shelves in Rochester
an amber-hued bottle with a blown-in design of a hop vine
in full fruit. Within was a potent liquid. "Hop Bitters, the
Invalid's Friend & Hope" had started a long and profitable
career, enhanced by the special appeal it made to the teetotal
trade.

Remember [one advertisement read], Hop Bitters is no vile,
drugged, drunken nostrum, but the Purest and Best Medicine ever
made, the greatest Blood Purifier, Liver Regulator, and Life and
Health Restoring agent on earth, tonic and stimulating WITH-
OUT INTOXICATING.

The total-abstinence element, then at the height of its social influence, read, bought, partook, and were gladdened in
heart, blissfully innocent of the medicine's secret content of
low-grade, high-powered whiskey. Swiftly the Bitters rose to
be the fifth best-seller in the patent-medicine field, and Asa
T. Soule, the proprietor of the company that manufactured

it, opened branches in London, Antwerp, Melbourne, and Toronto. Side lines were put out—Hop Cure for coughs, Hop Pad to comfort distressed abdomens, and an "absolute and irresistible cure" for drunkenness, narcotics and tobacco. The proprietor became a millionaire.

Mr. Soule, who composed all his own advertising, was a master of the persuasive phrase. His fellow-townsman, my father, who was not among his admirers, used to say of his copy that it "would convince a hale man that he has an incurable disease and that Hop Bitters will cure it." Grandfather, a militant foe of the Demon Rum, was seldom without his three-a-day dosage of Mr. Soule's inspiring concoction.

Up to 1879 the Hop Bitters proprietor was just another successful businessman in a community teeming with successful businessmen. Born into a Quaker family in which he was the eleventh child, he had inherited the commercial shrewdness of that sect without the handicap of its ethical standards. He had been a farmer, a patent-rights broker, a peach grower, a real-estate operator, a banker, a hotel manager, and a road man for a cough cure before turning up in Canandaigua, New York, with a little capital and buying (some said cheating) out the owner of Doyle's Bitters, an alleged extract of hops. Mr. Soule changed the name, fortified the formula, and moved to Rochester in 1873.

Six years later, he entered the professional-sports arena, a move not wholly unconnected with his zeal for promulgating the virtues of Hop Bitters. At that time, he was a rather handsome, watchful-eyed, pleasant-mannered, and surprisingly youthful man of fifty-five, precise in speech and dress (it was rumored that he paid sixty dollars for his black, diagonal, made-to-order cutaway suits at Witherspoon & Griswold's, in the Arcade), of moderate habits, without social ambition, a known Sabbatarian, and a generous contributor to the Presbyterian church and other worthy causes.

My boyhood memory of him centers upon a children's party of unique magnificence that he gave at his home on non-fashionable Lake Avenue, where soda water in six flavors was served from an improvised fountain by an aproned attendant and there appeared for the entertainment of the awe-stricken guests an authentic professional magician, complete with wand, silk hat and goldfish bowl. At the close of the evening, the host rapped for silence and addressed us as "my young friends," which made us feel gratifyingly grown up. He exhorted us to be good children, clean and polite, and advised us that a bottle of Hop Bitters, the Invalid's Friend & Hope, should always be kept at hand in case of sickness. As a dramatic climax, he—not the magician—plucked a silver dollar from the ear of an astonished blonde and ringleted seven-year-old, who thereupon burst into startled tears.

Mr. Soule's tastes and habits, before he permitted them to be diverted to the professional field, were fairly standard for his period and status. He drove a fast pacer, sharpshod, in the free-entry ice races on the Genesee River. He offered modest prizes for amateur aquatic sports on nearby Lake Ontario. It was said that he patronized cockfights, which were illicit but winked at, and whispered that he attended dogfights, which were illegal and frowned upon by the best people. As a loyal Rochesterian, he subscribed for a season ticket to the ball park and manifested some technical interest in the game by writing letters on the subject to the Rochester *Democrat & Chronicle.*

One of these communications was the denunciation of Sunday baseball which so stirred my grandfather's admiration. Another considered adversely the newfangled claim that a ball could be made to curve in midair. This theory Mr. Soule denounced as contrary to the laws of nature and he offered a reward to anyone who could prove him wrong. Nothing in his career thus far had presaged his abrupt incursion into the arena of professionalism.

Gamblers ruled and corrupted practically all sports outside the amateur field at this time. Contest-fixing was the accepted practice. "The methods by which the athletic classes [a social rather than an academic use of the word] and their confederates gain their living has become pretty generally known," the Troy *Times* editorialized. And the New York *Times*, more outspoken, referred casually to "that class of crimes known as athletic sports." A Rochester editorial writer was exaggerating little if at all when he asserted, "There is no sport which is not contaminated and, in large measure, controlled by the gambling fraternity. A square contest of skill is hardly to be expected." The basketball scandals of recent years would have been accepted by the sporting world of the seventies as standard procedure.

Although tainted by the prevailing lack of morality, baseball in the mid-seventies had developed from a fad into a frenzy. Clubs sprang up wherever nine people could find a vacant lot. There were college teams, school teams, village, town and city teams, ward teams, church teams, butchers' teams, undertakers' teams, railroad teams, Erie Canal teams, teams of bachelors, teams of married men, old men's teams with every player certified as being more than forty, brewery teams, distillery teams, and teetotallers' teams.

Haverley's Minstrels had a nine with an infield quartet, which not only sang between innings, but burst into harmony upon the completion of a double play. A formidable deaf-mute team played out of Columbus, Ohio, and there was a one-armed men's nine that was the wonder and admiration of all beholders. The Mormons triumphantly toured the nation with their squad. The diamond was further embellished by a female club whose players developed such a penchant for getting into jail on charges of disorderly conduct that substitutes frequently had to be called in to fill out the roster. Ungallant sports writers darkly hinted that the ladies practiced a profession long antedating baseball.

The field was divided between simon-pure amateurs, regular professionals who charged admission, and semipros who passed the hat "to buy new uniforms for the boys."

Poor, indeed, in public esteem, and in its own, was the city which was unrepresented by a league affiliation. Such was Rochester's prospective plight at the close of the 1878 season. Because of the character of its performance, which had for several years been both inferior and suspicious, the local team had fallen into disrepute. Rochesterians were a sports-loving folk; they accorded the players a loyal support "beyond what their merit deserved until the players, themselves, began to go crooked," a local commentator wrote. Then gate receipts dwindled. There were internecine bickerings. The season of 1879 opened with the city unplaced.

"Must we go to Syracuse or Buffalo to see a game?" the *Democrat & Chronicle* dismally inquired. Worried citizens echoed the lament. Asa T. Soule responded to it.

"I have faith in Rochester," he solemnly informed an emergency committee formed to confront the crisis. "Our city shall be in the field. Hop Bitters, the Invalid's Friend & Hope, will come to the rescue."

Overnight, Mr. Soule became Rochester's hero. The newspapers acclaimed him a public benefactor. Crowds followed him. Clergymen stopped him on the street to shake his hand. A variety artist extolled his patriotism from the stage of Corinthian Hall in a topical song of which the refrain alone sticks in my memory:

> Hail to Asa Soule!
> Rochester's fairest jool.

Mr. Soule bought the bankrupt Albany club, transferred it to his home community, and put it into new uniforms with the legend "Hop Bitters" blazoned in scarlet against gray across the chest. The local ball park, rechristened Hop Bitters

Park, threw open its gates of welcome with an address by the
mayor and music by the Artillery Band, G.A.R. The new nine
obliged by winning two games straight against amateurs.
"The Hop Bitters nine expect to give every club in the country a dose before the season is over," exulted the *Democrat &
Chronicle*.

Mr. Soule concurred. "Every player will receive a tablespoonful of Hop Bitters before each game," he announced.
"We shall march from victory to victory."

Both major leagues had closed their rosters before the Rochesterians belatedly took the field. They therefore joined a hy-
brid congregation representing New York and New England
cities, in which they promptly slid to ninth place in a league
of nine. By early July, the Rochester *Union & Advertiser* was
peevishly complaining:

Will anybody tell us what ails the Hop Bitters nine? They have
now lost eleven games in succession. Mr. Soule will have to re-
organize it or quit the baseball business.

Mr. Soule did neither. He doubled the pre-game dosage of
his tonic, and the inspired players responded by climbing ar-
duously to eighth place over their bribe-ridden Manchester,
New Hampshire, rivals. They did not long retain that status.
Financial dickerings with the gamblers' ring having been
proven against them, the Manchesters disbanded. Thereupon,
the Hop Bitters again became tailenders and so remained.

Stung by the criticisms of a city turned captious, Mr. Soule
now deviated from the paths of strict rectitude. Troy had a
notable first baseman. Rochester was weak in that position.
Secret advances were made by Mr. Soule of such a nature
that the Troy papers howled bribery and corruption and,
what was worse, proved it. After an obscure and embittered
controversy, Mr. Soule and his team were officially read out
of organized baseball.

Undismayed, the resourceful magnate formally disbanded his organization and, in midseason, formed the New Hop Bitters Baseball Club. This was a wildcat body without league affiliations, and so could not be barred from non-official contests. Recanting his skepticism about the curve ball, Mr. Soule bought from the One-Armed Nine a left-hander with a powerful inshoot and proceeded to fling challenges far and wide. Thanks to the pitcher's skill, the nine did fairly well against Washington, Albany (reorganized), Providence and Worcester, and better against Rochester's perennial rival, Buffalo.

After the regular 1879 season, the New Hop Bitters team hit the Western trail, ending up in Salt Lake City where they took on the supposedly formidable Mormon representatives. Score of the opening game: Hop Bitters, 28; Latter Day Saints, 2. Two other contests were also won by the invaders.

"Is there any other game you can play?" the manager then inquired politely.

"Cricket," the Saints' representative replied. "Know anything about it?"

"I've heard of it," the Rochesterian said modestly.

Accordingly, the teams met at cricket, and the Easterners won by an unrecorded score. Commenting upon the game, the unsaintly Salt Lake *Tribune* of September 7, 1879, observed:

And new abideth Mormons, dust, and Hop Bitters, but the worst of these is Hop Bitters.

Meantime, Rochester had been flooded, during that summer of 1879, with sartorial advertising of the Soule panacea. Such members of the original, outlawed Hop Bitters as had not been absorbed by the New Hop Bitters, recruited themselves up to quota and carried on locally for what gate money they could pick up, wearing their old uniforms. Several Amateur Hop Bitters nines came into being in the city, and at least four Junior Hop Bitters, all equipped with uniforms of Mr. Soule's beneficence. In and around Rochester, there were also a Towpath Hop Bitters Club, a Flower City Hop Bitters club, a Genesee River Hop Bitters Club, and a short-lived Sunday School Hop Bitters club, all bearing the medical insigne. The Third Ward Eaglets (ten-year age limit), on which I played shortstop, nobly rejected an offer of bats, balls, caps and shirts to change our name to Baby Hop Bitters. The "Hop Bitters" we could have taken, but the "Baby" was too much for youthful pride to swallow.

The sports-plus-medicine combination was destined to turn sour upon its deviser. Upstate newspaper wits began to make a butt of the Soule team. It was variously called the Liverpads, the Curacoffs, the Rumbleguts, and the Gambler's Friend & Hope. The Buffalo *Courier* reported:

The Hop Bitters have already been challenged by the Castorias, the Vegetines, and the Gargling Oils.

The Amsterdam *Courier's* baseball expert carried derision still further:

Bull's Body Syrup are billed to play Pierce's Pile Drivers and the Worm Lozenges will tackle the winners.

All this hurt the patent-medicine man's feelings. The Rochester *Union & Advertiser* spoke for him:

Mr. Soule is very indignant at the Buffalo and other papers because they don't call his club by their right name.

At one point, the "medicated sportsman," as a contumelious Trojan speaker had called him at the time of the filching of the first baseman, threatened to withdraw entirely from baseball, but soon thought better of it.

The season of 1880 found him still in the field, but with a difference. The barbs of the wits had found their mark. Before the summer's end, Mr. Soule abandoned the Hop Bitters uniform. The simple legend, "Rochester," now decked his outfit. As the officially titled Rochester Baseball Club, it was restored to the National Baseball Association in a four-ply league with Washington, Baltimore, and Albany. It did not do well.

"The new uniforms, at least, are satisfactory," was the best that the once loyal *Democrat & Chronicle* could find to say of it.

Little else was. The aroma of scandal still hung in the local air. Fresh allusions to a hookup between the gambling element and the players appeared in the papers. The manager went on a drunk with four hundred dollars of salary money lifted from the till, and although Mr. Soule, who was of a tolerant disposition, made good the deficit and took him back, the effect upon morale was unfortunate. The members played worse and worse. The public attended less and less. There was not even the indirect advertising value left for Hop Bitters. Mr. Soule quit the game with some pointed reflections upon civic ingratitude.

Baseball, however, had not been his only athletic interest. Contemporaneously, he dipped into aquatics, thereby involving himself in the most resounding scandal of the nation's sporting history.

Next to baseball, single-shell sculling was the most popular form of athletics in the United States at that time. Some two dozen topflight professionals, European and American, were in the field; a regatta with a fat purse might call out as many as twenty able contestants. Thousands of spectators could be reckoned upon for a race between two champions. To the same degree that baseball was the national game, sculling was the international sport.

It was perhaps a shade more fraudulent than baseball. No contradiction was adduced to the Utica *Herald's* charge that professional rowers in general were "controlled in the interests of the lowest class of thieves, gamblers and cutthroats." The contestants' opinion of their own ethics is indicated by the fact that guards were set over the boathouses before all important races lest interested parties sneak in and disable the racing shells. One disgruntled ex-champion opened his embittered heart to a Buffalo reporter, averring "that he could tell enough about boating rascalities to fill an encyclopedia, and he hoped he would go to h-ll if ever he touched an oar again."

Two popular heroes ruled the waters in 1879—Charles E. Courtney, of Union Springs, New York, and Edward Hanlan, of Toronto. Courtney claimed the United States championship. Hanlan claimed the Canadian championship. Both claimed the world championship.

The upstate man's background was the more spectacular. As a youthful carpenter without aquatic experience, he had built his own boat, entered a regatta on Cayuga Lake, and outdistanced a large field of professionals. Thereafter his career was checkered, not to say spotted. At his best, he was unbeatable; at all times, unreliable.

Peculiar circumstances attended his occasional defeats. Once, just before a race, some miscreant poisoned his iced tea, surely an unusual beverage for an athlete to indulge in at such a time. Another time, a submerged wire wrecked him in mid-course without leaving any mark on his shell. Again, in a two-man contest on a broad course, he mysteriously lost his way and wandered into foul water. On occasion, his speed seemed unaccountably to desert him. Notwithstanding, he was the idol of his countrymen. Mr. Soule was one of his open partisans.

Hanlan, eight years younger, was simply and solely a first-class workman in his chosen calling. With his clumsy, humpy and dogged stroke, so different from Courtney's smooth style, he had vanquished opponent after opponent on both sides of the Atlantic. His reputation was clean; he had never been implicated in any of the prevalent chicaneries of his trade. His one meeting with Courtney had resulted in victory, but the beaten man's backers emphatically considered the test unsatisfactory and inconclusive, complicated as it was by a near foul.

Naturally, there was a public demand for another trial. Those two cantankerous characters, Commodore William H. Vanderbilt and James Gordon Bennett, came forward in the spring of 1879 with an offer of a six-thousand-dollar purse, which was satisfactory to the oarsmen. But the financiers fell out over some detail, quarreled all summer, and then withdrew the purse.

Enter Asa T. Soule to fill the vacuum: He and his Hop Bitters Company would put up the stakes. In September, he summoned the rivals and their backers to a meeting at the Brackett Hotel, in Rochester, the aftermath of which was a powerful stench. The sessions were private, Mr. Soule presiding; but even so the *Democrat & Chronicle* scented "some very curious shenanigans." Publicly, it was given out that all terms were settled and the Hop Bitters prize of six thousand dollars had been deposited in the City Bank, payable to the referee. Chautauqua Lake was selected as the place; October 16th as the date. William Blaikie, a former Harvard stroke and author of the best-seller *How to Be Strong and Stay So*, was agreed upon as referee. His was the only reputation that survived the event unsmirched.

Chautauqua, theretofore the source of cultural radiations, now became the sporting center of the United States. Gamblers and sharpers from all parts converged upon it. Mayville, the principal town on the lake, swarmed with underworld denizens; Quimby & Forse, the great New York odds layers,

set up their "sentry boxes" for the taking of bets, on its downtown corners. Thimbleriggers, punchboard operators, and three
card-monte experts chanted their seductive lays. Loose females
flaunted exotic finery on hotel verandas. Room and board rose
from five dollars a week to twelve dollars a day. A Presbyterian
clergyman cried from his pulpit, "The seven plagues of Egypt
swarm about us and Hell's foul rays are focused upon our unhappy village."

Mr. Soule was early on the ground. He was vastly amused
at being taken for a Baptist minister by a faro-board operator.
In the character of a primitive five percenter, he exacted commission from railroads, excursion and sightseeing boats, grand-
stands, hotels, boarding houses, and "all the games, straight
and skin," as he boasted to a Utica newspaperman. "Not to
mention the advertising," he added. This last was considerable. Not only was the contest widely exploited as the Hop
Bitters Prize Race, but a railroad spur to the scene was called
the Hop Bitters Branch and Courtney tactfully christened his
shell the Hop Bitters.

Betting was fast, furious and variable. Most of the sports
seem to have placed their money on the assumption that the
race was fixed and that they knew which way. All the stig-
mata of hippodroming were present. Wild rumors kept the
odds wild. Hanlan was reported by the Associated Press to be
so out of condition that he would be unfit to row before
spring. Courtney not only suffered from ague and sore hands,
but had, in the delicate words of the *Democrat & Chronicle*,
"blistered that part of his body liable to be blistered under
such circumstances, and the coloring of his worsted pants
poisoned the abraisure [sic]."

The New York *Herald* asserted that neither contestant was
doing a proper amount of work—"not as much as a good,
stiff university crew would do four days before a race."

Hanlan paid a private call on Courtney, inspiring rumors
that (1) he had sold out, (2) that he had bought Courtney

off, (3) that the race would be a dead heat and the championship would carry over to the next year. Two days before the date set for the race, an unidentified man, who may or may not have had inside information, waved a hundred-dollar bill from the Mayville Post Office steps and offered to lay it against twenty that Courtney would not come to the scratch. There were no takers.

The pool boxes were so unsettled by the rapidly shifting odds that several of them closed their windows, and one wildcat bookmaker went crazy and jumped into the lake.

Mr. Soule gave out reassuring statements. He had visited both opponents, he said, and in his opinion (for publication), each was fit, ready and determined to row the race of his life; anything to the contrary was falsehood put forth to influence the odds.

As the promoter sat at breakfast on the vital morning, an emissary came up at the double and whispered in his ear. Mr. Soule dropped everything, climbed into his waiting rig, and drove at top speed through excited crowds that already cluttered the road leading to the Courtney camp. The oarsman's quarters were barred and guarded, but the early caller was at once admitted. He found Courtney seated in the living room, his head in his hands, surrounded by silent henchmen.

"What's this about your boat, Charley?" Mr. Soule demanded.

"Sawed," the oarsman replied in a hollow voice. "Sawed halfway through."

"When? How?"

"Last evening, while the boys were in town playing casino." (Courtney's nephew and another youth had been employed to guard the boats.)

Mr. Soule was scandalized. "You don't mean to tell me that you left your boathouse unprotected!" he cried.

Frenchy Johnson, Courtney's Negro trainer, spoke up.

"They broke in the water-door," he said. "When I looked in at nine last evening, there was both shells sawed."

Still more astonished, the promoter turned back to Courtney. "You heard about this last night and you never notified me?"

"Mr. Courtney didn't know nothing about it till this morning," Johnson explained. "He's a mighty nervous gentleman, Mr. Courtney is, specially before a race, and I didn't want to spoil his good night's rest."

By this time, the training camp was a bedlam. A rapidly increasing crowd was milling about outside, shouting and threatening. A committee of newspapermen angrily demanded admittance. Referee Blaikie burst in, having neatly spilled a guard who tried to block him off. He confronted Courtney.

"The race must be rowed," he said.

"How can I row without a shell?" Courtney replied.

"You can have your pick of a dozen shells," said the referee.

"I won't row in any shell but the Hop Bitters," Courtney mumbled. "You can't make me."

Mr. Soule interposed. "Let's not get excited, gentlemen," he said. "What do you propose, Mr. Blaikie?"

"To give the word 'start' at the set time," the referee said firmly. "And you had better be there, prepared to row," he warned the sullen oarsman.

With that, he left. So did Mr. Soule. He had urgent financial business in Rochester.

Hell broke loose on Chautauqua's shores. The streets of Mayville seethed with embattled partisans, arguing, cursing, denouncing. Quimby & Forse declared all bets off and returned the wagers, holding out one per cent as a handling charge. The newspaper committee returned from the camp, having stormed the stronghold and forced a statement from

Courtney: he would not row. From Hanlan's quarters came the charge that Courtney had sawed his own boat. Why, the Hanlan men asked, had the hired guards left their post unless through collusion? Courtney's irrelevant retort was that Hanlan had offered to split the purse with him two days before. Local opinion was heavily against Courtney.

When, later that day, Referee Blaikie gave the word, "Go!" Hanlan rowed the course alone, disproving the canards about his condition by breaking the record for the distance. He was officially declared the winner.

Little financial good it did him. When, with Mr. Blaikie, he presented himself at the City Bank in Rochester to claim the purse, a civil cashier said, "Sorry, gentlemen; no funds."

The provident Mr. Soule had got there first and drawn out the six thousand dollars. The Hop Bitters Company, he later explained, had offered the prize for a race. There had been no race. Therefore there would be no award. If Messrs. Courtney and Hanlan chose to arrange another match, the company would be ready with the money.

Everybody concerned, except the placid Mr. Soule, was now good and mad. Noisome exhalations from the September meeting at the Brackett Hotel began to ooze forth. A Hanlan backer produced a telegraph blank with what he asserted to be an offer from the Courtney representatives scrawled upon the back:

E. Hanlan: I hereby agree to hand over to you the sum of three thousand dollars being half of the Hop Bitters Company prize should I be declared the winner.

The Courtney people denied any knowledge of this document and cited another alleged agreement. This was that Mr. Soule had secretly put up a stake of two thousand dollars for the loser. Courtney now called upon the promoter for the two thousand.

Again Mr. Soule answered with the no-race-no-purse argument. He did not deny the offer; indeed, he intimated that it had been made, for the reason that he had not believed that Courtney could be enticed to toe the mark without a win-or-lose assurance. However, he would gladly put up a thousand dollars, to be claimed by Courtney if he would now row the course and better Hanlan's time.

Courtney would have none of it. One more gesture the promoter made in the interests of advertising; he put up a thousand-dollar reward for the detection of the boat sawyer. It was never claimed.

The newspapers cried out against all these maneuverings. "The whole thing is a disgrace," the New York *Herald* fumed. The Troy *Times* declared that the nation had not been so shocked and enraged "since the firing on Fort Sumter."

The general belief was that both contestants were through. Mr. Soule knew better. Confidence in the infinite gullibility of the human race is a cornerstone of the patent-medicine vender's creed. Give people a little time to forget, Mr. Soule figured, and they would be ready for another plucking. Aquatics would die out of the papers in the closed winter season. Next spring, he would put on a repeat performance. His six thousand dollars was intact; on behalf of the Invalid's Friend & Hope, he would let bygones be bygones and again put up the Hop Bitters prize. He so notified Courtney and Hanlan.

All the latent nobility of the rival oarsmen's respective spirits rose in response to the sportsman's generosity. The atmosphere became that of a love feast. Courtney gave assurance of his unbounded confidence in Asa T. Soule and Hop Bitters; he would row for them any time, anywhere, against any challenger. Hanlan publicly expressed his conviction that "Mr. Soule is the soul of honor," which had not been his precise opinion after his call at the bank. The newspapers beat their tom-toms. The rivals exchanged defiances. The book-

makers quoted the odds. The credulous sporting world took
sides with undiminished fervor and rancor. Interest focussed
upon Washington, D.C., where the race was set for May 19,
1880.

Then came the word that everything had been fixed up be-
forehand; Courtney's manager was privately laying his bets
on Hanlan. On the day before the contest, Courtney pro-
fessed to have developed a racking headache and would have
withdrawn had not his desperate backers threatened him with
dire bodily reprisals.

Too late to save the money of those backers and his own,
Henry C. Carr, of Union Springs, Courtney's neighbor,
friend and original backer, spoke out: the headache was a
pretense. "The race was sold long ago," said the disgusted
Mr. Carr.

Both contestants took the water in apparently prime condition. At the start, the American spurted ahead, stroking
with his customary smoothness and skill. The Canadian
quickened his lumpy stroke, and crept up foot by foot. Thereupon, to quote a poetical-minded reporter, "Courtney wilted
like a tender flower in the harsh blast of winter." The imaginary headache was still with him. Trailing his oars, he
brought out a handkerchief and laved his fevered brow in
cool Potomac waters. The next thing his infuriated backers
knew, he had turned at right angles and wavered completely
off the course. Hanlan was declared the winner and went on
to become the undisputed champion of the world.

Courtney's racing career was finished. He threw out a few
feeble challenges but they were ignored. Fellow-racers, many
of them with records far from immaculate, boycotted him.
He returned to his home waters of Cayuga Lake to instruct
a four-oared crew of schoolgirls in the art of oarsmanship.
Thence he went to Cornell, where he is still held in reveren-
tial memory as the most successful coach of all time.

The fiasco on the Potomac was too much for the long-suffering stomach of the American sportsman. The newspapers howled "Fake!" Bets were repudiated. Rowing, as a public spectacle, had suffered a blow from which it has never recovered. From that day, interest ebbed. Mr. Soule made feeble attempts to inject once more his Hop Bitters into the waning game, but the public would have none of it. The name of the nostrum vanished from the sporting columns.

Hop Bitters, itself, was losing its grip. A local rival, Warner's Safe Kidney & Liver Cure, manufactured by H. H. Warner, was outselling it. One of Rochester's rising notables was a comet hunter named Lewis Swift. Warner built Swift an observatory on East Avenue to the greater honor of the Cure, and announced a reward of a hundred dollars for each new celestial discovery. Every time a fresh comet swam into Astronomer Swift's ken, Warner's Safe Kidney & Liver Cure got honorable mention in the press.

Asa T. Soule observed and envied. Obviously culture was the ticket. The University of Rochester, like all small colleges, was chronically in need of money. Why not Hop Bitters money? An endowment of a hundred thousand dollars or so ought to persuade the institution to change its name for the better.

"If there's a Warner Observatory, why not a Hop Bitters University?" Soule said to his friend, Ernest Willard, of the *Democrat & Chronicle.*

"My God, no!" the editor replied. "People would call it Cathartic College. They'd invent the degree of Bachelor of Booze and pin it on you. They'd make a guy of you in Latin, Greek and Hebrew. Have you forgotten what the newspapers did to your Hop Bitters ball team?"

Advice was wasted upon Mr. Soule when he had a fixed idea. He made advances to the University trustees. They turned him down with an asperity that injured his feelings.

He shook the dust of an ungrateful community from his feet and went to Kansas to found Soule College, at Dodge City. A gift of real estate to the value of fifty-two thousand dollars made him temporarily popular, though nothing was then done about buildings or faculty.

Soule then embarked on some extracurricular activities that did not commend themselves to the people of Dodge City. He constructed an irrigation system which failed for want of water. He built a railroad which went bankrupt for lack of traffic. He invested heavily in real estate and encouraged others to do the same on the theory that he could negotiate the transfer of the county seat from Ingalls to Dodge City, thereby making a nice profit. The Ingalls citizens fought and beat him in the legislature.

Political methods failing, he resorted to direct action. At the head of a gang of professional bad men, including the formidable Bat Masterson, he raided the courthouse at Ingalls and captured the records. Before he could take them away, the forces of law and order besieged the building. The bad men proved to be not as bad as advertised. They meekly surrendered.

Disillusioned with the West, Mr. Soule returned to Rochester to die. As he had neglected to devise any funds to Soule College, that posthumous foundation also died after a brief struggle. Thus no monument remains to Asa T. Soule, once Rochester's favorite son. The Invalid's Friend & Hope has long since disappeared from drugstore shelves. Collectors are only mildly interested in the amber bottles, with the agreeable bas-relief of the fruitful hop. They value them at half a dollar apiece.

THE INIMITABLE
MR. CARLYLE

Culture descended upon the United States with a heavy impact in the 1880's. Nowhere was it more gratefully absorbed into the local mores than in Rochester. Its prophet and oracle was Thomas Carlyle. Reading groups held symposia upon him. His obiter dicta were echoed from pulpits. Visiting lecturers profitably analyzed his more obscure pronouncements at an admission fee of a quarter a head. A select assortment of local pundits organized themselves into a Carlylean Circle and discussed their demigod from scholarly angles in erudite fortnightly essays.

Though a fervent Carlylist of long standing, Grandfather did not join. He felt, I think, a sense of proprietorship in the dour Scot, and resented the intrusion upon his preserves by these newcomers who attempted to read all sorts of occult messages and meanings into the philosopher's most forthright passages. He regarded them as faddists. I have heard him apply the derogatory term, "toosey-woosey" to their unbridled enthusiasms. In time he came to cherish an "ambition"—as he would have put it—to the whole organization.

To us young ones, Mr. Carlyle was a blight upon the day. Once a month, at least, Grandfather forcibly improved our minds by reading aloud from his works. And on one painful occasion John and I were taken to a lecture on the subject by the old gentleman, the lecturer being one of our teachers at the Rochester Free Academy, Professor Glenn. He was a leading member of the Carlylean Circle and a tireless and minute analyst of the Master's philosophy.

"The man deems himself a veritable sapient on the subject," Grandfather told us as we entered the hall. "We shall see."

The title of the reading was "Thomas Carlyle—Incomparable and Inimitable." Grandfather's one commentary on the effort (aside from subdued snorts and sniffs during the delivery) was withheld until the three of us were out in the air.

"Incomparable, yes," he said. "Inimitable? Hah!" The word had put ideas into his head.

A fortnight later, on a glowing January day, we five regular Saturday callers entered the cottage sitting room to find the Boston rocker unoccupied, Grandfather was in the kitchen, undergoing a domestic operation at the hands of our step-grandmother, the nature of which was made plain to us by his voice, raised in admonition.

"That will be sufficient at the back, Mrs. Adams." Then, more sharply, "Mind my ear, ma'am."

Our attention was unhappily focussed on a small, reddish-brown book, splayed open upon the marble-top stand. I tiptoed over to ascertain the particular affliction in store for us.

"*Heroes and Hero-Worship,*" I read.

"Oh, *dear!*" said Jenny.

"Might be worse," her brother, Sireno, said.

"How?" John demanded.

"*Sartor Resartus,*" Reno answered. "All those darn thees and thous and thines."

John directed a sour glance at the stand. "All those Odins and Thors and Valkyrs!" he sniffed.

"And lookit at what kind of a day we're missing," young Charlie mourned.

We gazed out upon the glittering enticement of the snow. There would be cutter racing on the frozen Genesee River, the horses from the winter quarters of the trotting circuit sharpshod and shaggyhaired. The ice on Archie Cossett's father's rink would be slick as a window pane. Pinnacle Hill back of the Wide Waters would be echoing to the shouts of "Shinny on your own side!" There would be bellywhop coasting on the mounds opposite Mt. Hope Cemetery.

"Drat Mr. Carlyle and his heroes!" Jenny muttered.

There was a stir in the other room, "Just one moment, Mr. Adams," cautioned his wife's voice.

Grandfather's tall and solid form appeared in the doorway. Whiskers and hair were trimmed to a nicety. A potent but agreeable odor of Barboline scented the air. We all rose. The old gentleman greeted us, took his seat in the rocker, bade us sit down, fitted his silver-framed spectacles firmly to the bridge of his nose, and reached for the book.

"We shall consider today some thoughts from Mr. Thomas Carlyle," he announced.

He settled himself to read. We settled ourselves to endure. Somehow the ordeal seemed more than usually irritating that afternoon. Not even the reader's enunciated periods, as he built up to a specially eloquent finale, moved us to anything but resentment.

Oh, does not every true man feel that he is, himself, made higher by doing reverence to what is really above him? No nobler or more blessed feeling dwells in man's heart. This is to me the living rock amid all rushings-down whatsoever—the one fixed point in modern revolutionary history, otherwise as if bottomless and shoreless.

He paused and let the book rest on his knee.

"I trust," he said, "that you take the meaning of our author."

At this point Grandma summoned the old gentleman to the kitchen to consult with "my man, Geordis." Rebellion broke out among us. Charlie gave the volume a contumelious shove.

"Why'n't he ever talk about somebuddy a fella ever heard of?" he blurted.

Reno supported this view. "Yeah. Who cares about those old roosters! What's the matter with America? I guess there's no flies on George Washington and Abraham Lincoln and James G. Blaine and—and . . ."

"Buffalo Bill," I put in.

"Moody and Sankey," said Jenny who had been caught up in the previous summer's revival.

"Sam Patch," Reno offered. The famous cataract jumper who had met an untimely death at our own Genesee Falls was still a local godling. Not to Jenny, however.

"Sam Patch drank," she said.

"I don't care if he did," her brother retorted. "His soul goes marching on."

"That's not Sam Patch," John objected. "That's John Brown's soul."

"Rats on John Brown's soul! You can have John Brown for your hero if you want him."

"I don't want him," John declared. "My hero's General Custer, the deathless warrior of the trackless plains."

"Deathless warrior, indeed!" Jenny sniffed. "You've been reading dime novels, John Adams."

"And how was old Custer so deathless with a coupla hundred Indian arrows through his gizzard?" Reno added.

"Gizzard isn't a nice word," Jenny snapped.

Futher bickering was checked by Grandfather's return.

"So you have been disputing over heroes," he said as he settled into the padded comfort of the rocker. "With, I may add, a regrettable lack of decorum."

We looked at one another in awkward silence.

"*Si monumentum requiris, circumspice,*" he continued mildly.

Our R.F.A. Latin was not up to this. "Well, never mind," he said after a pause. "It was merely a hint that while you are seeking a hero, you might look nearer home."

"Mr. Asa T. Soule?" I ventured.

"I had in mind a less conspicuous figure of whom I have spoken in connection with the great epidemic of 1832."

"You mean Simmy," Jenny said, her eyes ashine with romantic light. "The poor little man who died a heroic death taking care of the cholera patients."

"Hmm," returned Grandfather. "Heroic death? Not precisely. The lamentable fact is that Simmy fell into the canal while in liquor and was drowned. A poor, nameless roustabout, but nonetheless an authentic hero."

He went on to recount Simmy's deeds of valor at a time when panic swept the town and city officials deserted their posts to flee to the country. The little man was quite without fear, exposing himself to the dread contagion with total disregard for his own safety. By a miracle he escaped the disease.

"The only recognition that an ungrateful community accorded him," Grandfather said, "was to make him a deputy constable pro tem with a tin badge. Yet it is pleasant to know that he left behind him one enduring memory. . . . Is that someone coming up the path?"

Nobody was on the path. It was a trick to distract our attention from a minor feat of legerdemain on the old gentleman's part. When we turned our eyes back to him he had already raised the Carlyle volume to a reading position and was clearing his throat. A respectful hush followed. He pronounced impressively:

Those dim, unillumined figures of small renown and great deed, men of private valor, of obvert nobility, of a genius of the soul more profound, it well may be, than the loftiest attainments of the mind —what just estimate can mutable history make of them? Fare we now in our jewel-quest to that far, trans-Atlantic world. There rises from the distant fulgor of the past an all but nameless one, now inhumed beneath unmarked sod beside the stupendous lacuna which the genius of Governor Clinton forged across the breadth of the great Empire State of New York; the forgotten hero of the dread pestilence in which Death missed his most candescent mark.

"Wh-wh-why!" John stuttered in his excitement. "Governor Clinton! He must mean our canal."

"What else, indeed!" Grandfather said.

"And the hero of the pestilence—that's Simmy," Reno added.

We gazed with reverence at the book in his hand. The once detested Mr. Carlyle was grappled to our souls with hoops of steel. He had immortalized a citizen of our beloved Rochester.

Grandfather shifted the book to one hand while he extracted a handkerchief from his pocket and wiped his glasses. An oblong of pale blue writing paper fell from between the pages and fluttered to the floor. It was covered on both sides with a close-written script. John pounced upon it. He read disconnectedly the words that leapt to his eyes.

". . . . genius of the soul . . . mutable history . . . jewel-quest . . . stupendous lacuna . . . Is that what you were reading from, sir?"

"It is," the old gentleman replied blandly. "You may return it to me, John."

"Yes, sir," said John, looking slightly dazed.

"Grandpa," Jenny said excitely, "did Mr. Carlyle really write that about Simmy?"

"Have I ever stated in any way, form or manner that this is the work of Thomas Carlyle?"

"N-n-n-no, sir," said the puzzled girl. "But . . ."

"It sounds exactly like him," I said.

"I am pleased to have your endorsement, Samuel," Grandfather said. "As a matter of fact, I wrote it, myself."

We gaped at him.

"Great Gosh! What for?" John asked, finally.

"A little experiment, and, I am encouraged to believe, a successful one," the old gentleman smiled. "Are you familiar with the phrase, 'trying it on the dog'?"

"They do it with plays, don't they, sir?" John said.

"Yes, the phrase derives from the drama. To change the simile from stage to stable, you young folk have been trial horses. The result has been gratifying. The inimitable Mr. Carlyle is perhaps more imitable than the erudite Professor Glenn supposes."

"But what are you going to *do* with it, Grandpa?" Jenny's query was urgent.

Grandfather's left eyelid drooped in what may not have been a wink, but was certainly near to it. "It would make a very interesting relic if accidentally discovered and brought to the notice of the learned Circle," he remarked. His tone altered and became stern. "I impose upon all of you absolute secrecy in this matter. If anything leaks out, I shall know where to impute the blame and it will go hard with the offender."

Hastily and meekly we offered our assurances of silence. Grandfather's plan, whatever it might be, was, indeed, safe enough with us. None of us had any desire to rouse the grandfatherly wrath.

"Why, very well," he said, appeased by our earnestness. "I shall now make a visit to the Reynolds Library."

Folding the blue paper to fit into an envelope upon which he inscribed a few words, he tucked it into his breast pocket, bade me fetch his overcoat, and instructed Reno to have Horace G. hitched to the cutter. Away he drove, leaving us to whispered conjectures.

Nothing happened for ten days. Grandfather frowned down several timid attempts on our part to broach the subject of Thomas Carlyle. Then, one afternoon, he appeared at my father's study with a pleased smile upon his usually austere countenance.

"Myron," he said to Father, "have you ever considered becoming a member of the Carlylean Circle?"

"No, sir," Father replied. "I have too many other matters to keep me busy."

"Too bad," the old gentleman said slyly. "Too bad. This is their day of glory."

He went on to set forth the facts which were to develop into the literary sensation of the season. A senior from the University of Rochester, engaged in research at the Reynolds Library, had come upon a strange document halfway down a crack at the rear of the shelf which housed the complete works of Thomas Carlyle. It was a grimy and dusty envelope, inscribed in faded ink:

DO NOT OPEN UNTIL A.D. 1900.

(Signed) T. C.

The student took his find to the librarian who naturally opened the envelope at once. Within was a passage which the librarian read with protruding eyes. He was, himself, a member of the Circle and familiar with the Master's work. This was it. There could be no doubt about it. The style proclaimed in every line that here was a holograph from the immortal Thomas's own hand. The U. of R. student was astonished to hear the librarian utter a faint whoop.

Fifteen minutes later a messenger burst into Professor Glenn's classroom at the Rochester Free Academy with a momentous message. Dismissing his class without explanation,

the professor hurried over to the Reynolds Arcade and went
into conference with the librarian and the student. Within
an hour messengers were circulating through the city, sum-
moning all members of the Carlylean Circle to an emergency
meeting at 7.30 P.M. News of prime importance was forecast.

The meeting was a triumph. The Reynolds Library trove
was hailed as a historico-literary discovery of the first rank.
The local connection gave it special value and interest. The
Circle officially sponsored it and sent out reports to cultural
organizations of other cities on a note of patronizing self-
congratulation subsequently difficult to justify. Why or how
or when Rochester was thus favored, the fervent Carlyleans
did not pause to explain. Somehow the sage had chanced
upon the record of a forgotten Rochesterian of heroic pro-
portions, and this was the glorious result. Who knew but
that the famous Scot had even visited Rochester at some
time? That there was no record of any American visit mat-
tered nothing. Here was documentary evidence.

Where there was one document, there might be more.
Local residents were exhorted to search their premises for
further possible Carlyleana. The resultant treasure hunt was
prosecuted with a fervor which made a shambles of half the
attics in town.

The stimulus to local culture was immeasurable. Miss Ada
Kent contributed to the *North American Review* a titillating
article (returned with thanks) showing that Carlyle might
have been in Rochester in 1852, or, if not then, in 1863, or,
failing either of those dates, in 1871. Professor Glenn, in a
paper read at a special meeting, attributed the excerpt to a
lost chapter of *Heroes and Hero-Worship*. Lawyer Paris Clark
challenged this thesis and advanced the theory that the passage was from an unfinished volume on the United States.
Professor Burton of the University took issue with him, on
the ground that Carlyle disliked this country and would have
been unlikely to write a book about it.

A lady in Geneseo dug out an intricate cipher from *Latter Day Pamphlets*—cipher interpretations were much in vogue at the time—showing that the author *had* visited these shores, incognito, probably in 1860. A minor poet in Brighton composed a 600-word ode to the memory of the heroic Simmy which he attempted to read, without success, before the Circle. A spiritualist from Wampsville wrote that he was the reincarnation of Mr. Carlyle and would be glad to appear before the Carlyleans and explain all about the manuscript for his railroad fare.

Here and there a voice of scepticism was raised. It was drowned out in the acclaim of the great discovery. The membership of the circle doubled. A waiting list was started. The appointment of a special committee was announced with instructions to commission a portrait bust of Carlyle and submit plans for the building of a club house. Several babies, born that spring, were named for the Scotch philosopher. The *Post Express* boasted editorially that the cultural glories of Boston were dimmed and that Rochester was destined to become the literary center of the nation.

The bombshell exploded at the June meeting of the full Circle. It was delivered at the hands of Archie Cossett's father, himself a caustic Scot. Mr. Cossett had been one of the few sceptics in the membership and had narrowly escaped a vote of censure for the vigor with which he expressed his heretical opinions. Now he rose to address the chair, holding aloft a sheet of writing paper of a pale blue hue, familiar to every eye in the gathering. A buzz of excited anticipation passed through the assemblage.

"Mister-r-r Chairmon," he began, his burr accentuated by his own excitement. "I hov here a communication which I wish to pr-r-resent for the meeting's conside-r-r-ration."

"If there is no objection, you may proceed, Mr. Cossett," Professor Glenn, in the chair, said uneasily.

Mr. Cossett read: "Will the honorable body which sponsored the alleged Carlyle document, bearing in mind the date of Thomas Carlyle's death, 1881, explain the fact that the stationery of the document is of a type first issued in 1883, as can be verified at the Scrantom & Wetmore bookshop which carries it in stock?"

There followed a swelling murmur interspersed with calls of "Shame!" "Sit down!" "Put him out."

The chairman hammered for order. "Mr. Cossett," he said in a shaken voice, "have you verified this scandalous charge?"

"I hov so," the Scotchman replied. "It's true, every wor-r-r-rd of it."

A representative of Scrantom & Wetmore present, confirmed the recent date of the paper.

The meeting ran wild. Charges and countercharges filled the air. Professor Glenn was requested to resign his chairmanship. The session broke up in a welter of mutual recrimination. The organization, itself, did not long survive the event. Its membership dwindled and the Circle dissolved.

Grandfather never publicly admitted his part in the catastrophe. To us children, however, he disclaimed responsibility for the demise of the Circle. It would have come about anyway, he said. He was probably right. For there was already in process one of those swift and inexplicable changes of literary allegiance so typical of the era.

The philosopher, Thomas Carlyle, was supplanted in public esteem by the poet, Robert Browning. No longer did the intellectual avant garde go about intoning the Scotchman's sonorous pontifications. Instead, when two cognoscenti met, they assured one another that God's in his heaven, all's right with the world, or asked, in conscious solicitude, What porridge had John Keats?

Within a year, Grandfather had Carlyle practically to himself in Rochester.

A DEAL IN GEMS

Normally there was no better-controlled temper in Rochester than that of Grandfather Adams. Something dire must have happened to rouse it, we five visitors surmised as we paused on the stoop of the South Union Street cottage, listening fearfully to the burst of wrath that sounded from within.

"Low bridge. Everybody down," John warned. We huddled for consultation.

"A politicaster!" the wrathful voice boomed. "A jimber-jawed, vituperous, injurious politicaster!"

"Is politicaster a swear-word?" Charlie asked in an awed whisper.

"Grandpa *never* swears," said Jenny severely.

"Well, it sounds like it," Charlie insisted.

It did sound like it. There were other noises from the sitting room.

"He's pounding the table," John breathed.

"He's mad at something." Reno's interpretation seemed reasonable.

"Let's make a sneak," I suggested.

"We'd only have to come back again." Jenny pointed out an irrefutable fact. Our weekly visits were foreordained and mandatory.

John tiptoed forward and opened the door a cautious crack. From the kitchen came our step-grandmother's composed counsel.

"Don't fret yourself so, Mr. Adams. Take a swallow of your medicine. The children are here. Come in, children."

We entered and made our manners. Grandfather was sitting in his accustomed Boston rocker. Beside him on the stand was the amber bottle containing his favorite restorative. At his feet the editorial page of the Rochester *Democrat & Chronicle* lay, crumpled, John picked it up and smoothed it out.

"Throw it in the fire," Grandfather snapped.

Opening the door of the Franklin stove, John did so. Our step-grandmother's placid face appeared in the kitchen doorway.

"Never mind your grandfather, my dears," she said. "Anything that belittles his pet Erie Canal always puts him in a twidget."

A correspondent, signing himself "*Civitas*," had, it appeared, written a letter to the paper, stating his conviction that the canal was obsolete and should be filled in forthwith to make a roadway. Grandfather glared at the stove in which this wicked heresy was burning brightly.

"Foolishness never dies," he said. "Before De Witt Clinton's mighty project was half completed, the York State air was full of just such anti-canal huncamunca. Palmyra from whence this *Civitas* quill-pusher vents his spite, was even then a hotbed of contentiousness. In fact, a cabal was formed there." All of us knew something of our narrator's activities on the canal-building project operated by his elders. It was Charlie's fond belief that most of the excavation between

Rochester and Buffalo had been done by Grandfather's own capable hands.

"Did they try to stop you, Grandpa?" he asked.

"They did. We outwitted them prettily."

"How?" Reno said.

"Through certain mining operations."

"Oh, my!" from Jenny. "Gold-mining?"

"Not gold. Strategy," the old gentleman replied.

When the news of the Erie's coming first spread, he explained, most of the landholders along the route enthusiastically favored it. But there was a considerable opposition, partly political, partly economical, partly from the stiff-necked old fogy element which instinctively resented all progress. Of this latter type was Tod Jamison, a local obstructionist, whose sheep-run lay athwart the Adams contract for a hundred yards or more.

Such was the lay of the land, that a detour around the Jamison property would have involved an extra mile of excavation. Thus Tod was in a position to be troublesome, had he known of his advantage. He did not know. Nobody knew. For reasons of policy, the Adamses had kept not only the location but the very existence of their contract secret.

"I know," broke in Reno, the shrewd. "So's they wouldn't raise the price of the land on you."

"Precisely," Grandfather said with an approving smile.

That was the year, he continued, that the large, red gem was found in a split rock at the fork of Ganargwa Creek after the ice went out. Eighteen-nineteen, was it: No, 1820. There was quite a to-do over it. Otherwise sensible people went bogueing about the country (at night mostly so that others would not find out what they were up to and get ahead of them) cracking open stones with sledges and now and then coming upon something. The learned Dr. Josiah Noyes, Professor of Mineralogy at Hamilton College, came down to investigate and stayed at the Adams homestead in East Bloomfield, a few miles from Palmyra.

His presence there was a turn of luck for the Adamses. He was an ardent Clintonian and canal advocate. So, when he learned of the opposition in Palmyra, he readily fell in with the plan which Deacon Adams and his son, Myron, had been maturing. He even added a few embellishments of his own devising.

Grandfather proceeded to draw for us a word-picture of Silas Bewar's smithy on Main Street, which was the unofficial town forum in the days when Palmyra was a self-contained, self-contented community, aloof from the principal lines of traffic, with the Erie Canal still no more than a distant portent on the far eastern horizon. To the smithy Grandfather escorted Dr. Noyes and presented him to the assemblage.

A dozen solid citizens were disposed upon chairs, benches and kegheads, watching the smith fashion a beetle-ring. A heavy-shouldered work-dog who might have been a Newfoundland had not several other strains intervened, panted upon the treadmill which filled the bellows and kept the forge-fires glowing. From time to time he whimpered in boredom. The smith admonished him: "Hush thy clamor, Demetrius, or thee will get no bone for thy supper."

At the moment of the newcomers' entry, Tod Jamison was inveighing against the hated "canawl." Grandfather described him as "a gross and bumptious ignoramous, bloated with rum and speaking with the voice of a thunderpump in a bog; burble-bloomp! burble-bloomp! burble-bloomp!" It was a creditable imitation of a swamp-bittern.

As the orator came to an end, Grandfather continued, Decker Jessup, the cobbler, (Bespoken Boots and Shoes; Free Fittings) spoke up. "Well, neighbors, like it or lump it, she's a-coming. The Grand Western Canal's a-coming."

"So's Christmas," Carlisle Sneed, the tinker, sniggered. He was the recognized humorist of the village and could be relied upon for a risible contribution to any conversation.

"Who says the canal is coming?" the proprietor of the general merchandise store demanded. (T. Lay; Buys Dear— Sells Cheap.)

"The Honorable De Witt Clinton," answered Stonefront Sarcy, so-called from the architectural elegance of his emporium. "And I guess he knows."

"De Witt Clinton don't know enough to stamp dirt into a rat-hole," Lawyer Upcraft growled. (Ephraim Upcraft— Legal Advice—Testaments, Mortgages, and Indentures— Uncurrent Notes Bought & Sold.)

The slur exasperated L. St. John of the Eagle Tavern. (Superior Accommodation for Man & Bestial.) "Clinton is an honest man," he averred. "That's more than can be said for some note-shavers hereabouts." He had lately purchased some red-dog notes from the Upcraft collection which had proved permanently uncurrent by reason of the issuing bank's collapse.

Silas Bewar interposed. He was a Quaker and a lover of peace. "Contentious speech makes ill-friends," he pointed out.

"What do we want with a canal, anyway?" This was Orlen Barnes of the rope-walk. "It'll cost money."

"It'll fetch trade," a little man in a bright bandanna neckcloth (Cassius Moore, Greengrocer—Live and Let Live) suggested.

"And circulate specie. That's what this town needs," asserted Daniel Heyl of the Literary Lottery. (Fortune Smiles on All at Heyl's.)

"It'll fatten every weaselskin in the county," the tavernkeeper confirmed.

"Not mine," Jed Parris, the six-horse coachee growled. "What happens to the merry turnpikes if travel quits dry land and takes to chancy water?"

"You can turn fish, old Breakbones, and tow a hawser in your teeth," the whimwhamsical Mr. Sneed proffered.

"Don't harstle yourself over it, Jed," the lawyer advised. "Up Rome way where the canal is finished, they say it's not boatable at all by reason of leakage."

"Being an Oneida County man, thee might have a word to say to that, Friend Professor," Silas Bewar said, turning to Dr. Noyes.

"Why, yes," the professor said. "I can answer for the Erie being boatable from Utica to Salinas, having, myself, traversed it last week in a packet of thirty tons, sixty feet long and drawn by three swift horses at four miles per hour."

There were exclamations of surprise and admiration, mingled with murmurs of disbelief. The ropemaker said incredulously, "But you don't think it will ever get this far, do you?"

"In my belief, it will span the state."

Ephraim Upcraft wagged a monitory finger beneath the scholar's nose. "You are dream-struck, sir. How is it to surmount the hills? How is it to cross the great marshes and the violent rivers? Hark ye here, Schoolmaster," he accosted a weedy young fellow near the door. "This gentleman claims that Clinton's Ditch will cross York State."

Parmalee Jones smiled in a superior manner. The school trustees had recently improved his wages from twenty bushels of wheat per month to ten dollars cash, thereby giving him an unwarranted estimate of himself. "I can prove him wrong by the system of physics," he said.

"So do," L. St. John challenged him. "I'd admire to hear it."

The pedagogue addressed the stranger. "Lake Erie to Hudson's River; such is old Clinton's project, I believe."

"It is."

"The Lake is higher than the river by a considerable measure."

"Five hundred feet," the other confirmed.

"Then, since water flows downhill, all the contents of the canal will discharge into the river and be dissipated in the depths of the Atlantic Ocean. Q.E.D.," he concluded and gazed about him for approval.

"Have you ever heard of locks?" Dr. Noyes asked mildly.

"*I* have." The answer came from the proprietor of the Canandaigua Street Human Hair Dispensary. (Arjalus Cady —Wigs, Toupees, Frizzes, & Ringlets for Ladies & Gentlemen.) "There is a canal in France with more than a hundred of 'em. I have read it in print." He was a book-learned man.

"If the Frenchies can do it, stands to reason we can," Daniel Heyl declared. "Huzza for the American eagle!"

"You'll huzza out of the other side of your big mouth if the canal ever gets here," T. Lay growled. "By what I hear, it brings naught but ill with it; rats and snakes; chintzes and moschettoes."

"Chills and ague and the fever-shakes," the coachee added.

"And the wild Irish to overrun the land and murder us in our beds," Parmalee Jones contributed.

"You will live to welcome them," the professor said. "Those same wild Irish are prime diggers and free spenders, as they can well afford at a dollar a day."

"A dollar a day!" the schoolmaster repeated in a squeak of resentment. "And I teach puling abecedarians for a third of that wage."

"Buy yourself a shovel and do some honest work for once in your life, Parm," Carlisle Sneed advised. He cut a caper.

"Canal fly east,
Canal fly west,
Canal fly over the cuckoo's nest . . ."

he chanted. "Either way I don't see as it puts an extra bawbee into my chicken account." He raised fowls as a side issue to tinkering.

"You are wrong, sir," the professor said. "The Grand Erie confers prosperity upon one and all. Land which it penetrates enhances in value. Merchants along the route profit by the high-waged diggers. Tools and machines must be purchased for the work. Contractors pay handsome prices to feed their labor. You will yet see ten-cent beef, fifteen-cent butter, and eggs at a shilling a dozen."

"Eight cents a dozen I touch for my eggs, and say thankee," the humorist said. "Mister," he added earnestly, "if eggs ever goes to a cent apiece, I'll go home and kiss a hen."

"I'm betting on the canal," the tavern keeper cried. "This town needs a good stirring up and Clinton's Big Ditch is the ladle to stir it with. Once the boats run, the dollars will come a-rolling in. Palmyra will outgrow Rochester and be as big as Canandaigua, I wouldn't wonder. Hallelujah-day is coming. Mrs. St. John's pianoforte will wear silk pants on its legs and we'll all be millionaire-men."

"You're exalted in the head," Lawyer Upcraft snapped. "It'll never reach here. I'll stop it, myself. I'll take it up to the Supreme Court."

"What's your grief on the canal, Mr. Upcraft?" the wigmaker asked.

"Anything that the scoundrelly Clinton is for, I am against."

"There's political principle for you!" Daniel Heyl gibed. "No more gumption than a mudchunker under a colic-root."

"Don't you miscall me, you ingling gamester!" the lawyer warned.

Everybody began to shout. Politics, prophecies and recriminations crossed in the smoky air.

". . . best thing for the town" . . . "bankruptcy and ruination" . . . "Palmyry forever!" . . . "taxes, taxes, taxes" . . . "when water runs uphill" . . . "live to see it" . . . "the law courts will have a say" . . . "five dollars a ton? Hunca-munca!" . . . "chatter like a clape" . . . "button your own lip" . . . "dummock" . . . "pack o' scrimshankers" . . . "Federalist muckworm!" . . . "poxy Democrat!" . . . "drop that forge-bar."

"Pax! Pax!" Silas Bewar's mighty voice quelled the tumult. "Is this a smithy or a rostrum for windy parmateers? Take thy factious bickerings out into the highway if thee must argufy. Medad Pomeroy must still have his beetle-ring and who is to ply the metal if I hifer here listening to thy silly whoobub?" He set aside the finished forging and addressed the work-dog. "Up, friend Demetrius! Our fire sinks low."

The sleepy-eyed mongrel lumbered to his feet, yawned, stretched, and cast a resentful glance at the treadmill. Whining, he crawled up onto the moveable strip. The machinery clacked. The bellows puffed. The forge glared red. The smith grasped tongs and hammer. Canal or no canal, man and dog must toil.

The debate was resumed in a more modest tone, from the economic viewpoint.

"Who's to pay for all these pribbles and prabbles?" T. Lay demanded. "I'd be obliged for an answer to that."

"You are," Orlen Barnes said bitterly. "I am. We all are. Taxes, taxes, taxes. All for bobbery that nobody wants."

"Perhaps thee can tell me, Friend Josiah, what the cost of this enterprise will be," the smith suggested.

"It will not be cheap," the professor admitted.

The humorous Mr. Sneed clutched himself across the breast. "Say it slow and say it low," he besought. "I have a limsy heart. What's the tally?"

"Six million dollars."

An awed hush followed the shocking statement. It was broken by the smith.

"It is a great sum," he said soberly. "I misdoubt that it could be availed."

"The Honorables, the Canal Commissioners hold that it
will pay for itself in time."

"Clintonian quacksalvery!" Lawyer Upcraft barked. "How
can it pay for itself?"

"Freight and passenger tolls."

"There you have it!" Orlen Barnes cried. "They tax us and
then they toll us. The country is going to perdition."

Tod Jamison, who had been silent for an unusually long
time lifted a dogged voice.

"Not a taxable stiver do they get out of me for their poxy
canawl."

Carlisle Sneed winked elaborately at the company, con-
veying that he was about to convulse them with his spe-
cialty. "Better learn your merinos to swim, Tod Jamison," he
said.

"What's a sheep want to swim for?" the wool-grower
growled.

"Or jump like a frawg," the humorist amended.

"Jump what?"

"Two rod and better of dirty canawl water. It's going to
spang through your holdings. I've seen the maps."

Glances of uncertainty passed among Grandfather's
hearers. Reno blurted out, "How could he have seen the
maps? You said it was all secret, sir."

"So it was. Your objection evidences discernment, Sireno.
Carlisle Sneed had seen no map. He was practicing a form of
hoodwinkery which, in the reprehensible game of draw
foxes, is known as a bluff."

Tod Jamison took it sorely, the old gentleman proceeded.
He turned red as a tom-turkey's wattles. He pounded his
fist upon a barrelhead until it boomed like a drum.

"I got a musket," he shouted. "I got powder—du Pont's
best. I got ball. I got my free-born American rights. The first
ditcher thrusts spade into my soil, I'll load his gizzard with

lead, was it the whole be-dotched Canal Commission their scurvy selves."

"So do, so do," Lawyer Upcraft cried in warm approval. "I will defend your action up to the Supreme Court, if need be." He adjusted his gray castor to his balding head and stalked out.

He did not hear Professor Noyes say in mild tones: "Violent measures are uncalled for. Surely some composition can be reached otherwise."

"Tod is a hard nut to crack, Professor," the lottery man put in. "What's your notion?"

The mineralogist drew a sizeable rock from his pocket and advanced to the forge. "Will you oblige me with the use of a hammer, sir?" he said courteously to the smith.

Silas Bewar handed him the tool. A shrewd blow laid open the stone. Glints of red fire sparkled in its interior.

Carlisle Sneed leaned forward, his eyes bulging. "Rubies, by cremany!" he ejaculated. "Whereja find it?"

"At the foot of Van Altemer's Nose," the other answered. This was the name given locally to one of the rugged hillocks bordering Ganargwa Creek.

"Huh? What's that? The Nose is on my proputty," Tod Jamison said.

The mineralogist held up the rock to his view. "You would be well advised to protect your interests in that property, sir," he said.

Tod squinted at the sparkling surface. "What might this be wuth, Mister?" he asked.

"Nothing. The stones are too small to be merchantable. Other and more valuable deposits may lie on your land, however. Such as this." He touched the glowing carbuncle in his neckcloth.

"Did that come from hereabouts?" the shepherd asked hoarsely.

"It did."

"And the like of it is on my proputty?"

"It may well be so."

"How'll I find out?"

"That, sir, is matter for an expert."

"Be you one?"

"I may fairly make that claim."

"What's your hire?"

"My services are at your disposal, Mr. Jamison. But not for hire. Are you open to a proposal?"

"Guess I might be," Tod answered cautiously.

"Very well. In conjunction with my young friend, Myron Adams, whom you all know to be a citizen of probity and enterprise, I offer you a contractual agreement."

At this point of the narrative Grandfather broke off to take from his pocket a key. "Fetch me my ort-book from the cabinet, John," he directed.

The bulbous scrapbook in which the old gentleman kept his memorabilia was brought and set upon the stand. Profiting by the interruption, Jenny gave voice to misgivings.

"Were there really rubies there, Grandpa?"

"Certes there were rubies," he assured her.

"Real rubies?" she said incredulously.

"York State rubies. Some call them garnets."

"Worth real money?" she persisted.

"Dr. Noyes's neckpin was valued at ten dollars. Ten dollars was real money in those days. Still is."

"How did they get there?" Reno inquired.

"The garnets? I don't know. Nobody knows. But there they were, imbedded in the solid rock for anybody to discover. And here"—he turned the pages of the ort-book—"is a true copy of the contract between Todhunter Jamison, party of the first part, and Noyes & Adams, parties of the second part, to explore for them."

He read the document. It set forth that, in consideration of fifty dollars, legal tender, paid in advance, and a fifty per centum share in any and all gems, jewels and precious stones or metals exhumed from the Jamison property, the owner thereof gave to the parties of the second part exclusive rights to dig, delve, mine, sap, burrow, trench, tunnel and excavate, and to traverse said property by wagon, sledge, barrow, boat, or drag without let or hindrance in furtherance of their prescribed occasions.

Reno, our budding business genius, cocked a knowing head at the contract. "Did Tod Jamison sign his name to that, sir?"

"Tod Jamison," Grandfather answered, "was an unlettered oaf who could not print his name in charcoal on a limed wall. He signed with an X mark, witnessed to by T. Lay and Arjalus Cady. Next day the mining and prospecting firm of Noyes and Adams started work with ten mechanics, presently increased to forty. By the time that Tod got back . . ."

"Back from where, sir?" John ventured to interrupt.

"Albany. Exalted by the possession of so great a sum as fifty dollars, he coached to that licentious city and spent every cent of it in a month of protracted and liquorous kantikoy."

"And you dug for the rubies, sir?" I asked.

"We mined, as per contract, Samuel."

"How many did you find?" This from Jenny.

He referred to the book. "Precisely thirty-two dollars worth. Here is the entry."

"You couldn't have dug very hard," she commented disparagingly.

"Never were you more mistaken," he rejoined earnestly. "Our mechanics labored like Titans. In that month we traversed the Jamison property with a channel forty feet wide and four feet deep."

"Forty by four," John repeated. He had a memory for detail. "Wasn't that the contract size of the Erie Canal, sir?"

The old gentleman's eyes twinkled. "By a curious coincidence, it was, John."

"And you were really digging the canal all the time," Jenny said reproachfully. "How could you play such a mean trick on the poor man!"

"No trick at all," the old gentleman retorted. "We were digging, delving, mining, sapping, et cetera strictly within the terms of the Todhunter Jamison contract. That the Honorables, the Canal Commissioners officially approbated our achievement when completed, may be regarded as a gratifying fortuity."

"I'll bet Mr. Jamison was mad," I said.

"He exhibited symptoms of discomposure," Grandfather confirmed.

"Did he shoot a Commissioner?" Jenny asked apprehensively.

"No. His indignation subsided when wool and mutton prices began to rise. He made so much money from his sheep that he forgot the rubies. In fact, he so far forgot his ambition against the canal, itself, that I sold him Erie stock in the sum of five hundred dollars upon which he gratefully drew six per centum to the day of his death."

Grandfather Adams set aside his ort-book. "A petition was circulated by Lawyer Upcraft, opposing the canal," he said. "It was signed by every makebate, dawplucker and malcontent in the neighborhood."

"It didn't do any good, did it?" I asked.

"It did no harm, certes. Nothing could stop the progress of the Grand Western Canal."

"Did it really cost six million dollars?" Reno, who was our financial expert, asked.

"Seven," Grandfather answered.

"Geewhillikins!" Reno exclaimed. "Was it ever paid off?"

"Down to the last bawbee. In less than ten years."

"I s'pose everybody in Palmyra got rich," Jenny said, "just like the stories in the *Youth's Companion*."

"The town enjoyed what is now called a boom," Grandfather replied.

"But it never caught up with Rochester," John said jealously. He was an upholder of local pride and prestige.

"No," Grandfather agreed. "It never quite did that."

Young Charlie, unconcerned with commercial details, pursued his own line of interest.

"Did Mr. Sneed kiss his hen?" he inquired.

"If he did not, Charles," the old gentleman answered, "he was guilty of gross ingratitude. Before our contract was finished, I was paying him fourteen cents a dozen for his eggs."

GRANDFATHER STORIES

by Samuel Hopkins Adams

A REVIEW BY JOHN P. MARQUAND
Reprinted from the Book-of-the-Month Club News

Grandfather Stories can easily stand among the rarest of literary events, for a series of circumstances that can hardly be duplicated came into perfect combination before such three-dimensional living history could be written. First off, its author had to be the possessor of two grandfathers both alive and active in his youth—one of them a nonagenarian, still sprightly, with a fine memory, a love of reminiscence and a lively past. Next, the author himself had to be a highly experienced writer, also well along in years and yet with a mind that was utterly uncalcified—one who had not lost an iota of his skill or his God-given gift of total recall. Through fate and fortune, Samuel

Hopkins Adams, with his distinguished literary career, is surely the only living American who can fill these specifications. *Grandfather Stories* is more than a literary curiosity. It is a kind of legerdemain that simultaneously re-creates the heyday of the Erie Canal, with its overtones of the old frontier and pre-Civil War folkways, and, besides, Mr. Adams' own American boyhood in the 1870s. His narrative, also, because of its complete unselfconsciousness, attains the stature of an American saga, though this may be a term too portentous to apply to such a universally entertaining book.

In the 1870s and '80s, usually in the winter and spring, the five young grandchildren of old Mr. Myron Adams, among them Sam, were obliged to pay their grandfather regular courtesy visits in his small but comfortable dwelling in Rochester, New York. In their early years, the children were appalled by this ordeal. The house was decorated in a lugubrious Calvinist manner, with prints of weeping willows and tombstones. Its most interesting mural item, to the children, was a certificate of membership in an anti-horse-thief society; it was something, the children thought in their ignorance, to have a grandfather who was a horse thief! Grandfather Myron himself was as formidable as his background. He was, to young Sam, almost entirely a beard from which issued a gruff voice that delivered, in archaic English, homilies on the behavior of the young. Beside him stood a bottle of patent medicine known as Hop Bitters, from which he helped himself at intervals during their conversations. It was only when the old man discovered that the children were convinced he

had actually once been a professional horse thief that the ice was broken and young Sam entered into a wonderful bygone world which his readers may now share with him.

Myron Adams had been born at the end of the 18th century and had never lost all the attributes of an American Federalist. His vocabulary was Johnsonian. He always disliked the steam cars. His fondest memories ran back to the early days of the Erie Canal, and his grandson, Sam, has brought those recollections of The Big Ditch back to us with the definition of newly minted coins. As a youth Myron Adams had pulled stumps when the Canal was being dug. He had lived through fearsome gales and blizzards; he had managed the business affairs of a traveling circus; he knew the man in Troy, New York, whose wife invented the linen collar. Grandfather Adams in his later years would have no truck with a young man named George Eastman who had invented a button picture box in Rochester—because he had been exposed to the bunkum of many con artists in the great days of the Canal, including a pair who had invented a machine for killing bedbugs. In fact, old Myron Adams had been exposed to

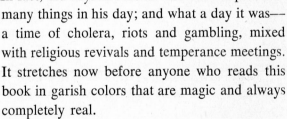

many things in his day; and what a day it was— a time of cholera, riots and gambling, mixed with religious revivals and temperance meetings. It stretches now before anyone who reads this book in garish colors that are magic and always completely real.

One becomes increasingly intrigued by the wealth of rich detail, such as the time when Grandfather, while selling circus tickets, was offered a Tuscarora scalp in lieu of hard money. The vividness of all this reminiscence is what makes this book remarkable. It progresses and grows from page to page so perfectly that one begins to seek the reasons for such an achievement. Excellent writing is part of the answer, for Samuel Hopkins Adams is a master of the form that lies somewhere between the short story and the anecdote. But good writing alone does not wholly explain the vitality of *Grandfather Stories*. The true secret of its success lies in the man who wrote it. The unconquerable spirit of Sam Adams is inherent in his work, and his trained observation is always tempered by his irrepressible humor, his gentleness and his human understanding. It will be many years before another such book can be written, and until then this one will stand by itself in many ways, a masterpiece in the art of reminiscence.

BOOK-OF-THE-MONTH CLUB, INC.
345 Hudson Street, New York 14, N. Y.

SAM PATCH'S
FEARSOME LEAP

It was Grandfather's eighty-second birthday. The grandchildren were gathered at the South Union Street cottage to do him honor. There were scalloped oysters, potato chips, lemonade, and three kinds of pie, pumpkin, mince and pieplant. For this was, on a modest scale, what the old gentleman called a "gala."

He sat in his favorite Boston rocker, with his ort-book open on his lap. Within were pasted the memorabilia of a long life ranging from printed rewards, offered by the Wayne County Horse-thief Society, of which he had been a distinguished member, to announcements of meetings of the Philopeuthean Society of Hamilton College, of which he had been a somewhat less distinguished member. In such reminiscent mood as was likely to beset him on anniversaries, he would refresh his memory by dipping into the oversized volume. Now he said musingly: "Joseph B. Gregg. *Anno domini* 1829. Wasn't that the year? Yes, of course it was."

"The year of what, sir?" John asked obligingly.

"The year the Grand Western Canal sprung a leak at Pilgrimport."

The name was vaguely familiar. I repeated it. "Is that up around Lyons?" I asked.

"That which once was, now is not," the old gentleman said somberly. "The pilgrims, long since departed, are forgotten. The Erie abandoned that once prospering town and it died."

"Did the canal leak away from it, Grandpa?" young Charlie asked.

"No. The Honorables, the Canal Commissioners ordained in their wisdom that the line should be straightened. The leak had nothing to do with it."

"Betcha it wasn't in *our* part of the canal, anyway," Reno said confidently. We of our generation maintained a proprietary and hereditary pride in our ancestral workmanship.

"Betting is an unworthy practice," Grandfather rebuked him. "However, Sireno, you are correct in your assumption. The Adams contracts held water."

"Maybe the pilgrims didn't know how to build canals," Charlie suggested.

"The pilgrims were not canal-builders. They were gooseherds. I was there buying goosedown the day the leak started."

The breach was very annoying to him, he explained, because he had planned to boat it to Rochester. Now he must change his schedule.

"But for that mischance, however," he added, "I might not have met the puke."

At the word Jenny gave so ladylike a start that some of the lemonade spilled over her shirtwaist.

"Why, Grandfather!" she protested faintly.

John, our inquiring mind, asked, "What's a puke, sir?"

"A puke," Grandfather said, "is an inhabitant of Missouri. This one made no bones of it. I had walked out along the canal berm to see for myself how low the water was, when I came upon him sitting there. We greeted each other, and he said, 'My name is Bulimy Joe Gregg. I'm a puke from Missouri, and I don't care who knows it.'"

"But what does it *mean?*" John persisted.

"I don't know. Nobody knows," Grandfather replied. "Now, everybody is aware that Tennesseans are rightfully termed mudheads, but if you apply that name to a man from Tennessee, he is likely to squale his walking stick at your jaw, whereas a Missourian puffs up with pride in terming himself a puke. All Missourians are braghards."

"What was the Missourian doing so far from home?" Jenny asked.

"At the moment, he was sniggling for eels," the old gentleman replied. "He sat on the berm and beat his arms for warmth, and his language was forbidding. The water was getting lower every moment, and he did not like it. 'What ails your dratted little river?' he said to me. 'It's dreening off.' I informed him that it was no river, but the Grand Erie Canal. 'Well, it's running down,' he said. 'Streams don't run down where I come from.' He then asserted that if the minikin little dribble that I called a canal were dropped into the Big Muddy—he meant the Missouri River—it wouldn't even leave a dirty streak. He added that any true puke could lick three times his weight in bobcats and five in dandiprat York Staters, and asked what was I going to do about it."

"Why did he want to fight you?" Reno asked.

"Missourians are always spoiling for a fight," said Grandfather. "I told him he might better mind his line—there was a fish on it. He pulled in a five-inch stickleback and pricked his thumb on the horn, and his language was worse than before. After he had calmed down, he wanted to know when the Erie would be boatable. I told him that since it was November, and near the close of the season, there would probably be no navigation till spring. He looked glum and asked how he was to get to Rochester. 'Coach it,' I said, and informed him that I had decided to do the same, as I was planning to attend the great spectacle there."

"What spectacle?" Charlie asked. "The circus?"

"More notorious than any circus," replied Grandfather. "Sam Patch. He had been bridge-jumping and cataract-leaping for money in any town that would pay for it. Everyone thereabouts was talking of him. He proposed to leap the Upper Falls of the Genesee from top to bottom the next day. My new acquaintance had heard of Sam, and he said he ambitioned to see the fearless leap."

Jenny's mind was elsewhere. "What did he look like?" she asked dreamily.

"Sam Patch? A meager, wizened, inconsiderable little hoddy-doddy," said Grandfather.

"I mean the gentleman from Missouri," Jenny said.

"Oh! He was a fine, upstanding blade," Grandfather answered. "Very vigorous for a man who would never see thirty-five again, and with a stout opinion of himself, for no better reason than that he was from Missouri. In his conviction, a Missourian could do anything that any man could do, and do it better. 'What of these falls of yours?' he asked. 'I'll warrant they're no great shakes.' 'They may not be Niagara,' I told him, 'but one hundred sheer feet from top to bottom is not to be sneezed at.' 'Pooh!' he said. 'Our maize-corn grows that high in Missouri. How much will this Patch get for making the leap?' There would be a collection, I told him, in the taverns and taprooms. I guessed that it would run fifty dollars upward. 'Fifty sweet dibs!' he said. 'I'd jump off a belfry into a horse trough for that! Let's go look at these pistareen falls of yours.'"

Grandfather was not pleased to hear Rochester's grandest sight spoken of in terms of a deteriorated twenty-cent piece, but he passed it over and invited the Missourian to accompany him. The man agreed, and they took the Champion Line coach to Rochester, where they repaired to the Exchange Hotel to engage quarters. Every room had been taken by the advance crowd.

"We were lucky to find standee," the old gentleman said, and, seeing our puzzled looks, explained. " 'Standee' was the privilege of occupying one's length on the floor of the taproom or the hallway. Sixpence was the proper charge, but the innkeeper mulcted us of a shilling apiece. We had to pay it. It was standee or the open street for us. We located our spaces on the taproom floor, and my new friend chalked his name in his with a flourish—'Bulimy Joe Gregg from Missouri.' "

"Bulimy?" Reno repeated. "What does that mean, sir?"

It meant, Grandfather said, a ravening appetite, and he added that Joe Gregg claimed to have earned it by devouring a whole buffalo hump at one sitting.

"Whatever the merits of his claim," Grandfather concluded cautiously, "I never saw the man who could deal more powerfully with a two-bit, sixteen-dish dinner. The Exchange Hotel made no profit on *him*."

After dinner, Grandfather went on, Joe suggested that they have a look at the hero of the occasion. They learned that Mr. Patch was making the rounds of the barrooms, taking up his collection and cadging drinks from his admirers, and after a brief search they ran him to earth in Bement's Recess, where he was eating pickled oysters and apple slump, and drinking kill-divvle, a popular heartener of the day.

"He was a pawky young scrawn, puffed up with vainglory but plainly nervous," Grandfather said. "His bear was dozing in a corner."

"Bear?" cried Charlie eagerly. "Did he have a bear? What for?"

Grandfather explained that Patch had a bear specially trained and that after Patch jumped, another collection was customarily taken up, and then the bear also made the leap.

"Cracky!" said Charlie. "I'd rather have seen the bear."

After a third round of lemonade had been poured, Grandfather dipped again into the ancient scrapbook and gave us a brief biography of Sam Patch.

Patch, born in Pawtucket, Rhode Island, in 1807, was a mill boy and then a weaver. As a lad, he became adept at the popular local sport of plunging from bridges or high buildings into the Seekonk River at Pawtucket. That this accomplishment could be put to commercial use was not brought home to him until he moved to Paterson, New Jersey, in pursuit of his trade as weaver. There, after several purely amateur leaps, he was invited to perform at an Independence Day celebration, and received a fee. Perceiving that this was an easier way of livelihood than a sunrise-to-sunset schedule at his loom, he became a professional, exhibiting his skill at water-side fairs and celebrations. He devised a slogan for himself (Grandfather pronounced it "slo-*gan*," after the Indian fashion), which attained to national usage: "Some things can be done as well as others."

When Patch came to Rochester on the occasion in question, he had already made descents of eighty feet into the Niagara River and one hundred into the Genesee. This performance, however, was to be a still greater achievement, and the platform built for it was one hundred and twenty-odd feet above the pool below the falls.

Grandfather put his scrapbook down within easy reach and proceeded with his story. He said that the Missourian, after examining young Patch with a disparaging eye, went up to him and expressed the belief that he would never meet his engagement the next day. It was evident that Sam had already had enough to drink, but now he took another gulp.

"Why not?" he quavered.

"I guess you don't know what day tomorrow is," the Missourian said.

Sam fell back upon his slogan.

"Some things can be done as well as others," he declaimed, but without conviction.

"Not on Friday," Gregg retorted. "And not on the thirteenth. And tomorrow," he intoned ominously, "is Friday, the thirteenth."

At this point, Grandfather told us, he decided to go back to the taproom of the Exchange Hotel and get some sleep, but Gregg sat down at Sam Patch's table and began filling his ear with depressing predictions. At midnight, the Missourian returned to the taproom, and Grandfather awoke as he sat down in the space beside him.

"I've fixed that young buck's flint," Gregg boasted.

Grandfather was puzzled. "What are you trying to do?" he asked. "Boggle tomorrow's performance?"

Gregg chuckled. "I've tucked him in his bed and sung him to sleep with the Indian death song," he said, and raised his voice in the lament—a series of wails that brought angry protests from the other men on the floor. "He was snivelling like a scairt baby when I left."

"I still do not take your meaning," Grandfather said. "How will it advantage you to frighten the poor fellow out of his wits?"

"Listen!" Gregg returned. "I'm a fast man with my clacker. I've been on the theatrical stage, I have. I've trod the boards with Lafayette Stepanfetchit and with Buffalo Dixon. Let me get my gab in with the crowd at the falls tomorrow and I'll talk that cheap jobbermow right out of his trick and that purse right into my pants pocket. Fifty sweet dibs!"

"I suppose you'll make the jump yourself," Grandfather said scornfully.

The Missourian winked. "Maybe I will and maybe I won't,"

he said. "That ain't figgered out yet." Then he set his carpet-bag for a pillow, spread his greatcoat for cover, and was off to sleep at once.

By virtue of an early start the next morning, Grandfather and his Missourian found places for themselves on Brown's Island, an artificial islet carved out of the west shore of the Genesee at the brink of the Upper Falls in the excavation of Brown's Millrace. It was shaped like a slightly curved and rather thick finger, and was bare except for four well-grown trees and the platform from which Patch was to jump. This scaffoldlike structure, rising more than twenty feet above the ground, was at the very tip of the finger. It was made of raw boards, and had a railing that was open at the front, over the falls. It was decked with insufficient strips of bunting, which, in Grandfather's opinion, gave it a scabrous aspect. He told us that it had seemed to him to be actually leaning over the smooth curve of the great cataract.

The day was raw, rainy, and dispiriting. From a staff at one corner, the national flag flapped wetly in the November gusts. One hundred and twenty-odd feet below the platform, the deep pool at the foot of the falls eddied and foamed.

From this vantage point, Grandfather could see the strands on both sides of the river filling up with spectators. Some of the more adventurous spirits clung like bees to the scarps and ledges of the precipitous cliffs. Upriver, the mill roofs were black with human clusters, and traffic was clogged on the Buffalo Street Bridge. Newcomers were arriving steadily, for the event had been widely forecast in the press, and excursion schooners from lake ports as far away as Canada had been bringing in their quotas since the previous day. Even Bulimy Joe was impressed, though he took occasion to assert that he had seen just as many folks at a fur traders' rendez-vous on the prairie.

Half of Rochester was present. The fashionable Corin-

thians of the "ruffleshirt" Third Ward were out in force,
elegant with beaver castors, Taglioni greatcoats, and beribboned and beleaded canes—Everard Peck, Fabricius Reynolds, Hamlet Scrantom, Parliament Black, and others of
Grandfather's familiars, with whom he had played the newly
popular game of baseball in Mumford's pasture lot. There
was also a contingent of the tough element from the canal
basins and the river front. Ladies minced about, finified in
their gala best. Grandfather saw more than one Paisley shawl
that could not have cost less than twenty dollars. Several
officials, journalists and other prominent citizens occupied
favored places on the platform itself.

A cheer was raised as Sam Patch wormed his way through
the crowd, followed by his manager, and mounted to the
platform. He was dressed in a close-fitting white outfit—
"Fadged to the skin," was Grandfather's description. His face
was splotched from drink. His eyes and lips twitched. He
peered nervously over the edge of the chasm at the surface of
the river, which, when the eye glimpsed it through scurrying
blobs of wind-tossed vapor, looked a mile down.

Patch fell to pacing back and forth, flapping his arms
against the chill. His manager circulated among the spectators, taking up a final collection in his hat. When he reached
the spot where Grandfather and his companion stood, the
Missourian held up a silver piece and shouted, "Two bits
to help bury the poor looby."

Sam heard. He looked down at Bulimy Joe with a forced
grin. The manager climbed to the platform and, while Patch
counted the money in the hat, made his announcement.

"At two P.M. precisely, Mr. Patch will fearlessly make his
fearsome leap of one hundred and twenty feet into the yawning abyss. At three o'clock precisely, his bear will make the
same jump."

The bear was led forward, made a bow, lumbered to the
edge of the platform, and whimpered unhappily at the void.

Two o'clock sounded from a church tower. Sam Patch un-
wound a black silk handkerchief from the platform railing
and fastened it about his loins. He straightened up, struck a
pose, and spoke to the gathering. His address, which Grandfather read to us from a clipping in the scrapbook, was brief:

Napoleon was a great man and a great general. He conquered
armies and he conquered nations. Wellington was a great man and
a great soldier. He conquered armies and he conquered Napoleon.
But he could not jump the Genesee Falls. That was left for me to
do. I can do it and I will.

The roughs in the crowd had begun to yell at Patch, Grandfather went on, derisively demanding that he make his leap
at once, when there was a diversion on the cliff opposite the
platform. Halfway down, the shale had crumbled beneath
an overgrown urchin perched precariously on a ledge, precip-
itating him into space. Wild yells accompanied his descent,
until he was lucky enough to lodge, unharmed, in a treetop.
Patch profited by the respite to take a long pull from a flask
offered to him by a kindly ringside patron, and when he was
once more the center of attention, he began to play for time.
He hitched up his clothes, adjusted the handkerchief with
minute particularity, and loosened the top of his shirt. Amidst
growing murmurs, he stumbled across the platform, caught a
fold of the flag, and pressed it to his lips. At this, the Missourian bellowed out, "That's right, kiss it good-bye!" and
followed this injunction with a chilling rendition of the Indian death song.

Sam flinched. He turned a look of appeal upon his manager, who caught the cue and tried to make a speech, of
which only fragments were audible above the rising clamor of
discontent: ". . . unfavorable conditions . . . a brief delay
. . . your patience kindly bespoken."

Suddenly Bulimy Joe swarmed up a pine that overlooked

the platform—like a squirrel with a tick on its tail, as Grandfather put it—and, from a point level with the tremulous
performer, addressed him.

"Come out o' there, you two-penny headpiece, and let a
true-blue puke show what he can do."

Poor Sam's head wobbled on his shoulders. He had begun,
uncertainly, "Some things can be done—" when a burst of
cheers for Bulimy Joe drowned him out. Joe scuttled upward
another yard and thrust himself out from the tree bole in a
graceful and athletic curve, landing on the flimsy platform,
which shuddered under the impact of his descent. He waved
a courtly salute.

"Ladies and gents," he boomed. "Give *me* the scads, and
with your kind permission, *I* will make the leap into the
yawning abyss."

A wild acclaim answered him. Sam Patch staggered over
and clawed at his shoulders. "No!" Sam gasped. "No!"

Gregg growled, "Get out! You're drunk."

"I ain't," Sam yelled.

"And scairt," the Missourian added.

With that, Sam gave him a look of mingled hatred, misery
and terror.

"I'll show you," he quavered. "I'll show you if I'm
sc-c-c-cairt."

He whirled about and, with knees buckling, scuttered
along the side rail, grasping it hand over hand as he went, a
pathetic figure of panic. When he reached the opening at
the front of the platform, he closed his eyes, flexed his knees,
gave a hoarse shout and jumped clear. Halfway down, his
body, still perpendicular, disappeared in a fog patch. When
it emerged, it was falling in a sidewise slant and the arms
were flailing the air. A woman shrieked. The single shrill
note echoed back from the opposite cliff through the silence.
When the plummeting form struck the surface, face down
and arms outstretched, Grandfather said, it looked as if a

fountain had spurted from the depths to meet it. And that was the end of Sam Patch.

"Strong drink did it," Grandfather moralized.

"Didn't they ever find him?" Reno asked.

"Yes," the old gentleman answered. "At the river mouth, the following March."

Rochester, through the wide-spread fame of the tragedy, sprang into valuable prominence in the public prints, he went on. Sam Patch was celebrated for years in song and drama. Fully a decade after his death, a comedy called *Sam Patch in France* was holding the boards, although Sam had never been nearer France than Paterson, New Jersey. As for poetry, Grandfather opened his book again and read us a long dithyramb, which concluded:

There's none alive could ever match him.
Oh, cruel Death, thus to dis-Patch him!

"What became of the bear, Grandpa?" Charlie asked.

"I know. The poor, faithful bear followed his master to a watery grave," Jenny said, clasping her hands sentimentally.

"The poor, faithful bear," Grandfather said, "bit the manager and made his evasion into the nearest woodpatch. He was through with show business."

"And the puke," John said. "Would he really have jumped?"

"I don't know," said Grandfather. "Nobody knows. When the confusion subsided, he was gone. So was the manager's hat with the collection in it."

"Didn't you ever hear of him again?" I asked.

"I did," he replied. "In the elegant upstate town of Cazenovia. Through a guttersnipe. That was in '34, as I recall."

"Who was the guttersnipe?" Jenny asked.

"In Thespian parlance," Grandfather said, "a guttersnipe

is a cheap broadside announcing a theatrical show. This was a third-rate troupe of dust-eaters, shun-pikers, and swing-kettles. Not a known name in the lot."

He opened the scrapbook once more and held it out for our inspection, unfolding a flimsy playbill that was pasted into it. The bill was headed, *"Sam Patch, a Tragedy in 3 Powerful Acts."* Below was a cast of characters, concluding, *"And Sam Patch* . . . Rendered with Notorious Success by his Old Friend and Loving Associate . . . Joseph B. Gregg of Missouri."

A SLAVE IN THE FAMILY

Before Grandfather Hopkins bought the point on Owasco Lake, the family gathered, summertimes, at the rambling, old Grant Avenue mansion on the outskirts of Auburn. There we had a regular and famous visitor, Harriet Tubman. It was a gala day for the household when Old Harriet came to call on "Doctah an' Miz' Hopkins." She would arrive, empty basket suggestively pendent on her arm, having covered the two miles from the small Negro quarter at the other end of town in a swinging half hour or so. The basket meant that Harriet had fallen upon slack times and was expecting her meed as a casual family adjunct. What little odd-job helping she did around the town failed to support her reliably.

To us grandchildren, she was more than a casual adjunct; she was an institution in the Hopkins household. Our great-aunt, Sarah Hopkins Bradford, had written two books about her, the proceeds of which were turned over to Harriet as the royalties came in. That, plus the interest of Lincoln's Secretary of State, William H. Seward, and other prominent local men, accounts for her having settled in Auburn after her war service was over.

Aunt Sarah's idea was that the money should be a sort of current fund for the relief of needy colored people. Harriet's notion was different. Her method of administering a fund was to give away all the money she had upon her at the moment and trust to the good Lord to fill the void. Whatever the amount on hand, it was chronically insufficient.

Aunt Sarah's books gave us grandchildren not only a literary but a proprietary interest in their subject, of whom we bragged shamelessly to less richly endowed playmates who did not have an ex-slave in the family. While other youngsters of the late 1870's played Scouts and Indians, our standard make-believe was Slaves and Overseers, with Harriet as heroine. Competition for the star part was rancorous. By her own uncertain reckoning, she was then about sixty, bent and wizened but still powerful, and with one of the blackest and plainest faces I have ever seen.

Harriet's historical importance did not impress our youthful minds. To us, she was merely a tribal teller of tales, a never-failing source of adventure and romance. We knew vaguely that she had been the friend of great folk—Mr. Ralph Waldo Emerson, Secretary Seward, and Miss Susan B. Anthony, whom, to our horrified delight, we had once seen, when she was on a lecture tour, wearing what looked to us like pants. John Brown and the Reverend Thomas Wentworth Higginson had paid tribute to Harriet's achievements. Queen Victoria had sent her a rich shawl and personally invited her to visit England, a courtesy that she was unable to accept. Later, a bronze bas-relief of her head was to adorn the front of the Cayuga County Courthouse, and much later a Liberty ship was to be named for her. All such honors, had we applied our reasoning powers to them, would have seemed perfectly logical and natural. We should have regarded them as a suitable recognition of Harriet's entertainment value.

They rested, in fact, upon an unquestionably solid historical basis, for Harriet Tubman, called by the Abolitionists
"the Moses of her people," had played a great and inspiring
part in the troubled events leading up to the Civil War. That
efficient and secret enterprise, the Underground Railroad, was
already well organized in 1849, when she ran away from slavery on a Maryland plantation. In the next decade, several
hundred blacks, supported by a resolute clique of white Abolitionists, shuttled back and forth between the Northern and
Southern states, rousing the slaves, forming them into bands,
and running them across the borders of New Jersey, Pennsylvania and Ohio into freedom, delivering a total of perhaps
seventy-five thousand. Of these "engineers" or "conductors,"
Harriet was the most notorious, the most persistent, and the
most successful.

She operated along the Eastern, or Seaboard, line of the
Underground throughout the 1850's. In those ten years, she
plotted innumerable excursions and conducted some twenty
major raids to smuggle Negroes out of the Southern states.
She was the despair of the slave patrols, who for many years
did not even know who she was. Broadsides and dodgers advertising her for capture referred to her as a man, the black-
hunters being deceived, perhaps, by her sobriquet of Moses
or by her other nickname, General Tubman, admiringly be-
stowed upon her by John Brown in recognition of her strate-
gical ability.

Other "conductors" were seized, killed, mutilated, or jailed,
and their charges haled back into servitude. Harriet never lost
a passenger. If one of her band turned fainthearted and
showed signs of wavering, she would draw the pistol that was
always at her belt and exhort him, "Keep on, brothah, or
die." Rewards totalling forty thousand dollars in gold were offered for her apprehension. "Dey might catch me," she would
promise her Abolitionist supporters, "but not alive," and she
would touch the butt of her pistol.

By 1860, her name had become an inspiration to every Negro who hoped for freedom. Unfortunately, by that time her identity was known; accurate descriptions were circulated; her position became too precarious for her to take further risks. That violent divine, and not too reliable witness, the Reverend Thomas Wentworth Higginson, from whose Worcester pulpit Harriet spoke more than once, assured his fellow-Abolitionists that she would be burned alive if caught in slave territory. She was taken to Canada and told to stay there. Meantime, she had stolen her ageing parents from Maryland, an extra-hazardous venture, since her mother had insisted upon taking along her feather bed and a hencoop full of chickens. Harriet had found it necessary to steal a horse and wagon to carry them.

At the outbreak of the war, Harriet returned to this country, and in 1862 was sent to General David Hunter at Port Royal, South Carolina, then in the hands of the Union troops. General Hunter, having learned of her tremendous influence and prestige with her own race, and her spectacular skill as pathfinder, had requested her aid. What her exact military status was under him is doubtful. Earl Conrad, in his able study, *Harriet Tubman, Negro Soldier and Abolitionist*, states that for a time she drew rations as a soldier. Certainly she wore a uniform and bore arms. Probably she received no pay, since, though attached to the General Staff and assigned to the organizing of a spy and scouting corps, she made and sold pies and root beer to maintain herself. She was especially active in the up-river expeditions, helped to direct the gunboats, and led one raid that freed seven hundred and fifty slaves. Later, she volunteered as a nurse and served in the encampments of the Northern forces.

The postwar ebb of patriotic fervor left her stranded. Nobody wanted to hear her exhortations, which, delivered with the fire and art of the born orator, had been such a popular lecture-platform feature of an earlier generation. Constantly on the verge of want, she did a little nursing, a little cooking —she had not lost her light hand with pastry—and a little assorted choring, and was helped out by the charitable Auburn folk, the Sewards, the Pomeroys, the Osbornes, the Beardsleys, and the Underwoods. No matter how hard up she might be, her house and larder were always at the disposal of any of her fellows needier than herself.

Bits of Harriet's history seeped through to us children, mainly in the form of uncorrelated autobiographical incidents from her own lips. While the business of filling her basket with provender was proceeding under Grandma's benevolent eye, the urbane and somewhat worldly theologue who was our grandfather, having invited the guest to take a chair on the sunken lawn, would say, "Harriet Tubman, will you sing for my grandchildren?" (Thrills of anticipation down our spines.)

"Now, Doctah Hopkins, I'se hawss in my froat." (We knew this for mere self-depreciation and were undismayed.)

"Just one song, Harriet. Perhaps your throat will clear."

Whereupon the old Negress would clap her stringy hands upon her bony knees, rock her powerful frame, snap her eyes, and raise a voice that resounded up to the cupola. It was baritone rather than contralto, that voice, and produced a strangely moving effect of mingled challenge and appeal.

"Farewell, ol' mastah, don' think hahd of me.
I'm on my way to Canaday, where all de slaves is free. . . ."

Or

"When dat ol' chariot come,
I'se gwine to leabe you.
Boun' for de Promise' Lan',
I'se gwine to leabe you . . ."

"Thank you, Harriet Tubman," Grandpa Hopkins would say. "Will you take off your hat and have some refreshment?"

Yes, Harriet would have the refreshment, thank you kindly, but she wouldn't take off her hat. Bitter disappointment on our part, for, having once heard a visitor say, "To think there was forty thousand dollars in gold on that head!" we always hoped to see the dent that so much weight must surely have caused. But the black straw, with flowers that looked more dead than artificial, always remained stiffly in place. As if that were not enough, Harriet wore, jammed beneath it, a sort of turban. Her dress was of an incomparably fusty black, coarse and wrinkled, but clean.

Incited by the rest of us, once when no elders were present, my cousin Julia, the senior grandchild, darlingly broached the subject of the gold.

"Aunt Harriet, wasn't the gold awful heavy?"

"Whut gol'?"

"The gold on your head."

"Ain' totin' no gol' on *my* haid."

"You did once, didn't you? Is that what makes you fall asleep?" (Harriet had been since youth subject to brief cataleptic seizures.)

A strange sound made itself heard without really issuing from her stringy throat. It resembled a red squirrel's annoyed "chuk-chuk-chuk" and was identifiable as mirth.

"Ain' got no gol' on my haid. Got a fraction."

"How'd you get it?"

Before her escape from the plantation where she was a slave, Harriet explained, she had blocked the pursuit of a young Negro running away from a flogging. The irate overseer had hurled a two-pound scale weight at her, fracturing her skull. For several months, she lay moribund.

"When I got up," she said solemnly, "I knew I had to follow de No'th Stah. Me an' my people."

"Following the North Star" had been one of the bywords of the Underground Railroad.

Persuading old Harriet to give details of her sorties was difficult. It was not so much modesty, I think, that kept her close-lipped, as a deeply ingrained reticence about secrets that had once meant the difference between slavery and freedom, or even between life and death, for herself and others. Appeals to her vanity, however, sometimes proved successful.

"Show us your mark, Aunt Harriet." (She was susceptible to the title.)

"My whippin's? Sho'! Dey almos' gone."

"Come on, Aunt Harriet. Please!"

After a little more pretense of disinclination, she would draw down her dress and exhibit the cruel weals on neck and shoulders.

"Didn't it hurt awfully?"

"Dey nevah make Harriet hollah. I go back dere attawahd." The gleam in her button-bright eyes indicated a successful raid.

"Did you always know just where to go?"

"I go where God call me to."

"Were the other darkies waiting?" (We knew they were, but we wanted to hear it all again.)

"Dey waitin' to hear Harriet sing."

"What did you sing?" (More strategy on our part.)

"A song of peace. Dat mean all well."

"S'posin' it wasn't?"

"Den I sing 'Moses' ["Go Down, Moses"] Dat mean dangah, hide yo'self."

"Sing it now."

"You chillun is sho' pesks." But she would oblige us with a stanza or two in her marvelous, resonant voice.

To keep her going, we would inquire solicitously, though we well knew what the answer was, "How did you know how to bring them out?"

"The good Lawd was my guide. He fotch us thoo. Besides, I tote a map."

"You couldn't read a map, Aunt Harriet." (She could not read anything, being totally illiterate.)

"I tote it in my haid."

According to the testimony of unimpeachable witnesses, Old Harriet had possessed a miraculous geographical instinct, never forgetting any detail of a route she had once traversed. Thus she was able to pilot unerringly her little, scared bands along unfrequented paths, lying up by day in swamp, cave, or abandoned shack, and dodging the patrols by night. Her genius for recognizing locality and an attendant knack of concealment gave her special value later to the Union forces.

Saturday night was her favorite time for slave-running, since the God-fearing Southerners would not get out their printed offers of reward on the Sabbath. Once the band was gathered and instructed, she was in undisputed command. She would never reveal her technique of flight. When our grandmother once took her to a matinée of *Uncle Tom's Cabin*, she expressed approval of the theme but was critical of Eliza's escape across the ice, declaring the affair ill-managed and intimating that she could have handled it better.

"Bloodhoun's!" she said disdainfully, eyeing the two disconsolate mastiffs who appeared in the role. "I nevah made no min' of bloodhoun's."

Indeed, Old Harriet was said to have a way with all animals and, when we knew her, was reputed to be able to calm a fractious horse with a quiet word.

The adventure about which Harriet would talk most expansively was a publicly conducted rescue in Troy, New York. Passing through that town on her way to a prewar Abolitionist rally at which she was to speak, she learned that an escaped Negro, Charles Nalle, was in local custody and was to be restored to his master. She gathered a crowd and harangued them with the fervid eloquence always at her command. The town fire bell was rung by her sympathizers, and the street outside the United States Commissioner's office filled up with blacks and whites. When the marshall, backed by his deputy and the local police, ill-advisedly undertook to transfer the prisoner to another court, Harriet rushed him. A policeman clubbed her.

"I knock um squawkin'," she told us gleefully.

The deputy grappled with her.

"I choke um till his tongue stick out like dat." Harriet's imitation of a strangling man was extremely graphic.

Nalle was knocked senseless in the struggle.

"I th'ow um acrost my shouldah like a bag o' meal and tote um away outen theyah."

Here enters an element of mystery and an ellipsis. In Harriet's veracious, if incomplete, account, rescuer and rescued presently turned up in Schenectady, fourteen miles away, in a buggy drawn by a blooded horse.

"Where did you get the horse and buggy, Aunt Harriet?"

"I fin' um."

"Where?"

"A gemmun in Troy had um."

"Did he *give* it to you?"

"I got um."

"Who was the gentleman?"

"I din stop to ast, but he was a good judge of hawssflesh," Aunt Harriet would say complacently.

The woodcut frontispiece of Aunt Sarah's *Scenes in the Life of Harriet Tubman* displays its subject in her scout uniform, "all fine-an'-fitten." A voluminous bandanna swathes her kinky hair. A small knapsack hangs beneath her armpit, and her right hand grips a grounded musket. She was inordinately proud of that woodcut. Reference to it never failed to loosen her tongue.

"I fit on de Calm-bee Rivah [the Combahee, in South Carolina, up which she piloted the federal gunboats]. I fit up de creeks an' in de wide ma'shes. Alligatahs longah'n a pine plank. Turkles big as a do'."

"Did you shoot your gun?"

"I shoot um. Bang! Bong!"

"Did you kill lots of people?"

"Nevah kill nobody."

"Why not?"

"Whuffoh I want to kill folks? Nobody nevah kill me." Which, though unsatisfactory to our bloodthirsty childish instincts, appealed to us as logical.

Some of the reminiscences of her work as a volunteer nurse were delightfully gory. There was one account of an amputation that began: "Tie down his ahms. Stick a bullet in his mouf."

"What for?" one of us would ask.

"To bite on. Saw his laig off."

"Didn't he yell?"

"Yell an' kick an' flounce. Bite de bullet clean thoo. I had to hol' um down."

"You must have been awful strong."

"I could tote a flour bar'l on one shouldah."

Many years later, when the pressure of bone on the brain caused by Harriet's skull fracture necessitated an operation, she resolutely refused an anesthetic, asking only for a bullet between her teeth. Though the surgeon dreaded risking so delicate an operation upon a sentient subject, he yielded. Harriet lay motionless as a log, mumbling prayers through teeth clenched on the bullet.

Disease had no personal meaning for her. She could not remember a sick moment other than the recurrent disability produced by her fracture.

"Nevah had time for such foolishness."

God would not let her be ill; He had too much work for her. Her relations with the Deity were personal, even inti-

mate, though respectful on her part. He always addressed her
as Araminta, which was her christened name. Harriet was her
slave name, which she accepted for convenience.

In the hospital camps she would nurse a case of scarlet fever
or small-pox with as much indifference toward contagion as if
it were chicken pox or stomach ache. For the latter, she had a
sovereign remedy, a one-day "yarb" cure, especially effective
for dysentery. All her postwar life, she made trips to whatever
woodland was adjacent, for the purpose of digging the root
that was the basis of her remedy. The identity of the plant
was her well-kept secret.

Harriet held Grandfather Hopkins in veneration, though
she had more affection, perhaps, for our grandmother, who
looked after her wants, scolded her for her improvidence, and
even bullied her a little. My last recollection of her is at
Grandmother's funeral service, during which, although a specially invited guest, she sat in the kitchen in her shabby gown
and absurd headgear, rocking to and fro and weeping silently.

The big house on Grant Avenue was swept away in the
architectural currents of a growing city, and the grandchildren
of the household were scattered afar. Through the elder
branch of my generation, I kept casual track of Old Harriet.
She moved to the Harriet Tubman Home, a frame house on
Auburn's lovely, elm-vaulted South Street, but on the city's
outskirts, beyond the limits of fashion. The house had been
built from funds raised in Auburn and was formally opened
as a home for needy Negroes in 1908. There Frank Drake, of
the New York World, who had married into our family, sought
Harriet out and wrote for his paper a "special" article that
reawakened interest and brought in welcome contributions.
For a time, the home had a matron and a handful of inmates,
who paid, when able, three dollars a week for their lodgings.

But the Auburn Negroes showed a disappointing lack of
interest in it. When my cousins Julia and Winthrop visited
Auburn and went to call on Harriet, they found her vigor-

ously tidying up the yard. She was then well over ninety, but the broom strokes were powerful and rhythmical. The place was run-down, but well kept. Poverty was evident, but no real want, since Harriet was receiving a belated pension.

All through the lush years of pension graft, when every camp follower, malingerer, and bounty jumper was battening on federal handouts, Old Harriet, who had recruited something like a regiment of soldiers and had been scout, guide and nurse, for devoted years, was passed over. To her patriotic mind, this was all right; she owed her services to the country that had set her people free. When the government got around to granting her a skimpy eight dollars a month, and when it subsequently raised her pension to twenty, she received both sums with equal gratitude. This and help from a few surviving friends were sufficient for her needs at the time of the call from the two Hopkinses.

Leaning on her broom handle, she addressed the visitors with calm dignity.

"Good mawnin'. Who is you?"

"We're Dr. Hopkins' grandchildren," answered Julia.

Harriet fixed her with a beady eye.

"Don' go an' think you can ride to Hebben hangin' to yo' granddaddy's coattails," she warned. It was her way of putting the younger generation in its place.

After Old Harriet's death in 1913, the simple house on South Street carried on for several years, occasionally harboring some wandering or indigent Negro. Then, for a period, it was neglected. Decay undermined it. Scavenging raiders, seeking repair material or firewood in the lumber shortage of the war years, stripped it to a skeleton.

Local pride came to the rescue. Money was found to restore the house and clean up the grounds. A New York State official standard marks the spot as a historical monument. Today it is as fresh and neat as if strong old Harriet herself were still there in the body to keep her home tidy with mop and broom.

GRANDFATHER ATTENDS
A VENDU

Illness in his family called Grandfather's "man Geordis" from his duties, including the care of Grandfather's horse, Horace G. On the second day of the man's absence, the horse disappeared.

Grandfather was deeply distressed. To us visiting grandchildren, he expressed his conviction that Horace G. had been stolen.

"The race circuit is holding at the Fair Grounds," he said. "All trotting men are horse-thieves."

As the missing animal's best gait was a lopfooted, five-mile-an-hour shamble, he could hardly have been an irresistible temptation to a racing man, however thievishly inclined. Our guess was that Horace G. had merely gone gypsying. Grandfather did not take kindly to the suggestion.

"Is it likely that my horse would forget seventeen years of loving care and commit a willful evasion?" he demanded bitterly. "No, no! He has been misled."

John, young Charlie and I offered awkward condolences. Sireno was more practical; being farm-bred, he was wise in the ways of livestock, and asked if Horace G. had been pastured out that spring.

"Yes," Grandfather answered. "In Cook's ten-acre, out beyond the Liberty Pole."

"C'mon, fellas," said Reno.

We found the truant in the pasture lot, led him home in triumph, and were rewarded by the warmest blanket approbation we had ever heard from Grandfather's Draconian lips. We were knowledgeable and officious boys, he told us, and he was proud of us. He gave John a quarter and directed him to fetch five bottles of sarsaparilla from the corner grocery. Just then, Jenny arrived, and the old gentleman tossed a nickel after the departing John and grandly bade him make it a round half dozen. Plainly, there was jubilee in the air.

When John returned, we all sat guggling for a time in pleasurable silence. Outside, a hand organ approached. Ordinarily, Grandfather did not approve of street music, but now his feet began to shuffle.

"A spry tune," he said. "A tune of merit."

"Yes, sir," John agreed. " 'Turkey in the Straw.' "

"Hunca-munca!" Grandfather retorted. " 'Turkey in the Straw,' indeed! 'Hoggee on the Towpath.' The work gangs used to sing it before the Erie Canal spanned the Great Montezuma Marsh." He raised a husky baritone.

"Hoggee on the towpath, picking up straw.
Along came a Dutchman. Haw! Haw! Haw!"

"It's a pretty song," said young Charlie politely. "What does it mean?"

"Surely I do not have to tell you what a hoggee is," Grandfather replied. "The straw of the song would be leakage from a pathmaster's sack. It was used to plug breaches in path or berm. As for the Dutchman, he might have been Dunderhead Van Rensselaer, or Piet Van Altemer of Van Altemer's Nose, or Rip Van Winkle. I don't know. Nobody knows."

The hand organ passed on, and we fell silent again. Grandfather took a pull at the pop. His eyes closed. He said dream-ily, "I remember one day, when I was driving my team along the towpath, and around the bend came a hoodledasher mak-ing its three-mile-an-hour. There—"

"Came a *what?*" John asked.

"A hoodledasher. Surely you know what a hoodledasher is?"

"Yes, sir," young Charlie was brash enough to say. "Did it escape from the circus?"

"Certainly not!" Grandfather pretended to be annoyed. Privately he was pleased, as always when he succeeded in stumping us. "A hoodledasher is not an animal."

"Is it a fish?" I ventured, my mind on the canal.

"An intelligent surmise," the old gentleman said sardoni-cally. "A fish that swims but three miles an hour." He ad-dressed us all. "Do not further exhibit your composite ignorance. A hoodledasher is two live and one dead."

Gratified by the baffled glances which we exchanged with one another, he proceeded to enlighten us.

For one reason or another—as an economy measure, or be-cause a horse had fallen sick, or a hoggee had broken his in-denture and run away—canallers of the early days often tied two or more cargo-less "dead" boats onto a "live" one, so that the latter's horses might draw them all. This hookup was called a hoodledasher. Why? Grandfather did not know. No-body knew.

"And there he sat on the live boat foredeck," the old gen-tleman continued, "as chirk as a chitterdiddle on a pokeweed, whistling away the time."

"*Who* was whistling, Grandpa?" John inquired.

"My grown-up poor-boy," said Grandfather. "But that was years after I lost my bay mare, Spiderfoot, the finest bit of horseflesh I ever owned, except perhaps Horace G."

Rome, New York, in 1820, was a very active and affording town, Grandfather said. On an October morning he rode

Spiderfoot into the village without a care in his twenty-one-year-old head but to turn an honest dollar into two. At the town hall, he reined in to look over the hoardings, for one never could tell what matter of interest might turn up: offers of reward for fugitive slaves; sales of furs, fish, cattle and rope; postings of errant wives whose husbands would no longer be responsible for their debts; the parmateering appeals of political candidates; sheriffs' warnings of jail-broken criminals; notices of runagate apprentices; and bids for "mechanics" to work on the swiftly progressing canal. One printed broadside caught Grandfather's eye. The Rome selectmen, having voted the sum of five hundred dollars for the relief of the poor, had resolved that "said poor be set up at Public Vendu by the Overseers, and go to the lowest bidders." The vendu was set for that very afternoon, and Grandfather resolved to go.

John said, "Lowest bidders? Didn't it mean the *highest* bidders, Grandpa?"

"Not at a poor vendu," the old gentleman replied. "At a poor vendu, the person on the block went to the bidder who offered board, lodging and care at the lowest rate per month, a sum the selectmen were obligated to pay from the fund they had voted."

"Just like slavery!" Jenny said indignantly.

"Not very different," Grandfather agreed. "The occupants of the poor-bench, when I arrived, looked quite as wretched as slaves."

"Couldn't the poor people do anything about it, sir?" John asked.

"Oh, yes," the old gentleman said. "If they did not choose to be bid off, they could lie out and starve or freeze. Humane persons did not approve of these pauper auctions. Nevertheless, they went on for many years. The 'New England system,' it was called. I suppose the custom derived from there. It was so well established in this region that a farmer of my acquaintance used to bid for the entire pauper list of Amsterdam, New York. Three hundred and fifty dollars per annum was his stated offer. Nobody ever underbid him, so he got the lot, year after year."

"Why did you go to the auction, Grandpa?" Charlie asked. "Did you want to buy a poor?"

"I had no such conceit at the time, Charles," said Grandfather. "I went there out of idle curiosity."

The Rome town square, the old gentleman continued, was shrouded in dreary, October fog. Sixty or seventy townsfolk stood about paying little heed to the auctioneer, a facetious fellow named Schley. It was an unpromising vendu, Grandfather thought. A scant dozen figures were huddled on the poor-bench. An obliging bystander identified several of them for the stranger's benefit. There were two recent widows, the local half-wit, a pock-marked redemptioner who had been turned out of the farmstead where she worked as not worth her keep, a county pauper who was not properly a town charge, a rheumatism-doubled cripple, and a befreckled urchin of ten or eleven, unknown to the informant. Among the whole sorry lot, this boy was the only one who kept a straight back.

As Grandfather dismounted, Auctioneer Schley was exercising his wit upon a bleary and tremulous crone who could hardly stand upright, she was so weak from hunger.

"Exhibit B for Beauty," the auctioneer said merrily. "Any traveling poppet show would hire her on sight. How old are you, Mrs. Nosegay?"

The answer was an unhappy mumble. Taking her chin between thumb and forefinger, Schley pulled down her jaw. "Look!" he cried. "No teeth! Can't eat! Cheap to feed! What's the offer?"

After a few scattered bids, the woman was knocked down to the lockkeeper's wife for twelve shillings, and her place on the block was taken by the frightened young redemptioner. On her quavering admission that she could cook and wash, she went to a quick-bidding canal-labor contractor and was led away, weeping. The rheumatic cripple followed, and was offered by Schley with the cunning suggestion that whoever got him would not have to keep him long. Bored and depressed, Grandfather was about to re-mount and go his way, when the auctioneer's raised voice checked him.

"Here's a fine bit of goods!" Schley called. "Up with you, spratling!"

The urchin rose and walked, straight, steady, and scowling, to the block. He was skeleton-thin. Shapeless pantaloons of well-worn fustian flapped around his legs. His coat was fashioned from a large jute bag. Oversized wooden shoes were held on his meager feet with strings. His wretched and defiant look moved Grandfather to a kind of admiration.

"How old are you, brat?" Schley began.

"Dunno."

"Come on! Make a guess, young Web. That's your name, ain't it?" he added, consulting his auction list.

"Yup."

"What's the rest of it? Web waht?"

"Web Loakes."

"Loakes, hey? Where's your folks-y, young Web Loakes-y?"

Amidst the paroxysms of merriment provoked by this sally, Grandfather heard the boy mutter, "Ain't got any."

"Well, well! Foundling, huh? Nobody around to stir up trouble about you. That's good. And you don't know how old you are. Call it ten. How you been living?"

"Traveling circuit with a show," said the boy. "Poppet and animal. I tended the bestial."

"What happened? You run away?"

"No. Monkey died. Bear bit the boss. Show busted."

"So you get you on the poor rates. Can you read?"

The boy stared at him. "No," he grunted.

"Well, I wouldn't expect it of you. Write nor figger, neither, I reckon."

The boy shook his head.

"See?" the auctioneer said to the onlookers. "No book learning to set him above his vittles. A stout fellow, too; stout and willing, ain't you, boy?"

"No," the boy said.

"*Yes!*" Mr. Schley corrected, cuffing him beside the head. "Now, what's the bid on this brisk spratling?"

A scissors-grinder opened with thirteen shillings, which pleased the auctioneer, though he feigned disappointment.

"You could keep him a year on that!" he cried.

The local whitesmith, who was looking for an apprentice, bid twelve. A taproom keeper cut a shilling under. A motherly-looking boarding-house mistress went to ten.

"Nine shilling!" came a bellow from a hulking citizen in a painted castor hat, who had been lolling against an oak.

Grandfather, who recognized him as Dunk Snedeker, captain of the line boat, *Try and Catch Me*, felt sorry for any human chattel who might fall into the Captain's brutal hands. It was none of Grandfather's business, however.

A Peter Funk—a spurious bidder, the accomplice of the auctioneer—now offered eight-and-six. Captain Snedeker underbid him, and was, himself, capped by the scissors-grinder. Again the Captain shouted a bid, and the Peter Funk kept the bidding going once more. It was now down to five-and-six.

"Five, blast ye all!" Dunk Snedeker bawled, glaring about him. "Any man unders that, he'll have me to deal with."

"That's no manner of talk," protested the official, discountenanced. "Don't let him scare you off, folks. Next bid?"

Nobody responded. The Captain was an ugly customer.

"Do I hear the four?" the auctioneer cried. "Well, four and the penny? Four and tuppence? Going, once. Going—Hey, grab him!"

The merchandise had plunged from the platform and was scrambling through the crowd. He was tripped, collared and dragged back. Grandfather caught sight of his face. It was filled with hate and terror.

"One shilling!" Grandfather called, startled to hear his own voice.

"Who spoke?" the auctioneer asked, peering around.

"One shilling," Grandfather repeated firmly.

"Done!" cried the auctioneer. "Get down, boy. The next article is—"

Grandfather heard no more. He was making for his mare, with one eye out for the Captain and one hand on the collar of the boy. He swung into the saddle, and the boy swarmed up behind him. Captain Snedeker was pushing through the crowd toward them. There was no chance of evading him. Grandfather pulled the mare around, set her straight at the Captain, and bowled him over like a ninepin.

"And that," the old gentleman told us, "is how I got my first apprentice."

"I think it was noble of you, Grandfather," Jenny said.

"Why, I was rather of that opinion myself," said Grandfather.

The old gentleman refreshed himself with more sarsaparilla, and went on. He did right by his charge, he declared. He took him home and treated him like a younger brother.

"I victualled him and clothed him and hided him for his own good when he needed it," Grandfather said. "I taught him reading and writing and the rule of three. When I took the road on my occasions, he went with me under indenture as my apprentice. He was sharp as the little end of nothing at a trade, but an uncompanionable roadfellow, with naught to say for himself. Surly blood there. Indian, I suspect, or perhaps gypsy. Nearly three years he was with me. Then, one misty, summer

morning when we had tented on the Cherry Valley pike below
Skunk's Misery, he was gone without sign or word, and so was
Spiderfoot."

"How sharper than a serpent's tooth!" Jenny said, sighing.
(The third-year class at the Rochester Free Academy was taking Shakespeare that term.) "What did you do?"

"I put out a broadside offering forty dollars for the mare's
return and inserted a paid runagate notice in the *Western
Farmer & Canal Advocate*," Grandfather replied. "Hand me
my ort-book, Samuel."

I went to his secretary desk and brought him the volume.
Grandfather opened it and found an old clipping. It read:

Two Cents and a Bucket of Ashes—The aforesaid will be
paid for the return of my evaded apprentice, Web Loakes, circa
twelve years; short, slim, black-haired and ill favored. No pock-
marks. All and sundry are warned against harboring him at my
charge.

Myron Adams
East Bloomfield, N.Y.

"And he was the passenger on the hoodledasher?" Jenny
asked.

"Yes," Grandfather said. "The whistling passenger was Web
Loakes, finified beyond belief in a brass-buttoned coat like a
packet master, a flowered sarsenet waistcoat, and prunella-
topped boots, no less. And I soon found he had a gift of the
gab quite different from my tongue-tied poor-boy of the
vendu."

Web Loakes waited until the hoodledasher veered in to give
space to an approaching boat, Grandfather said, and then made
a flying leap to the towpath where Grandfather had reined in.

"Good day to you, Mister," said Loakes, civilly enough.

"Good day to you, Web Loakes," Grandfather returned.

"You know me, then."

"I do. For all your pompous clothes."

"They're honest come by," Web Loakes said defiantly.

"I am pleased to hear so," Grandfather said. "What fetches you here?"

"To get justice. You put the ash-bucket on me."

"And deservedly."

"In your teeth," the other said. "I'm here to clear my credit. I want the wrong you put on me righted."

"Do you so? And how came you to knowledge of the ash-bucket?"

"I saw it in public print."

"That print appeared in 1820," Grandfather said. "This is 1827."

"Posts are slow out beyond the Big Muddy," said Web Loakes.

"Missouri country, eh?" said Grandfather. "What have you been doing out there?"

"Indian trading."

"And fared well at it, I take it," Grandfather said.

"I could buy and sell you like a pinch of kinnikinnick."

Grandfather considered this disputable, but, not caring to argue, he said pacifically, "I give you éclat for your dandiprat appearance. You are fit for the governor's gala."

Web Loakes, unmollified, said, "You posted me on the Horse-thief Society roster."

"I did," Grandfather said. "You stole my mare, Spiderfoot."

"Not me," said Web Loakes. "The gyppos stole her. I saw them."

"Then why did you not make an outcry?" Grandfather asked sternly.

"They stole me, too, with my head in a bag," Web Loakes said. "I can prove it by a sworn paper."

At that, Grandfather invited Loakes to be his guest in Rochester, whither he was bound on business. On the way there, Web recited an account of his adventures.

The gypsy band that stole him had pushed west, he said, by

turnpike and Indian trail to the huddle of fishermen's huts
that was later to be Buffalo. There the boy escaped. The
tail-wheel steamboat *Walk-on-the-Water* was about to cast off.
Though terrified by its snortings and roarings and spoutings
of vapor, Web sneaked aboard and hid. He was found, and
thrown off at Cleveland, half starved. A party of hunters took
him on as chore boy for their trip across state to the Ohio
River. There he caught a ride on a raft, which carried him to
the Mississippi, and, hearing of the wonders of the Far West,
he joined up with a family of Pittsburgh pioneers, in a six-
horse connywagon, who needed a helper with the stock.

Thanks to his apprenticeship, Web Loakes could read,
write and figure—accomplishments rare on the frontier—and
had no difficulty getting a job in a store. He accumulated a
bit of capital, and when an expedition set out for the fabulous Mexican city of Santa Fe, Web went along. He carried fishhooks, jew's-harps, hand mirrors, and tin whistles,
valuable fripperies that he could exchange for beaver and
otter pelts with the Indians along the way.

It was a hard life, Web said. He was shot by a spent Ara-
paho bullet, treed by a grizzly bear, island-bound for three
days in an Arkansas River spate, bitten by a centipede, and
jailed on general principles by the Santa Fe authorities on
arrival. Released, he marketed his pelts to such good purport
that when he got back as far east as Missouri, he owned a half
share in a Durham wagon, and four hundred dollars.

"He palavered me into expunging his name from the
horse-thief list," Grandfather said, "and into inserting a re-
tractive advertisement in the newspapers. On the strength
of that, he cashed a bank note at a trustful Rochester bank,
bought a saddle-horse, and went his way without farewell or
Godspeed."

"Was it a red-dog note, sir?" I asked, perceiving a chance
to show off my own knowledge.

"Not precisely, Samuel," Grandfather replied. "The bank

of issue was not wholly mythical. It was, however, defunct, rendering the note painfully uncurrent."

John spoke up quickly. "An Ontario note?" he said.

"Quite so," Grandfather assented. "Such was the local stigma, consequent upon the frequent failures of banks in that county, that the very name Ontario was much blown upon."

"And that was the end of Mr. Loakes, I suppose," Jenny said.

"Not by fifty years," said Grandfather, "though I never again set eyes on him. From time to time would come a memento from the West; a bedizened vest, or a buffalo robe. Once, it was a full-feathered war bonnet with what purported to be a Pawnee scalp inside. After the Civil War, Web sent me a certificate of stock in a turquoise mine, and a message: 'Hold this, and your descendants will be millionaire-men.' He was a great brag-hard."

"How I would love to have seen him!" Jenny said.

"Would you?" The old gentleman turned the leaves of his ort-book until he came to the photograph of an erect, richly mustachioed man in an ornate uniform topped by a superbly cockaded hat. Scrawled across the photograph was "Yours resp'y, Webster F. Loakes, Grand Commander, Wide-Winged Condors of the West."

"Whether, as he once wrote me, he was actually a member of the San Francisco vigilantes," Grandfather said, "or whether he served as a cavalry captain in the Confederate Army, I would not undertake to say. But here, at least, is authentic news," and he showed us the headlines of an article in a San Francisco newspaper of 1874.

DEATH OF A PRIZE LIAR
WEBSTER F. LOAKES, SELF-STYLED
HERO OF A THOUSAND CRISES,
EXPIRES IN DIRE POVERTY

"Did you know all along he was lying, Grandpa?" Reno asked.

"I had my suspicions confirmed by certain developments," the old gentleman answered mildly. "The Pawnee scalp proved to be rabbit pelt. The buffalo robe was mangy. The sworn paper about the gyppos, which he sent me, was a forgery. And the Wide-Winged Condors of the West existed only in their supposititious commander's fancy. The truth," he concluded, "was not in Web Loakes."

"There wasn't any turquoise mine, either, was there?" Reno asked with a grin.

The old gentleman turned a derisive regard upon him. "Doubtless wisdom shall die with you, Sireno," he said. "But there you err. There *was* a turquoise mine and still is, for aught I know. I disposed of my shares for nine hundred dollars in 1874. Therefore I would not too harshly judge Web Loakes. As my father, the Deacon, used to say, 'Man that is born of woman is seldom all of a piece.' "

CANAL BRIDE

Several years after my Grandfather Adams' death, a leather-bound ledger was found in a trunk of his. It contained a few scattered pages of a diary in a delicate, feminine hand. Who the diarist was I do not know; perhaps a relative. The explanatory notations are initialed "M.A." presumably for Myron Adams. The date of the manuscript is not stated, but is probably either 1827 or 1828.

Thursday. May I be preserved from the sin of vainglory, dear Diary. This be the humble prayer of one who but a short month ago was well content with life in the mansion of her respectable father in Buffalo. Now to find myself translated to the bosom of the Grand Erie Canal, mistress of the spanking Durham, *Starry Flag,* sixty tons burthen, out of Black Rock, N.Y., licensed for perishable freight and four passengers. Who would not be prideful over a destiny so pompous!

A great bobbery befell in the household when my captain came a-wooing.

"You, Dorcas!" my weeping mother said. "Daughter of an honorable judge. Graduated at great cost from a Female Academy of Elegant Learning. You, to throw yourself away upon a rough and rude canaller! Reflect, my child, reflect, ere it be too late."

My father bewailed that I should be sundered apart from all ties with decent home-keeping, dry-land folk. Could they but see me now, as I sit, easeful and ladyish, upon my spotless foredeck!

One hundred feet ahead our senior hoggee (canalese for a towpath driver—M.A.) guides the tandem sorrels that draw us. The younger boy is currying down the relief team between decks. The deckhand is fishing overside with a slab of salt pork. My husband, captain and owner, stands watchful at the tiller. Though I make my boast who should not, there is no master upon Erie Water more maccaroni and personable than Captain Angus Robie of the *Starry Flag*. He is arrayed in the uniform of his calling, in which he wed me; brass-buttoned blue broadcoat, sarsenet waistcoat, with neckcloth to match, tight yellow smallclothes, bespoken boots of prime morocco with prunella tops, and a high, glossy castor hat of gray with a mermaid entwined upon an anchor painted on the front. Looped about his neck, a cord of gilt twist supports his spyglass, balanced by his silver bugle. Finefied though he is, it would be a grievous error to misprize him as a weakling dandiprat. The weight of his fist is well known from Mountain Ridge to Hudson's River.

We are now in the Long Level, having passed through the massive five-fold locks of Lockport. For sixty-three miles to the Genesee River there is neither lock, block, nor stay to traffic. We could make our fifty miles a day were it not that we must stop to take on freights. Before me the stupendous prospect charms the eye. Forty feet from bank to bank the canal spreads. Its depth of four feet can support the mightiest bottom afloat. The hand-built towpath is three hundred and sixty-five miles long. As for the traffic, surely not all the argosies of Greece could equal this spectacle. There are line-boats, packet boats, ballheads, Durhams, gala boats, counter-sterns, toothpick scows, dugouts, arks, flats and periaugers, and always the slow rafts, all transporting such cargoes as were never before conceived of. Goods which cost one hundred dollars a ton carryage, Albany to Buffalo by waggon, the *Starry Flag* freights for six dollars in a fourth of the time. Where are now the malcontent politicasters who dubbed this greatest of man-made achievements "Clinton's Folly" and declared that the "Governor's Gutter" would go dry for lack of patronage?

Utica is our port. Below decks we carry cargo for the asheries, both pot and pearl; and fifty bales of cedar shingles for the fast-building town of Rome. Amidships we have fresh fish in barrels for delivery in Rochester, and such general merchandise as turnips, cloth in bales, gin in pipes, mirrors, furniture, axes, saws and mauls, and ten fine head of merino sheep. Every few miles we are hailed by farmers, standing on their private docks and offering us goods for transportation or wishing to bargain for what we have aboard.

We pass through a wild and ragged land. Few are the clearings. The farmsteads are mostly rough cabins. Everywhere the roadless forest stretches. Only the Grand Erie Canal brings to this desolate region the blessings of commerce and civilization.

Night falls while we are still in the wilds. Half asleep, I hear the steersman's call: "Look for a post," and the weary hoggee's grateful answer: "Post-o!" "Snub in," the steersman orders. We ease over against the berm for our nightberth. The gangplank is run out. The tandem tramps aboard, for we are no rich packet boat with fresh relays every twelve or fifteen miles. We carry our own draught-stock.

Nearby from a thicket comes a piggish grunting. A bear is busy with his nightly concerns. From afar the wind brings the desolate howling of wolves. There is a whirr of wings in the darkness, and the strange call of the thunderpump (swamp-bittern—M.A.), like a distant muffled drum. A canal lullaby to which I fall asleep again.

Friday. A rude awakening this morning. My husband's musket, with which he conquered the redcoats in 1813, belched its fire into the early-morning darkness with a desperate roar. He has shot a skulking wolf, and now jumps ashore to scalp the animal, which will put a ten-dollar bounty in our money-box. As everyone aboard is roused by the clamor, we make a timely start.

Shortly after sun-up, I observe a sorry figure plodding along the berm. The urchin, bone-meager and with a swollen face, might be twelve years old. In lieu of a jacket, he wears an old potato bag of bombast with holes cut for arms and head. Catching my eye, he removes his ragged coonskin cap with a flourish and addresses me. The following colloquy takes place, as he limps alongside in oversize wooden shoes.

Urchin: Got a job for a poor and honest young fella, missus?

I: What kind of job?

He: Ten shilling a week and found.

I: What could you do to earn such a wage?

He (confidently): I'm a canawller, I am. I can drive, steer, clean stable, bed down the critters, plug a leak, splice a rope, fight the rafters, and help with the scullion work.

I: How came you by that blackened eye?

He: Captain Ely Tugg of the *Three Brothers*, he gimme that for trying to knife him.

I (severely): It is very wrong for little boys to knife people.

He: Captain Tugg pay me in red dog.

I: What on earth is red dog?

He: Busted bank notes. Couldn't buy a chaw of tobacco with five dollars of 'em.

I: Captain Tugg must be a very wicked man to cheat a poor little fellow like you.

He: He's meaner than a hog-nosed blauser. (puff-adder— M.A.) I'll get him yet.

I: Then you will go to jail.

He: That's what I hope.

I: You *wish* to go to jail?

He: Soon as snow flies. No canawl jobs in winter. How will I eat if I can't get into jail?

I: Are you hungry now?

He: Certes, I'm hungry. No job for a poor and honest young fella, missus?

I: No. We are fully manned.

He (beseechingly): No prog? (victuals—M.A.)

I: Yes, you shall be fed.

So I made up a packet of ortings left over from breakfast. At last sight he was sitting on the berm, ministering to his galled heel with a scraping of butter from my half loaf of bread. There are scores of these wretched little pinklings canalside who take towpath jobs for ten dollars a season, and then are fobbed off by evil captains with depreciated currency or perhaps no wage at all.

What strange contrasts of misery and luxury upon these waters! Hardly had we left my minnikin job-seeker behind when we drew up upon a gala boat making poor progress behind jaded horses. She was cruel gay with bunting upon her rails, and silk pennants flying, and her name in high gilt lettering upon the stern: *May Queen of Geneva*, N.Y. There were revelry and tippling on the afterdeck, where lolled the owner and his friends. After making a night of it they were still in musical mood with their guitars and flutes. They bawled a rowdy canal song:

> "Two days out from Bowman's Flat,
> And the gin is running low,

> And I hardly think
> We'll get a drink
> Till we get to Buffalo."

Captain Robie at our tiller overbore their ditty with an impatient bugle blast for passage. Little did they heed. These young ruffleshirts and Corinthians deem themselves above rules and regimen, though they but make dalliance upon the face of the waters where soberer folk must earn their livelihood. By dint of fending pole and some regrettable profanity on my captain's part, we scraped by. As we passed, one young dandiprat gave over playing upon the gentlemanly flute and advanced to the rail. With his hat upon his heart, he unjustifiably addressed me as his "pretty popkin." So he stood, mouthing and blowing kisses, until our stern came abreast of him. Then, without word or warning, my captain out with his fending pole and fetched young Mr. Impudence such a clout aside the jowls as sent him toppling into the hold, amidst the jeers of his fellows.

Saturday. How happy I am to be in Rochester! Only a few years ago, the town was derided as "an emporium of mud and outcasts." Now it is the swiftest-growing city in our great nation. Here we shall take on fifty barrels of white flour from the water-powered mills along the Genesee River. We shall lay up in the basin. Other boats will be moored there. I shall visit and be visited by the wives of other captains. From them I shall hear what goes on in this fine, new water-world of ours.

My husband bought me the issue of the Rochester *Telegraph.* It is full of important political speeches, and missionary letters from Wild Africa, sermons, and pious poesy, and a romance. But not one item of what everyday folk like ourselves do. This I shall obtain from my round of visits. Let my scornful husband call them mung-meetings. (Mung-news in canal parlance means gossip—M.A.) I fetch back more information than he does from Bement's Fashionable Recess or the Coffee Exchange, where he foregathers with his cronies. Eager enough was he to listen when I returned this evening from my deck-to-deck promenade, with my news. Be my repository, dear Diary.

The line-boat, *Quaker's Choice*, which sunk in Joppa Basin last week, was found to have six auger holes in her hull. To what rude lengths will not jealousy drive some captains in their rivalry for freights!

The packet, *Young Lion of the West*, was mulcted in three different fines of ten dollars each for forcing the locks.

A five-foot sturgeon was speared by the watergateman in Lock 47.

The *American Spy*, Captain Porter Bell, had a man-child on Tuesday night. Mother and son are prospering.

The mistress of the counterstern, *Fair Play*, has a new seal's-skin overall; reputed to have cost 40 dols. How she will prank it over us other canal wives, who must content ourselves with the lowly mink or the humble beaver!

Sunday. This is the Sabbath. No keel stirs along the length of Erie Water, save only their cockahoop high-mightinesses, the packet boats, by special privilege of the Canal Commission. Honest trading craft must remain wharfed or basined at whatever risk and damage to their freights, while the through packets break God's holy law at four miles per hour.

Though bells are ringing in the nearby village of Perrington, we worship on the Gospel Raft of the Wembley brothers, equally powerful in prayer, exhortation and song. This day no less than two hundred canallers of all sects have attended. Captain Robie and I worshipped at morning service, three hours; afternoon baptism, two hours; and evening sermon, two hours. Now at 11:00 P.M., the good brothers are holding their Refreshment of Song. Across the waters are wafted the harmonies of their lap organ, upon which the old-est brother pumps with his elbow. I shall sink happily to sleep soothed and exalted by those distant voices singing sweetly of sin and the fires of hell and eternal damnation.

Monday. East of Rochester we pass through a new world, improved and nurtured by the canal traffic. Where before there was desolation and wilderness, we now come to a region of thriving villages, wharves, basins, frequent occupation bridges, and waterside taverns. Here the towpath has become a free-to-all highway for a vagrant world. Through the rising dust plod bands of homeless, kinless vagabonds, all the riff and the raff of the itinerant trades.

Item: A knife-grinder with cart and bell. "Sharpen 'em up, lady? Whet all your cutlery for sixpence."

Item: A bear-trainer with a sick bear and an unhappy monkey.

Item: A professional bouker, higgling his lewd prints for a penny. "Hairy Harry and others." A leer and a wink. Such fellows should be horsewhipped from the right-of-way.

Item: A goose-girl with a dozen of her charges, arguing in Dutch, against the Pathmaster's angry English, that her birds should have privilege of the path.

Item: Whiskey Johnny from Skaneateles, with his hogshead on wheels. "It's prime. It's pure. It's cheap." Not so cheap, say I, at two shillings the gallon.

Item: A poppet show of *Punch and Judy;* mortal risible, for a penny with their "quips and cranks and wanton wiles," as saith the poet, Milton.

Item: A barrow-man with old clothes; the day's bargain, a captain's uniform of the Palmyra Light Artillery for three dols.

Item: An aged fortune teller, with owl.

Item: Pomphret's Patent Chemical Bedbug Machine, fouling the air with a horrid stench from its funnel.

Item: Professor Popple, the magicker and quack medico, with a shoulder-sack, offering an Elixir Proprietatus, which, by his claim, "cures nettlerash, vertigo, gout, gangrene, and the Decline, and relieves all a lady's anxieties, or your money back."

Item: Fleetfoot, the Indian runner with three fellows of the Tuscarora tribe, on his way to exhibit at the Auburn Fair, where he will strive to out-do the record of a mile in six minutes and forty seconds, a speed difficult for the mind to compass.

Item: Three felonious woodsmen on their way to jail in charge of a constable, for felling the state's trees.

Truly, a great and wonderful world. Where, otherwise than on the Grand Erie Canal could one witness such a human panorama!

Tuesday. We lay up in the shadow of that strange hillock called Van Altemer's Nose, to take on hawsers from the East Palmyra ropewalk. In the evening a meeting was convened aboard the *Ploughboy of Brockport,* which canal wives were privileged to attend. The object was to protest a dire threat to our Canal. The Lake Erie steamboat, *Walk-on-the-Water,* out of Buffalo for Cleveland, has petitioned for a canal license. I am well persuaded that it would mean ruination, for I have observed that thunderous mechanism drawing in to her lake wharf. Never shall I forget the horrid din and clamor of her approach. Jets of noisome vapor spurted from her. Her paddle wheels flailed the placid surface into a maelstrom. A fearsome sight.

At the meeting, captain after captain rose to protest the invasion of our peaceful waters. A memorial was offered, recorded, and unanimously adopted: "Resolved: that the monster, Steam, be forever debarred from Trespass upon the confines of the Grand Erie Canal." The meeting then adjourned after giving three huzzahs for Governor Clinton

and Internal Improvements. (The *Walk-on-the-Water* was
debarred by the Honorables, the Canal Commissioners—
M.A.)

I was not idle at the meeting in my gathering of mung-news
for entry in my diary.

Smallpox has broken out upon the Erie. Two learned physicians are traveling the towpath by gig, with fresh kinepox,
offering free vaccination to "immigrants and indigents." For
myself, I should fear the results of the practice, though I
doubt current reports of a young man in Herkimer who, after
impoxination, sprouted horns and bellowed.

A hoggee of the packet, *Storm Queen*, was bitten on Saturday by a rattlesnake taking its comfort in the warm dust of
the towpath. A doctor on a passing boat bled, purged and
puked him, and applied a cataplasm of bread and milk upon
a wilted cabbage leaf, thus saving his life and, haply, his
leg.

An Indian found a red gem on the pebbly shore of Lake
Ontario, which he sold for 29 dols. to a Rochester whitesmith. (Probably a large garnet—M.A.)

In a dispute at Teall's Lock over precedence, the lockkeeper lost an ear by chewing.

Wednesday. We took on two passengers. The pair, who are
now berthed amidships, are a professor at Hamilton College
and his wife, returning from vacation. They pay 2½ cents a
mile, victual themselves, bring their own pallets and a tin
stove, and are no trouble.

A silly mishap has this day disfavored me with my husband. It was due to Farmer White's occupation bridge having sagged in the middle. These occupation bridges are built
by the Canal Commission where the canal cuts a landowner's
holding in two, dividing, it may be, his house from his barn.
Mortal nuisances they are, though measured to allow passage
of a boat's top-structure. My day's wash was out upon the
line, supported by poles of the proper height. Knowing

this, I paid no heed to the steersman's call of "Low bridge!"
There was a hideous crackle and crash as a protruding plank
caught my line and the week's wash went outboard. The
hoggee pulled up, the *Starry Flag* nosed over, and I was put
to the humility of fishing out my garments with a pike-pole
while two clownish soaplocks on the berm sang derisively:

"Low bridge! Everybody down!
Low bridge! We're coming to a town."

My captain took out his chronometer and counted nine-
teen minutes lost. "I have married an ignorama," he said.

I wept.

Thursday. The dawn is cool and crisp, and I pray that it
may so hold. For now we approach the five-mile crossing of
the Great Montezuma Marsh, a wasteland of tall water reeds,
quicksands, and the ravening marsh mosquitoes. Here the
building of the Canal came near to being terminated by these
pests. Under their savage attacks the Irish mechanics (day
laborers were termed "mechanics" whatever the nature of
their work—M.A.) went mad and sickened and died and finally deserted their camps and abandoned their contracts, so
that for four weeks not a spade rose or a pick fell. Nor would
the survivors return until the frosts killed the bloodsuckers.
The crossing was finished with the sturdy Irish toiling knee-
deep in icy sludge. I have a sovereign defense against the
venomous buzzers in my basket of fresh pennyroyal leaves,
which I rub into hands and face and neck. No mosquito can
abide its spicy odor.

The *Starry Flag* locks through to solid land at Cayuga,
and we are on our way to Weedsport, where we discharge
cargo for Auburn prison. Beyond the town at evening I had
my first view of a band of runaway youth, gathered about
their campfire. They were apprentices, of that ilk which is
advertised weekly in all the York State journals, to this purport.

"Reward! Two cents and a bucket of ashes for return of my run-away apprentice; thirteen years old, under-sized, pock-pitted, half-witted, answers to name of Zink. Persons harboring this thievish rascal do so at their own risk and cost, for I will be responsible for no expense.

"Elias Johnston, Malster;
"Spencerport, N.Y."

There were a dozen in this band, led by a youth of six-teen with an evil squint. They roam the countryside following the Canal and sleeping in hedgerows, hayricks and un-guarded barns. This group was armed with bows and arrows and long, reed blowpipes, through which they propel feath-ered darts, killing blackbirds for the two-cent bounty.

A small figure in a torn jacket of hum-hum and flapping pantaloons left the fire, climbed the berm, and accosted me in a hoarse voice, which gave me a start of surprise. Holding out to me a bark lunkin (homemade bucket—M.A.) on a pole, the creature impudently requested the "loan" of two pounds of flour. "White, not rye."

I said, "Are you not a female?"

"Certes."

"What are you doing here with these young ragmuffins?"

"I'm the cook."

"Where do you come from?"

"Troy. I was a doffer in the Bird of Freedom mills."

"A much better employ than this vagabondage. I daresay you earned a good wage. Eight shillings a week?"

"Ten."

"Many a young female of your age would be grateful for so much."

"Let 'em have it. A pox on it!"

"That is a very improper observation."

"A double pox on it. Fourteen hours a day at the looms,

and what happens at night? Locked in, horse-high and hog-tight. Come payday, who's at the window, first in line? My father waiting to nobble my wages. I'd rather eat dust on the towpath."

I gave her the requested flour, but rejected her suggestion that I add a jar of long-sweetening (sorghum molasses—M.A.) "for the night's luck." A strange and pathetic figure. Were I her mother, I should entertain apprehensions for her virtue in such lawless company.

Friday. Daily I return thanks to Divine Providence that I am a Canal wife. Truly, life on the Erie is enviable. Consider, dear Diary, my day. Unless there is special cause for an early start, I keep to my easeful bed often as late as six o'clock. While the horses are turned out and the *Starry Flag* cast off, I light the fire in Mr. Burden's patent stove from Troy, dispose my pots, pans and skillets, and get breakfast for all hands. Captain Robie does not believe in overfeeding, but we are sufficiently victualed to appease the men's appetites. The meal may consist of a pike or bass, fresh caught upon my overnight trawl line, a steak, bacon, sausage, and ham; a platter of scrambled eggs, baked pritties (potatoes—M.A.) boiled cabbage and squash, bread, both corn and white, pancakes, both wheat and buckwheat, with sorghum, maple or honey to choice; and, to wash all down, coffee, tea, milk, skimmagig (buttermilk—M.A.) and cider. Dinner will be heartier, with whiskey, rum, and, if we have a pipe in freight, good Holland gin.

With my dishes washed and restored, I draw my water buckets and sluice out our cabin with the firkin of soft soap, composed from my grandmother's recipe. I am proud of my Canal home. Our cabin on the foredeck is of oak, painted in blue and gilt. Every window has its curtain of striped dimity, work of my own hands. Outside stands my Dutch wasserbank of billstead (maple—M.A.), gay with potted ferns, marigolds, gerania, and the handsome though poisonous tomato. This, my floral display, is the advertisement to all and sundry that Captain Angus Robie of the *Starry Flag* has taken a wife.

Land wives must go to market. My market comes to me. Before I am done with my morning survey, the farm children are paddling alongside in their homemade bateaux. They offer eggs, fowls, vegetables and fruits in season, milk, butter and maple syrup. We chaffer gaily, spending five minutes in humorsome argument over the price of eggs. I proffer seven cents, pay eight, and am saving two on the store price. One great advantage I have is that my kitchen treasury, which is a tin pail, is filled with coined money. These farm folk, whose local medium of barter is flaxseed, goosedown, or gunpowder, are mortal impressed with the sight and feel of a shilling or a round pistareen. Many a cent am I advantaged on a bargain by the seductive clatter of the hard specie.

Dinner is at eleven o'clock. The towpath hoggee has his carried out, hot, in a pail. After all is cleared away, I have several hours of leisure before supper. I may check the boat's manifest and reckon up our freightage, for I studied Mathematicks at the Academy. Or I may fetch out my Griswold rocker and sit on the foredeck, as lady-like as the squire's wife in her parlor, with my silver-eyed blunt (a special kind of needle—M.A.) and a bobbin of fleak (fine thread—M.A.) making a neckcloth for my captain. He says that I have needle-worthy fingers.

As like as not a professional hunter will paddle up, easing his laden periauger alongside. He will have teagle duck, Canada goose, quail, snipe, and wild pigeon at prices below barnyard fowl. A haunch of venison or a set of bear's hands are sound economy, with prime store beef at the excessive price of nine cents a pound.

Supper at five is soon out of the way. Again I have my leisure spell. Other boats may be moored near us for the night. Then there will be polite visits back and forth and the exchange of the news of the day, very excitable, lasting as late as nine o'clock. I go to bed, grateful for all my mercies and asking myself what other life could be so affording and pompous as that on the Grand Erie Canal.

Saturday. Syracuse is a rising town by virtue of its salt deposits. We take on many barrels, during the loading of which I visit the shops. On Salina Street, my eye is beguiled by a red flag. It is an Almshouse Auction, with the Poormaster offering a huddle of miserable humanity as they might be slaves on the block. Town paupers and county paupers make up the lot.

Sunday. Our junior hoggee has a pigsney (sweetheart— M.A.) in Syracuse. I know because he once solicited me to write a cupidity (amorous missive, or love letter; derived from Cupid—M.A.) for him addressed to her. This morning he strutted down the gangplank, cruel finefied for his Sundaying and with a neckcloth never before seen upon those slinking shoulders. "How come you by that bit of cloth, Dobby?" I asked, though well knowing. The young scrimshanker had the impudence to reply that he hooked it up from canal-bottom while sniggling for eels. "Then must you have dried it well," I said, and added, "A Sabbath lie is twice punished." He but grinned and went on his sinful way with a flirt of the pilfered neckpiece. That it may choke him is my kindliest wish.

Now for my grist of mung-news gathered after church from other Erie ladies.

The steersman of the packet *Young Lion of the West* held a 100-dol. ticket in last week's drawing of the House of Fortune. Some folk have all the luck, and those not the worthiest.

A bogus-boat has been arrested near Amsterdam, three coniackers (counterfeiters—M.A.) jailed, and a large sum in false coinage taken. This may be the source of the light shilling I had in change last week from a notion-higgler. (An itinerant peddler of oddments—M.A.)

A 1½-cent-a-mile immigrant boat from New York was refused wharfage at Schenectady because of smallpox. Four deaths.

There was a turn-out of the mechanics (strike of the workmen—M.A.) in the snuff factory at Little Falls. They demand twelve sh. a week and medical service for sore eyes.

An explosion took place on board the *Mary Fidler* last Friday morning. The ignorant deckhand attempted to stimulate the sluggish fire with an application of Seneka Oil. This is the scum gathered from the surface of stinking pools in the southern part of the state by Indians, who sell it as medicament for bellybloat and costiveness. It is highly combustive. Notwithstanding, it is used by the foolhardy in lieu of whale oil in lamps. The *Mary Fidler's* cabin windows were blown out, and the reckless deckhand lost beard, eyebrows and a portion of his hair.

It is whispered that Captain Barker's wife, of the Durham freighter, *Humility*, surprised him on Saturday night in Van Hamm's congress hall, where public dances are held. He was performing that new and wanton step called the Rutland Wriggle in partnership with a young female, reputed to be a bonaroba (a woman of wanton morals—M.A.). Though she weighs hardly eight stone, Mrs. Barker set upon the giglet and beat her so soundly and deservedly that she fled along the waterfront, calling loudly for help and the constabulary. That be the fate of all such Cyprians!

In Friday morning's thunderstorm an electron killed two horses of the *Chief Engineer* and stunned their hoggee. The packet was delayed ½ hour.

Toll rates are to be raised on potash, pearl ash, planking, livestock, and other freightage. How can honest canallers make a living under such oppressions?

Mowbray, our deckhand, speared a fine twenty-pound snapping turtle this noon as it was crossing a meadow below the berm. Savory soup for the rest of the voyage!

Two sloops engaged in the owling trade (smuggling to and from Canada—M.A.) are supposed to have been lost in the Lake Ontario gale of last week.

Goody Merseran, the Montezuma Marsh witch, is dead.

Monday. Two miles this side of Teall's Lock we met the Blauvelt brothers' raft. Its chain-joined timbers were a shambles. The older Blauvelt, with a bloody rag around his head, was splinting the arm of one of his woodsmen. The other brother hobbled on a home-made crutch as he ministered to two wounded hands. Two other men stretched upon the logs, whether dead or alive it was difficult to say. I needed no information from Captain Robie to apprise me that there had been a fight at the locks.

Back of the raft there rose a wild whoobub; blaring and tooting and blasting and squawking in every tone of brazen fury. A long procession of boats had been held up at Teall's while the raft locked through, section by section, eight of them in all; an hour's delay for every craft behind, be it humble scow or privileged packet. Whilst the raft was but half through the lock, the infuriate captains and crews of two obstructed craft attacked with their fending poles. Though out-numbered, the raftsmen had their wood-axes, a powerful defense, and in this instance, successful. Now I am apprised (a) why all true boatmen have an ambition (grudge —M.A.) against the cumbering rafts; (b) why the Canal is called the "Raging Erie."

Tuesday. Tomorrow we should reach Utica, the end of our voyage. The Black Snake stretches before us, sixty level miles and more. (Because of its winding and twisting course between Syracuse and Utica, canallers call this stretch the Black Snake.—M.A.) Heaven send that we be not impeded by too many slow rafts or overtaken and pushed aside by too many swift packets! Given a clear course upon this lockless reach, we are capable of fifty miles by nightfall.

Wednesday. Utica, indeed! Fifty miles, forsooth! Here lies

the *Starry Flag* mudded down like a hog in its wallow three
miles east of the Castle (Oneida Castle—M.A.) and the
Grand Erie Canal no more boatable than my grandmother's
jorden. What a nightmare night! Misfortune overtook us at
sunset. I was awaiting the pleasant cry: "Look for a post!"
when there came a rataplat of hooves from the direction of
New Boston. A pathmaster appeared in a cloud of dust,
mounted upon a bespoken farm horse. He beat upon the
animal's neck, shouting loudly, "Breached! She's breached!"
Before we could ask him where or how badly, he was gone to
summon the Hurry-Up Boat. (Every section has its repair
boat, commonly called the Hurry-Up boat, with a skilled crew
of spade and shovel men under command of the section
superintendent.—M.A.) Captain Robie, peering forward, determined to make all the easting he could before the water
subsided beneath us. He ordered out the fresh tandem and
bade the hoggee lay to them. So for an hour we pressed on,
followed by other craft.

Bugling and shouts from astern bid us yield the right-of-
way. We edge over to the berm. Every keel, be it swift packet
or sluggish raft, gives free passage to the Hurry-Up Boat.
She foams into sight behind four straining horses, a slender,
thirty-foot "Needle," laden with timber, planks, tools, ropes,
and gear, making her twelve miles an hour.

The section superintendent shouts an order. "*Starry Flag*,
ahoy! Keep going till you ground." By this we know that the
breach must be a great one and that all available manpower
will be needed to staunch it. We make all speed for another
hour through shallowing water, until our keel scrapes bottom. We slow down. Captain Robie shouts to the hoggee,
"Mudlarked." We stop perforce, bemired until the breach
is mended.

Presently we hear a roaring. My husband orders all hands
out. We join a throng on the towpath and press forward. The
berm has breached above Farmer Tighe's corn lot, where

musquash burrows had weakened it, and a mighty torrent
pours down through the flat. Hundreds of men are plying
pick, shovel, and maul, throwing up dykes, driving posts, and
nailing planks between them to contain the flood. Scores of
women are tending gypsy fires, boiling coffee, cooking food
for the all-night toilers. On the upland, the ax-men from the
Hurry-Up Boat are furiously felling trees, trimming them,
and rolling the logs into the Canal to be floated down to
the endangered bank and chained together to form an emergency dam. This is the work of the repair gang, and a perilous matter it is. Already, one man has had his leg crushed
between logs. Three others have been caught in the current
and dragged out below, unconscious. A woman has fallen
into the fire and been burned. I have brought with me the
Home Medicator, which every proper Canal boat carries,
and now join a traveling herb doctor and two midwives in
ministering to the disabled.

Dawn finds the efforts unremitted. Ten o'clock Methodist
time strikes from the church belfry. The report comes from
the section superintendent that the dam is holding. A bugle
sounds. The shilling-a-nighters, drummed up from farmstead,
tavern and village, form a line at the paymaster's window
on the Hurry-Up Boat. The superintendent looks like a dead
man, but he still mounts guard at the critical spot and gives
his orders.

Our crew collects shillings, not we. Captains do not take
pay for saving their Canal.

We hire a farm flat to row us home in a scant foot of water.
I have never been so wearied in my life.

Thursday. The *Starry Flag* heaves herself out of the mud.
The Canal is boatable again. We are off for Utica. My captain has news of another charter there from a disabled Durham. Albany! Perhaps New York! To think of walking on
the elegant Bowery! Attending the theater and seeing the
mighty Forrest, the romantic Miss Robinson, the risible

Stepanfetchit. To visit a Broadway hotel! To see the coffee-house wits at their cards or draughts! To stroll with the fashionables upon the spacious Battery! Never shall I cease to felicitate my happy fortune. How rich, how affording, how pompous is the career of a Canal wife!